Sheffield - A Civilised Place:

A history and gazetteer of the making of the city.

Duncan Froggatt

With photographs by Angela Harpham.

© Duncan Froggatt

Published by Duncan Froggatt, Sheffield

Printed by Mensa Printers, 111 Arundel Lane, Sheffield S1 4RF

All images copyright © Duncan Froggatt or © Angela Harpham except where indicated otherwise.

Cover illustrations, top to bottom, left to right. Front: Sheffield Hallam University (© Catherine Harpham), Sheffield Station, Moor Markets, Sheffield Cathedral (© Mark Calvert), Norton water tower, St Paul's Place, Sheffield University, Lady's Bridge, Commercial Street Bridge, Park Hill Flats, panorama from Wincobank Hillfort, Ponds Forge, Flood Memorial, Kelham Island, Sheffield Forgemasters, Cementation Furnace, Victoria Quays, Botanical Gardens, Sheffield Wednesday, Sheffield United, Weston Park. Rear: Rivelin Trail, Winter Garden, Crookesmoor Park, Parkway Viaduct, Wicker Arch, Crucible Theatre, City Hall, Howden Dam.

I wish to dedicate this book to my maternal grandfather Leonard Saynor
who, although he died while I was a small child, helped develop my love of
history and inspired me to become a civil engineer.

Contents.

Acknowledgements ix

Sources and Further Reading x

Index xiv

Foreword.

As the City of Sheffield continues its renaissance in terms of post-industrial redevelopment and economic growth, it is important to stop and think about the feats of engineering that have enabled the City to progress as a civilised place. We too often take for granted the designs behind the scenes that enable hundreds of thousands of people to live in close proximity in an urban setting and facilitate our culture and social development. Duncan Froggatt, with his understanding and experience as an Engineer has written a celebration of Civil Engineering in the City of Sheffield and with his illustration of infrastructure and structures in the Gazetteers with map references, brings the City's Civil Engineering heritage and future journey to life for us all.

To sustain future growth, the City of Sheffield will rely upon the expertise of engineers to design systems that support our daily lives. Transportation, communications, water management, structural design of buildings for work, accommodation and leisure, will all continue to test and challenge the work of engineers as the City grows and the density of people increases.

With planned major works such as High Speed 2 (high speed rail) arriving at Sheffield Midland Station in the early 2030s, completion of the city centre retail, leisure and business quarter (Heart of the City 2) in the early 2020s, full operation of the UK's first tram train and further works to protect the City against flooding, the work of engineering continues and is vital for our future prosperity and growth.

In a world now dominated by mobile communications and the digital revolution, I was amazed to read about Sheffield having one of the first telephone exchanges in the world only 18 months after the first in New York.

Duncan Froggatt clearly sets out the distinct areas of life that have all relied on engineering design solutions that make up the essential components for being able to live a civilised life. This book is a true celebration of both the City and the people who helped design the systems and structures that support it.

This book is a timely reminder of the astonishing engineering achievements from the past to the present day that have shaped the lives of those living, working or visiting the City of Sheffield. Duncan Froggatt provides a valuable insight into the importance of civil engineering and its part in enabling civic society in Sheffield.

Nalin Seneviratne BSc LL.B. FRICS

Director – City Centre Development, Sheffield City Council

Sheffield

September 2018

Background

The entire landscape of Sheffield from the highest moors to a city centre street has been created by human activity. The ancient wild wood was cleared from what is now moorlands in the bronze age for agriculture and settlement. Climate change led to the abandonment of the settlements and the accumulation of the peat soils to be found today. However, the upland landscape continues to be managed for recreation, livestock, water, forestry and ecological conservation. At lower altitudes agriculture and settlement dominate the shaping of the land in more obvious ways – field boundaries in stone and hedging, farmsteads and roads and the fabric of our villages and city.

The rocks of the seven hills of Sheffield and a series of, originally wooded, damp valleys with fast flowing rivers is the basis of development of the city itself. The geology of the Sheffield area is predominantly Carboniferous Coal Measure sandstones and shales with seams of coal and iron ores. There is gritstone to the West and some alluvial deposits up to 6m deep in the lower river valleys. The ground falls from a height of 400-546m AOD on the gritstone edges, to around 200m in the valley heads dropping to ~45m at Lady's Bridge and ~32 m at Blackburn Meadows. This gave engineers the opportunity to quarry the stone and minerals needed to build the town and supply its industry. The local sandstones provide millstones for grinding an edge of metal tools (and foodstuffs). Other horizons are suitable for dressing into blocks for building while others are relatively flaggy and suitable for paving, roofing and general walling. Some of the clay soils can be used for brick making while beds of clay and ganister are also to be found that are suitable for making crucibles and lining furnaces. The local coal provided a source of heat and ironstone the raw material for the metal industry. However, Sheffield soon came to import the best quality iron. The valleys' woods also were managed to provide a source of charcoal and white coal for the early metal industries. We were also able to impound the rivers for power and water supply. The combination of geology, climate and topography were perhaps uniquely favourable to allow the metal industry to establish and thrive here.

However, there was also the challenge of building in relatively difficult terrain and at times overcoming the legacy of earlier developments. This has shaped the development of the city we see today.

The three essentials for life are shelter, clean water and food. To these we would add for human life in Britain energy for heating, cooking and illumination. For civilised life, transport and communication facilities and advanced technological processes would be added to allow the accumulation of wealth and so the development of knowledge and culture. A definition of civilisation is "the ability and mechanism of living together in an urban environment". Thomas Tredgold, in the 1828 Charter of the Institution of Civil Engineers, defined civil engineering as "the art of directing the great sources of power in nature for the use and convenience of man".

For millennia all technical knowledge was passed down from master to apprentice through experience and word of mouth. However, the introduction of paper to the western world and the development of moveable type printing allowed books to be come easily and comparatively cheaply produced. This in turn, together with political and religious changes, led to a huge expansion in literacy. From the 16th century onwards books began to be published on various technical subjects.

These early engineers set the path for the provision of infrastructure including clean water, sewage disposal, canals, roads, railways, bridges and tunnels, dams and harbours, most of which continue in use today. Increasingly over the subsequent centuries diverse people have studied aspects of technology and their knowledge transmitted to a wide audience through books, various forms of colleges and universities and learned societies. Modern demands for communication and energy have expanded engineering expertise to airports, telecommunications and new forms of power generation. Engineers have always been concerned with the effective and efficient use of resources. The need to balance environmental and social pressures with technical constraints adds to the complex challenges faced and resolved by engineers.

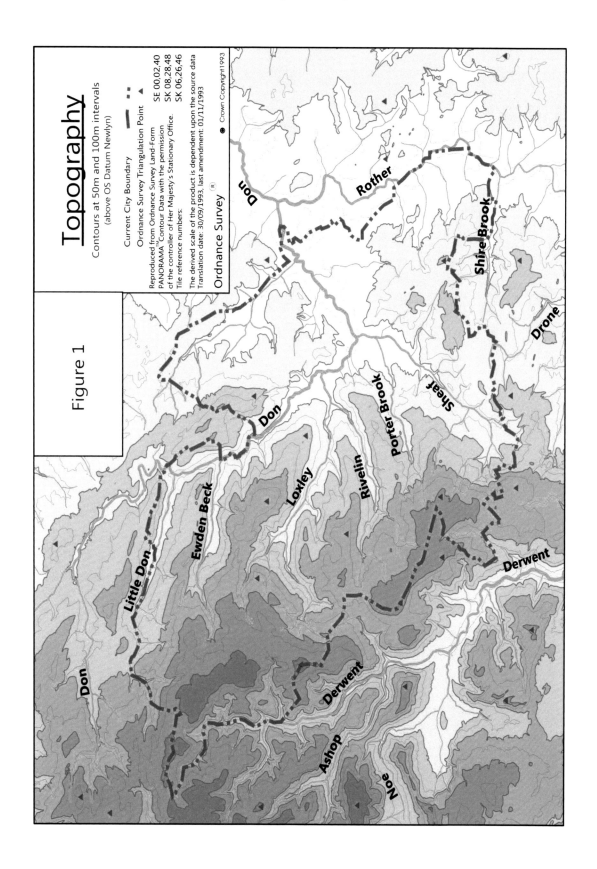

Figure 1

Topography

Contours at 50m and 100m intervals
(above OS Datum Newlyn)

Current City Boundary
Ordnance Survey Triangulation Point

Reproduced from Ordnance Survey Land-Form
PANORAMA™ Contour Data with the permission
of the controller of Her Majesty's Stationary Office.
Tile reference numbers:

SE 00,02,40
SK 08,28,48
SK 06,26,46

The derived scale of the product is dependent upon the source data
Translation date: 30/09/1993, last amendment: 01/11/1993

Ordnance Survey ®

© Crown Copyright 1993

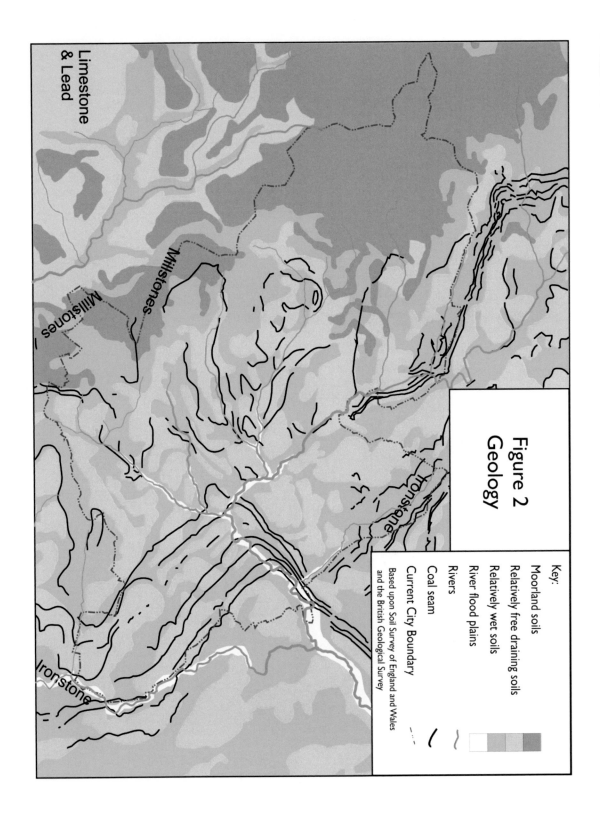

Figure 2
Geology

Key:
Moorland soils
Relatively free draining soils
Relatively wet soils
River flood plains
Rivers
Coal seam
Current City Boundary

Based upon Soil Survey of England and Wales
and the British Geological Survey

Limestone & Lead
Millstones
Ironstone

1.1   Wooded valleys interspersed by mainly pastoral farmland with moors on the high ground above characterise the natural landscape of the Sheffield region.

1.2   The fast flowing streams and managed woodlands provided the energy for Sheffield's early metal trades.

Shelter

Population growth and city expansion

Man has been present in the local landscape since earliest times. Actual evidence of settlement back in the Stone Age is somewhat lacking. However, this is quite normal. Not far to the south east at Cresswell Crags is to be found some of the oldest remains in the country dating back to 40,000 years ago and the country's oldest art from the last ice age 10,000 years ago.

By the time we reach the Bronze Age in the second millennium BC evidence of occupation improves. There are several areas of field systems of this period on the moors in the west of the city and more widely in the Peak District. They may well have been more widely present but evidence has been lost by later activity. While dredging a dyke at Chapel Flat near Blackburn Meadows, at the start of the last century, a large timber was found that had been worked. This is thought to be a Bronze Age log boat and is held at Sheffield Museum but is not on display.

There are remains of around nine hill-forts across the city and more in the Peak District. "Roman Ridge" is a linear earthwork extending 27 miles east from Wincobank to Mexborough. This is thought to be a boundary marker between the Iron Age tribes. The tribes known to the Romans as the Brigantes occupied Yorkshire and the Peak District while those known as Coritani were in the low lands of the East Midlands, broadly speaking. Enclosures thought to be of this period have been found by crop marks at various sites such as Handsworth, Woodhouse and Darnall. Wharncliffe Woods are believed to have been a quern stone manufacturing site in the Iron Age. Quern stones were used to grind corn by hand before rotary corn mills were developed.

The Roman occupation of the city area is also elusive. Coins have been found at many sites across the city. Romano-British field systems have been identified at Grenoside and an iron smelting complex at Broomhead reservoir. Whirlow and Lodge Moor are home to an estate complex and fragments of a mosaic pavement from the period and pottery was found at Sheffield Castle. They had built a road from their fort at Templeborough to Brough near the lead mining centres in Derbyshire and south to Chesterfield. However, the routes remain largely conjectural.

Sheffield became an important centre in Anglo-Saxon times although the details are again vague. By the 969 it is known to be held by Earl Waltheof of Northumberland for the King. The de Lovetot family held the manor from the time of Henry I. Thomas de Furnival established the Town Trustees and Church Burgesses in 1297 to run aspects of the town. The same year its market charter was granted. The following year is the first literary reference to a Sheffield cutler in the Reeve's Tale by Chaucer.

From the Mediaeval period onwards, Sheffield township comprised the town centre and Manor Park area to the south-east. This was surrounded by Attercliffe, Brightside Bierlow, Nether Hallam and Ecclesall Bierlow. All of the former two and parts of the latter two were incorporated within Sheffield by the early 19th century. The remainder of Nether Hallam and Ecclesall together with Upper Hallam were taken into the town in the mid 19th century.

Population estimates for this period for the city would be entirely speculative. It is thought that the national population doubled through the Iron Age to about two million before the Roman Conquest. During the four centuries of Roman control the population doubled again before declining due to worsening climate and civil unrest. The climate was warming again by the 10th century to create the Mediaeval warm epoch from c. 1000 to 1250. Generally, the population was growing in this period but no doubt disrupted by the Harrying of the North in 1069/70 and national anarchy in the 1120s and periodic famines. By the early 14th century the national population was thought to be over 5 million. The admission of the Bubonic Plague to the country in 1348 saw the population collapse to around 3 million in 1350 and 2¼ million 50 years later. Relatively reliable figure can only be obtained from the mid 16th century when registers of births and deaths were required. Despite the mini ice age from 1500-1850 the population generally grew strongly despite short term hiatuses due to outbreaks of disease, conflict and failed harvests. This is no doubt due to the increasing wealth of the population at large.

A census was carried out in 1616 to determine the town's population and likely need for almshouses. A figure of 2,207 is recorded. At this stage the national population would be approximately 5 million people. The town population had grown nearly to around 10,000 in 1736 and by a similar amount by the end of the century to reach around 46,000 by 1801. This doubled by 1831 and grew rapidly through the century as technology advanced drawing more people to the city. As the population grew, the township expanded and subsumed the neighbouring settlements within Sheffield.

Hillsborough, Wortley, parts of Tinsley and Catcliffe together with Handsworth and much of Norton joined the city in 1901. Further parts of Tinsley in 1912 and parts of the Rivelin Valley joined the city in 1914. The land for Blackburn Meadows power plant came into Sheffield while Rotherham had back the adjoining land for Steel Peach and Tozer's plant in 1919. Two years later the site of Blackburn Meadows waste water treatment plant and other sections of Tinsley and Handsworth together with Wadsley Bridge and Shiregreen became parts of Sheffield. Parts of Hathersage, Derwent and Gleadless were taken-in in 1929. The remainder of Norton, together with Dore, Totley, Bradway and Greenhill changed from Derbyshire to Yorkshire in the 1933-5. There was a proposal in 1937, never acted upon, to incorporate Todwick into Sheffield.

This growth pattern continued through the 20th century when the population grew from 381,000 to 517,000 by mid century. A decline in the latter part of the century as heavy industry lost workers together with further boundary changes results on the total figure being similar today. However, the 20th century saw a large expansion in the built up area as garden suburbs were built to replace the congested Victorian central tenements.

Mosborough, and parts of Eckington, Holmesfield, Killamarsh and Ecclesfield became parts of Sheffield in 1967. Bradfield and the remainder of Ecclesfield together with part of Wortley and also Stocksbridge became part of Sheffield in the 1974 local government reorganisation. In addition, there have been many small local adjustments to the boundary to maintain a rational route as areas were developed.

Housing development.

Evidence of the early housing is largely elusive.

It is not until from the later middle ages that tangible evidence of the habitation has survived. There is around a score of timber framed structures from this period surviving, generally hidden within later parts of the buildings. Firm dating evidence, where available, indicate 16th and 17th century dates. However, the technology was slow to evolve and some examples may be a hundred or so years earlier. The Bishops' House at Meersbrook Park and the Old Queen's Head in the city centre are the two most clear examples and date from the 15th century.

The town came to be largely rebuilt in brick and stone from the 18th century. Brick was becoming more affordable and is far more durable and fire resistant - an important consideration in a town of many "manufactures". The hearth Tax list of 1672 listed 494 households with 224 smithies in use among them. This was also the time when the town started to grow out of the confines of the mediaeval settlement. Early expansion was in the crofts around what became the West Bar area. Cementation furnaces were built in this area. Paradise Square was commenced in 1736. The Norfolk estate systematically provided new housing on their land immediately south of the old town towards Little Sheffield. This was followed by a westward expansion on land held by the Church Burgesses.

The late 19th century and early 20th century saw a large rise in population driven by the growth of the town's industries, notably in the Don Valley. Many of the industrialists that built new factories there also built extensive terraces of houses to provide homes for their workers within easy reach of the works.

Sheffield became a borough in 1843 following the 1835 Municipal Corporations Act. This gave the newly expanding industrial towns more control over their own affairs.

From the 1840s onwards, parts of the town were developed by Freehold Land Societies, most notably to the south and west of town. These forerunners of building societies allowed the artisan classes to build their own homes. Home ownership then enfranchised them with a parliamentary vote. The members of the society collectively bought an area of land to be divided into plots of up to ¼ acre upon which they built their own houses. The land purchase loan was repaid through contributions. The Freehold Land Societies bought large parcels of land and sub-divided the plots at typically ten per acre. Plot holders developed their house to their own requirements and means resulting in a diversity of style and size from modest to moderately large. A key feature of the schemes was that the plots would be large enough to provide a garden for the owner to cultivate and produce some of their own food and a beautiful environment. There were covenants restricting use of the plots to ensure a pleasant domestic environment away from the city's industries. Thus they can also be considered a precursor for the 20th century garden suburb and garden city movement.

Freehold Land Societies were not widely adopted across the country with only Sheffield and Birmingham having significant developments, as far as I am aware. In 1862 there were 37 registered Land Societies in Sheffield providing 3,154 plots over 564 acres and having built 23 miles of roads and associated drainage in the process.

These roads were then adopted by the council for a fee. Societies ranged in size from around a dozen plots to 250.

Elsewhere at this time, land owners built speculative housing for sale or rent to varying classes of workers. The new industrialist built large terraces of houses near their works to accommodate their workers. Often the houses were tied to employment and allocated according to one's position in the works' hierarchy.

In the absence of statutory building control, building standards were enforced by contract and monitored by the land owner's surveyor, such as Fairbank acting for the Church Burgesses for their development to the west of the town. Some of the records remain in the Sheffield Archive. Local Authorities were granted the right to impose building control by the Public Health Act of 1848. However, Sheffield did not adopt these measures until 1864 when a local by-law was passed preventing the building of back-to-back houses and led to the terrace housing construction seen widely across Sheffield today each with its own internal water supply, plus gas and electricity when available, and separate outside privy. These by-laws were updated in 1889 under powers granted in the 1875 Public Health Act.

The Housing and Town Planning Act of 1909 gave powers to councils to regulate suburban dispersal and relieve city centre overcrowding. By 1911, plans were drawn up allocating land for development. However, negotiations allow this to happen were interrupted by the first world war. Patrick Abercrombie was appointed in 1919 to revise the proposals with a report laid before parliament in 1924. This pioneering report became the foundation for all subsequent UK planning with zoning of land uses and low density suburban housing - "Homes fit for Heroes" as the slogan went. However, powers to implement and force the changes were limited at the time. Sheffield Council gained some further powers under the 1932 Town and Country Planning Act and the development control order was created two years later with bold plans for the city centre. These were only partly implemented over the next four years and then revised following world war two after the 1947 Town and Country Planning Act. J.G. Graves purchased Blackamoor to the west of Dore and presented it to the city as open space in perpetuity. This resulted in the country's first green belt being provisionally agreed around the city in July 1938.

Wincobank was the site of the first garden suburb with an informal layout varied house types gardens and open spaces. It was developed from 1903 onwards. This development was very successful architecturally and in terms of users satisfaction, but proved more expensive than initially planned. The large inter-war council housing estates of Manor, Arbourthorne, Longley, Parson Cross and Shiregreen provided spacious houses with the facilities expected today, gardens and local community facilities on architectural geometric layouts. However, the layouts did not reflect the hills of Sheffield and building cost constraints limited house design variation. Nevertheless, they provided homes and space for many families in far better conditions than they had hitherto experienced. In total 25,000 council houses were built in the inter-war period. The extensive estates to the NE of the city forms one of the largest concentrations of council housing in the country. The estates included shops, schools and churches and were laid out to the latest design principles being used in the garden city movement. The vast majority of these houses remain. Over the past 15 years or so a rolling programme of modernisation has taken place across the entire council housing stock. This has improved insulation and weather resistance and updated heating, plumbing and electrical services within the buildings. The houses built by Sheffield City Council were all well designed and exceeded the design space standards set out in the model specification in the Tudor-Walters Report of 1919 for local authority housing. In 1961 the Parker-Morris committee report *Homes for today and tomorrow* updated these earlier requirements with the revised specification being mandatory from 1969. This requirement to meet the standard was withdrawn by parliament in 1980. However, Sheffield chose to continue to apply the principles. For private housing there is only limited guidance in the planning guidelines and it is largely considered a matter for the market to decide. Consideration is now being given to reintroducing minimum space standards. As we become wealthier our demand for space tends to increase. From 2012, Sheffield has promoted *Building for Life12* as a standard for developments of more than ten houses. This, with the associated South Yorkshire Residential Design Guide, sets out minimum recommended standards for new housing in the city.

The first city wide development plan was approved by the council in 1952 but not authorised by parliament for a further five years. Nevertheless, Sheffield was amongst the first cities to implement development plans. Various local government reforms of the 1970s and 1980s delayed the completion of aspects of the planning controls and revision of the plans. The revised local plan was adopted in 1979. The Lower Don Valley came under special planning rules from 1988 with the creation of the Sheffield Development Corporation following the collapse of the steel industry. The Unitary Development Plan was published in 1991 and adopted in 1998. This became the Sheffield development framework from 2009 which is now being amended as the new Local Plan.

In the 1950s and 60s Sheffield embraced the modernist architectural movement under J.L. Womersley as City Architect. New multi-storey housing schemes were developed to replace damaged and slum housing. Most notable of these were Park Hill and Hyde Park built in 1955-61 and 1955-64 respectively. These became internationally famous with their streets in the sky. Elsewhere around the city were mixed estates of low-, medium- and high-rise units. In comparison with the pre-war estates these were designed to work with the topography of the city, most successfully at Gleadless Valley. They also were at a much higher population densities than the garden estates. Some of the tower blocks were demolished in the 1990s. Others have been given a new lease of life with over cladding to again improve insulation and weather resistance and new services and access control. While some sections of Hyde Park were demolished others were refurbished as accommodation for participants in the World Student Games in 1991 and subsequent use by the people of Sheffield. Park Hill, now a listed structure, is also being stripped back to the concrete structure and rebuilt and fitted out as part of an urban regeneration scheme. These schemes are a rare departure from the gradual evolution of housing design and construction over the last 300 years since brick became the predominant building material.

Council housing largely ceased in the 1980s and from then private house builders developed numerous estates, most notably the Mosborough townships developments to the south-east of the city. The planning of these provided for the creation of a series of small communities again with local services but with a mixture of sizes and tenure to improve a mixed social cohesion.

The late 19th and early 20th century also was a time of substantial privately built housing schemes often in the western suburbs. These ranged from small terraced houses to large detached country villas.

The council now has a target that all new developments built in the city from 2016 will be of high standards. All developments should a high standard of energy and resource efficiency; and make the best use of solar energy, passive heating and cooling, natural light, and natural ventilation. Existing building should be sympathetically enhanced and underused spaces brought into use when being redeveloped. New home developers are encouraged to have a Home Quality Mark assessment. The HQM is a five star scale of assessment from energy and water efficiency to accessibility, flood risk, security and comfort and sustainable use of materials. It is related to the Building Research Establishment Environmental Assessment Method (BREEAM) used primarily for non-domestic buildings. Non-domestic building in Sheffield are encouraged to achieve a BREEAM score of at least "Good", the second of a five point scale.

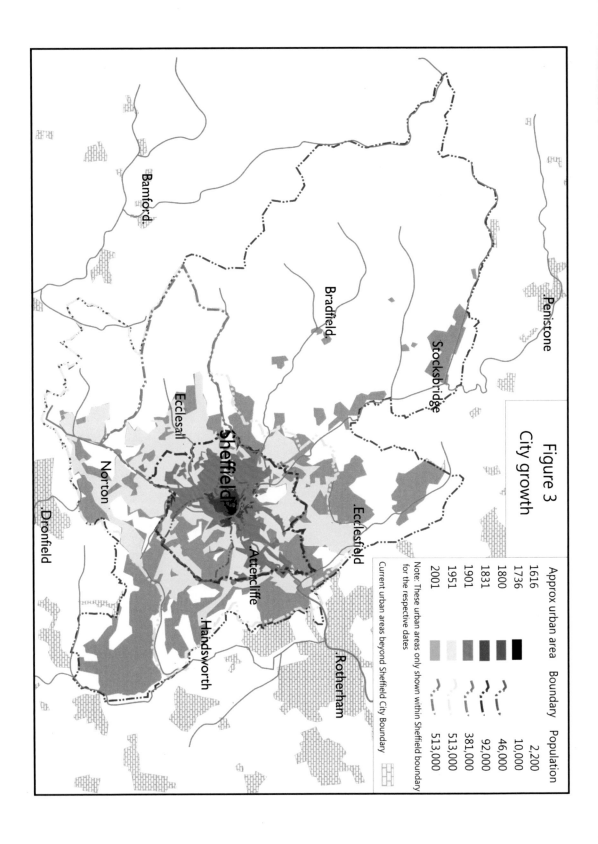

Figure 3
City growth

Approx urban area	Boundary	Population
1616		2,200
1736		10,000
1800		46,000
1831		92,000
1901		381,000
1951		513,000
2001		513,000

Note: These urban areas only shown within Sheffield boundary for the respective dates

Current urban areas beyond Sheffield City Boundary

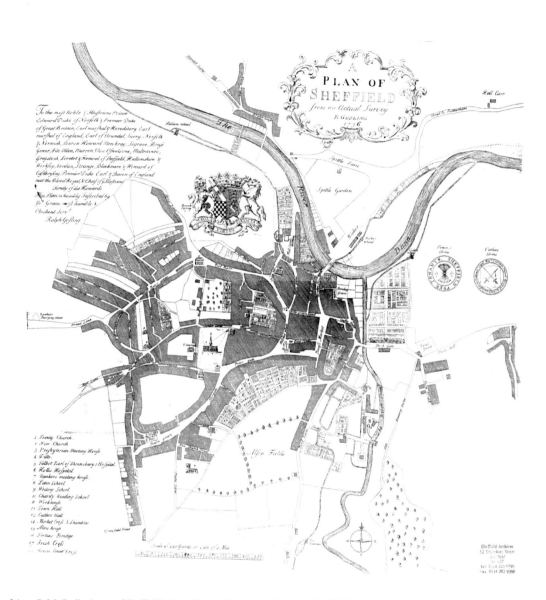

2.1   Ralph Gosling's map of Sheffield is the earliest surviving map of the town. In 1736 the town was
still largely still within the mediaeval settlement, but with some new development taking place in the crofts
to the north-west of the church.

2.2　Only very fragmentary remains of bronze and iron age houses have survived. There have been several research projects where attempts to reconstruct how they might have been made have been undertaken. These include at Calverton near Nottingham and in Cheshire. The nearest open to the public is at Ryedale Folk Museum.

They varied in size from around 4 to 18 m in diameter and will have housed extended families and their livestock in the latter case. In the late iron age and into the early mediaeval period they became rectangular producing the Yorkshire "Long house" where livestock were at one end of the building and the family the other. (This example is in the Cotswolds.)

These buildings can be seen at Ryedale Folk Museum at Hutton-le-hole in North Yorkshire.

2.3　The crofter's cottage is based on archaeological evidence of a 14th century dwelling.

2.4　Stang End cottage however, is a surviving building relocated from Danby and rebuilt in 1967/8 as it would have been c. 1700.

2.5   Bishops' House in Meersbrook Park is a good example of the larger timber framed houses of the region and was built in the mid 16th century. (Reproduced Courtesy of Friends of Bishops' House, © Ken Dash)

2.6   Moor Cottage, Totley, is a typical early 18th century stone built farmhouse. Like almost all old houses it has been altered over time. The house to the left was originally part of the range, but since divided into separate cottages. The lean-to extension is modern.

Approximate area of old town.

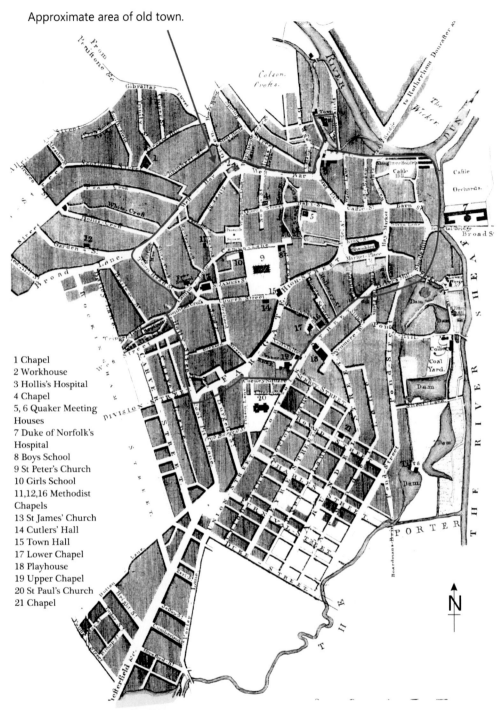

1 Chapel
2 Workhouse
3 Hollis's Hospital
4 Chapel
5, 6 Quaker Meeting
Houses
7 Duke of Norfolk's
Hospital
8 Boys School
9 St Peter's Church
10 Girls School
11,12,16 Methodist
Chapels
13 St James' Church
14 Cutlers' Hall
15 Town Hall
17 Lower Chapel
18 Playhouse
19 Upper Chapel
20 St Paul's Church
21 Chapel

2.7   Fairbank's 1797 map of Sheffield.

This clearly shows the regular grid of streets laid out over the previous decade south of the then new Norfolk Street. The Division Street area was similarly being laid out on a grid system at the time.

This contrasts with the street layout of the mediaeval town and early croft enclosures to the north.

The Alsop Fields area, south of the town centre, was originally for housing but quickly became a centre for cutlers.

(Reproduced courtesy of Sheffield Libraries and Archives)

2.8   Paradise Square is a good surviving example of well to do housing of the Georgian era. The east side was built in 1736 with the remaining sides completed in the 1770s and 1780s. It is now widely used as offices. It was a place of public meetings in the 18th and 19th centuries with John Wesley preaching to a packed crowd in 1779. It continued a a place of gathering for the Methodist and the Chartist movements.

2.9   Carr Road, Walkley, is one of the areas where Freehold Land Societies from the 1850s facilitated the building of individual houses by middle income tradesmen. This allowed them to become property owners and so eligible to vote. The societies were set up in several Sheffield suburbs, but were not common in other towns. These mutual societies collectively bought land and sold plots to members in return for regular modest payments.

This group of houses show the varying styles adopted. Here on the south side of the street the gardens are to the rear, those on the north side have large front gardens. Clearly laid out to afford the best growing conditions.

© Anna Ravetz

2.10   Both the existing landowners and the new industrialist built extensive housing to accommodate the workers, mainly near to the factories. In a few areas there were back to back houses but generally they were two-up two-down housing with a privy in a rear courtyard. Some areas and often facing the main roads were slightly larger houses with bay windows, off-shot kitchens and additional storeys. Houses were developed at a density of approximately 40 per acre.

2.11   Elsewhere, larger houses were built for the middle classes. These were sometimes speculative land developments and in places developed privately. Here the development density was around 7 plots per acre or less.

2.12 & 2.13   In the inter-war period both the public and private sector built extensive suburban estate often of semi-detached houses with gardens. Sometimes bungalows were built. On many estates the density of housing was around 10 plots per acre. Occasionally on the edge of the country, plots with large gardens or small holdings were created at densities of one to four plots per acre were created as "homes for heroes". This would allow young families to live in open surroundings and be at least partially self sufficient.

2.14   Private house developers in the 1960s continued to produce houses of a similar overall design to those in previous decades but with more provision for cars and larger windows being typical.

2.15   Council house developments in the 1960s experimented with a range of house styles, estate layouts and construction methods. Some were new forms of "garden suburb" with large amounts of landscaping.

2.16   Council housing took a variety of forms including low-rise block to higher rise towers. The tower blocks in the city have been refurbished in recent years to improve security, amenity and comfort. The blocks in Sheffield were carefully given fire proof cladding to improve the insulation and so reduce the energy costs of the building.

2.17   Suburban housing has remained on similar principles since but with a shift towards detached houses. Housing density remains typically 8 - 12 plots per acre, but can be as high as 16. However, with increased car usage more space is taken up by roads and driveways. Also areas of public open space are provided within the scheme. The net result being that (particularly back) gardens are smaller, by perhaps $\frac{1}{3}$ to $\frac{1}{2}$ the size of pre-war.

2.18 & 2.19 Both universities and indeed the private sector have invest heavily in recent years in accommodation for students.

The 21 storey tower block is the first phase of New Era Development's project to provide student accommodation and the China-UK Business Incubator – a trade-centre set to promote business between China and Sheffield.

Water & Wastewater

Water supply

Water is the most important ingredient in life. Without clean water, life as we know it would not exist. Civil Engineers have been providing clean water to society for centuries. Engineers continue to improve processes for the safe and efficient supply of clean water and the disposal of dirty water to the growing world population. In January 2007 an international poll by The British Medical Journal (BMJ) voted the advent of public sanitation as the greatest medical breakthrough since the BMJ was founded in 1840.

The first record of public water supply in Sheffield was Barker's Pool in 1567. It was a large cistern collecting rain and spring water. However, the cistern probably predates this by around 113 years as there is a record of a Barker associated with the district from 1434. The growth of the town in the 17th century and the increasing number of coal pits combined to increase demand and reduce the supply (by lowering the water table) available from the town's springs and wells. The pool was enlarged in 1631 and again in 1672-6. In all, the burgery spent £166 / 7 / 4 in the period 1616 to 1708, but only £7 in the subsequent 85 years. It was removed in 1793 as it had become a public nuisance. Barker's Pool supplemented around 20 wells around the town through this time.

The supply was supplemented in the 1690s by Peter Whalley of Nottingham and upon his death "the great English Engineer" George Sorocold of Lancashire. This scheme involved again enlarging Barker's Pool and pumping spring water up from a waterworks by the River Don near Lady's Bridge. The works were noted by Daniel Defoe as he journeyed through the area. However, they may never have been completed or were short lived in operation. Thomas Oughtibridge's View of Sheffield of 1720, 1740 and Nathaniel Buck's Prospect of Sheffield of 1745 may include some of the construction related to this. However, it is hard to interpret with conflicting information.

The 18th century records seem to indicate a size of Barker's Pool of around 20m x 35m – roughly the size of three tennis courts – in area and so may have held approximately 1,000m^3 of water.

In 1713 The Duke of Norfolk and Town Trustees granted permission for Goodwin, a merchant, and Littlewood, a millwright, to start another scheme. This was to pipe water from a spring at Whitehouse, Upperthorpe to Town Head Cross. Matthewman built a supply reservoir at the source spring in 1737 to supply the growing population of around 10,000. The growth of the urban area was mainly focused around the crofts south of Kelham Island.

In 1782 the Whitehouse scheme was enlarged and the construction of the first of the Crookes reservoirs was started by the Sheffield Reservoirs Company. By 1832 there were six large reservoirs and 4 smaller ones at Crookes. The lower Crookesmoor reservoirs supplemented the Whitehouse Scheme and supplied the lower part of the town via Watery Lane. The Great Dam and those above it at Crookes supplied the upper parts of the town via a cistern at Portobello.

The water was fed by wooden, probably alder, pipes of 7.5cm or 15cm bore. Latterly distribution to subscribing premises was possible. Some streets had a basic piped system from around 1759 when Fairbanks indicates pipes and 12 watercocks in the town. The first cast iron pipes are recorded in 1830. The town trustees erected a public water pump at the site of the pool in 1825 which was finally removed in 1876.

Although the annual average rainfall in Sheffield (Weston Park meteorological station) is 825mm there is considerably more rainfall on the moors to the west of the city forming the catchment to the rivers of Sheffield. These will have average rainfalls of 1200-1500mm. Harnessing this rainfall in the headwaters of the valleys provides a substantial high quality water resource for the city.

The Sheffield Water Works Company was incorporated in 1830 with John Towlerton Leather as Engineer and John Gunson his resident engineer. They immediately set about the construction of the Redmires reservoirs - completing the three in 1854. They also built a 2.2 ha, 1M m^3 capacity supply reservoir at Hadfield above Crookesmoor. These were linked by a conduit and cast iron aqueduct on 10m high masonry piers to carry the water across the Tapton Valley. In addition, by 1837, 25 miles of new cast iron supply pipes had been laid to replace and extend the timber pipe network.

A report on the conditions in Sheffield in 1843 reported that there was ample supply of water to supply water 3 times a week through pipes in principal streets to house cisterns. A Royal Commission of health of towns reported at the time. This estimated the population at 85,076 in 25,000 houses "most of which were better cleansed than most towns".

Following the London Cholera epidemic of 1848 the first Public Health Act was passed setting up boards of health and local sanitation authorities. Enabling acts were passed from 1853 for the construction of further reservoirs to supply the growing needs of Sheffield. Dale Dyke was completed in 1864 by Craven, Cockayne & Fountain contractors and infamously failed on 11/12 March 1864 releasing its contents through Sheffield. What came to be known as the Great Sheffield Flood. It was not until the 1980s that an eminent reservoir engineer, J. Binnie, was able to give a convincing explanation of the failure - an excessively large step in the deep puddle clay core. It was rebuilt at an amended location over the period 1867-75 with Thomas Hawksley as Engineer. Hawksley, from Nottingham designed leak resistant pipe fittings and was a strong advocate of constantly pressurised distribution systems which significantly reduce the risk of contamination of the water supply. Upon his advice constant pressure water supply was introduced in 1869. This initially led to a large increase in leakage from the pipes but eliminated the problem of leakage into the pipes contaminating the water supply.

Hawksley took over from Leather as engineer to the Sheffield company until 1887, when the corporation took over and he became their consultant.

The flooding from the Dale Dyke disaster eventually led to the Reservoirs (Safety Provisions) Act, 1930 which required all large reservoirs to be designed and supervised by qualified engineers. This legislation was subsequently replaced by the Safety of Reservoirs Act 1974. (A "Panel Engineer" was called upon to supervise the emergency measures to ensure the safety of Ulley Reservoir when damaged in the storms of July 2007 and its subsequent improvements.) Subsequent to the 2007 floods the Flood and Water Management Act was passed in 2010. Amongst other things it amended the 1974 Act extending its scope. However, in 2018 some of the provisions have yet to be implemented by the government. From 1910 all Sheffield reservoirs were being thoroughly inspected at least annually and works carried out if deemed necessary to ensure their continued safety.

A report of 1886 comments upon the high quality of the water in Sheffield. The extreme softness made it particularly appealing to the railway companies passing through the area. However, it was also noticed that this and the slight acidity caused a slow dissolution of lead from supply pipes. This was causing cases of mild lead poisoning in the population. The water company immediately introduced the pioneering step of dosing the water with controlled amounts of powdered calcium carbonate to control the pH of the water. This eliminated the problem of lead poisoning.

In 1888 the town corporation bought out the Sheffield Water Works Company and set about improving both water quality and connections to premises removing many stand pipes still present in poorer areas of the town. Langsett and Underbank reservoirs were a joint project with Rotherham and Doncaster corporations completed in 1907. The yield available to the various corporations was divided 18 : 8 : 5 to Sheffield Rotherham and Doncaster respectively. Midhope Reservoir was originally built by Barnsley Corporation Waterworks in 1896. Broomhead, came into operation in 1936 as part of the River Don compensation pumping scheme, together with More Hall reservoir.

It is notable that the Sheffield Water Works Company were required to provide over half of their storage capacity to act as regulating reservoirs to ensure adequate water flow in the rivers down stream. This was substantially more than was the custom in other areas where 25-30% was the norm. This reflects the continuing importance of the Sheffield Rivers to power the manufacturers of the town.

At the turn of the 20th century there were substantial increases in water demand. This was partly a result in increases in both population and industrial activity but also the increase in use of water closets which were replacing the earth privies. Use in 1860 was 52.3 litre/head /day had risen to 84.1 with trade use increasing from 39.1 litre/head/day to 67.3.

The corporation joined with Nottingham, Derby and Leicester in 1909 to create the Derbyshire Valley Water Board Derwent reservoirs project of Howden, Derwent and Ladybower reservoirs. Sheffield receives 25% of the water from this scheme. This water is tapped off the main supply aqueduct from the Howden and Derwent dams in Priddock Woods. From there it passes through a 4½ mile tunnel under Bamford and Hallam moors to the water treatment works below Rivelin Reservoirs. Edward Sandeman, the first president of the Institution of Water Engineers was the engineer. In 1925, after dam failures in Wales and Scotland, he publicly pressed for the legislation first proposed after the great Sheffield Flood be enacted. Thus the Reservoirs (safety provisions) Act 1930 came into being. He was also influential in a board of Trade Enquiry from 1918 to 1921 on water resources that laid the foundations for the modern water and sanitation industries. Sidney Winser was Sandeman's principal assistant and took over as board engineer when he retired. Messrs M. G. Weekes and W. F. H. Creber were the resident engineers. The work force was employed directly by the Derwent Valley Water Board who built Birchinlee Village "Tin Town" to house the work force and take care of their needs.

Ladybower is an earth fill dam and work started in 1935 and became operational in 1945. The engineer for this works was Messrs G. H. Hill & Sons, with Mr A. R. C. Ball their resident engineer. The contractor was Richard Baille of Haddington, Lothian. This reservoir allows the head waters of the River Ashop to be diverted into the Derwent reservoir. Flows from the River Noe, Peakshole Water and Bradwell Brook are taken to supplement the supply to Ladybower which act to regulate the downstream flow of the Derwent. However, in exceptional circumstances it is possible to pump water from the Ladybower reservoir into the Bamford aqueduct to augment the water supplies.

From 1919 in exceptional circumstances the facility existed to pump water from the river Don at Ickles near Rotherham to Damflask for release as compensation water in the rivers. This allowed more of the stored water in the reservoirs to be diverted to supply usage. This practice was operated between 1922 and 1962 when the practice was discontinued. Clearly, pumping up to 7.9M l/day would be an expensive undertaking best avoided.

In 1940, additional water mains were installed to link supply zones. This was to prevent areas losing all water supply in the event of a single pipe being damaged in an air raid attack. In addition, 54.55m^3 emergency service reservoirs were installed at hospitals, Darnall and Attercliffe and 88 smaller 5.45m^3 tanks at schools and designated shelters across the city.

Water supply was further supplemented in 1964 with the Yorkshire Derwent transfer scheme. In this case the river water is treated at Elvington, North Yorkshire where it is at an altitude of 7.6m AOD. Three pumping stations then deliver it along the 37 miles to a service reservoir at Hoober near Rotherham at an altitude of 138.7m AOD for supply into the local water network. Water is pumped at a rate of up to 3.3Ml/d through bitumen lined welded steel pipes up to 1.07m diameter. The pipeline, built by John Brown Ltd involved four river crossings, 13 railway crossings and 53 road crossings.

This is now part of the Yorkshire Water Grid which allows transfer of water around the region to balance supply and demand. The municipal water company was amalgamated into a regional board in 1974 and privatised in 1989 and is now part of Yorkshire Water plc. The water from the reservoirs, or grid, is filtered and chemically treated at Ewden, Langsett, Loxley or Rivelin Water Treatment Works and is then pumped to covered water supply reservoirs at Fulwood, Hadfield, Loxley, Manor, Norton, Tankersley and Wincoside.

By 1910 all the city's water was treated by filtration. John Gibb in Paisley had been the first to use sand filtration to purify a water supply for his factory in 1804. The process was then refined and the first public water supply to benefit from the process was at Chelsea Water Works in 1829 under James Simpson as engineer. The water is treated by slowly draining through a thick layer of fine sand. This effectively removes many pathogens. By 1852 it was a legal requirement for London water drawn from the Thames to be so treated. Mechanical filters were developed at the end of the 19th century. George W. Fuller developed a rapid sand filtration system in 1920 at Little Falls New Jersey, USA. This could treat far more water per hour and required far less space but is also far more complex to operate. Almost all public water in developed countries now undergoes some form of filtration.

The previously open service reservoirs were covered by 1934 and sterilisation (chlorination) introduced to improve further the safety of the water. The possibility of sterilising water by chlorination had been first mooted in Germany in 1893. The first large scale use was in Maidstone, Kent, in 1897 when it was used to sterilise the entire town's water supply to eliminate a typhoid outbreak. This was successful, whence the treatment ceased. In 1905, in Lincoln faults at a filtration plant allowed an outbreak of typhoid once again to sweep the city. Chlorination of the water supply again quickly stopped the epidemic. The chemical water treatment continued for a further 6 years until new reliably clean water supplies were available. The first permanent chlorination began in Jersey City, New Jersey USA from 1908 under the auspices of G. W Fuller and Dr John Leal. The process was quickly adopted world-wide being standard practice by the 1940s. Other disinfectant treatments are available, notably ozone and UV light. These are more expensive and leave no residue in the water. In some circumstances this purity is essential. However, for public water supply the residual low dose of Chlorine helps protect the water from the effects of any slight contamination during the process of transmission from the treatment plant to the customer.

The treatment of the water here in Sheffield is now carried out in stages. Firstly it has chemicals added which reacts with the mineral content to reduce the colour absorbed from the peat moorland soils. Next lime and ferrous sulphate are added. These cause very fine particulate material to clump together to form a floc (an agglomeration of particles) when aerated in flocculators. The scum is then mechanically scraped off taking 5 minutes each hour. Further lime is then added and the water passed through rapid sand filters to remove particulate and bacterial content. Periodically, these filters are back washed by simply reversing the flow to clean them and the sludge removed, once lifted from the sand, every 12 to 72 hours. Following filtration the water can be disinfected with the addition of Chlorine in the form of sodium hypochlorite produced by the on-site electrolysis of brine. Finally further lime is added to correct the pH and induce the oxidation of manganese salts which precipitate out of solution in sand filters known as manganese contactors. The water treatment works are rigorously monitored continuously and can be controlled both on-site and remotely from the Yorkshire Water control centre in Bradford. The works incorporate water turbines to recover energy from the system for re-use. In addition the plants have automatic diesel generator back up power supply to ensure the continued safe running of the plant even if the national grid connection fails.

Yorkshire Water offer public tours of their treatment works from time to time and also allow the public to walk in the vicinity of their reservoirs. Further details are available from Yorkshire Water.

There are now several thousand kilometres of pipes across the city from 914mm to 90mm diameter supplying homes and businesses across the city with over 100M m^3 of water every day, on average. Yorkshire Water continue to invest in the business to improve water quality and reliability of supply. It replaces or relines many kilometres of water main each year and continues to modernise the water treatment plants.

Their engineers and contractors are finding new ways to renew and repair the water supply pipes as efficiently as possible whilst avoiding as much disruption as possible to their customers.

Jointed cast iron pipes are being replaced with welded plastic pipes. This may be by digging a trench and physically replacing the pipe sections but this is very disruptive, especially where the pipe is in close proximity to other services such as gas, electric and telecoms. Frequently, the new pipe is inserted into the old below ground. For smaller diameter pipes the new plastic pipe may simply be pulled through the old pipe it replaces. The smooth surface of the plastic pipes reduces the friction on the water flow which compensates for the reduced pipe diameter. For the larger pipes the old pipe is burst apart underground to make way for the new by pushing a steel splitting cone in front of the new pipe.

Waste water

A report of 1727 describes the beneficial effect of flushing the town streets with water released from Barker's pool. Unfortunately, the effluent went straight into the Don. The river below Lady's bridge was an open sewer also taking the wastes from the towns slaughterhouses which were situated where Castlegate now is until around 1830. Although most privies were emptied as night soil, the growing population meant the system could not cope. The river was becoming polluted from various wastes dumped into it.

A seminal work by Dr John Snow in London in 1858 established the link between sewage and Cholera. That year a Royal Commission was established to look into the practice of treating and disposing of sewage. This went on to produce a series of reports through to 1915. The traditional practice of spreading on agricultural land had been effective in areas of low population with various caveats. However, the increasingly urbanised population required new thinking. In 1868 Sir Edward Frankland carried out laboratory tests on filtering effluent through various media and achieved successful biological cleansing. Although the mechanism was poorly understood at best. Early real world implementation was often unsuccessful. It took until 1893 for success to be reliably achieved with the trickle filtration through coke media. By the 1920s these techniques had been thoroughly researched and widely implemented. In 1914 two academics, Edward Ardern and William Lockett, chemists at Manchester's Davyhulme WWTW, published a paper on the treatment of sewage without filters. The activated sludge wastewater treatment process rapidly became the most widely used biological wastewater treatment process. This involves the aeration of wastewater in the presence of aerobic microorganisms and removal of biological solids from the wastewater by sedimentation and also the recycling of the settled biological solids back into the aerated wastewater. Lockett and Ardern were able to shorten the required aeration time for "full oxidation" from weeks to less than 24 hours which made the process technically feasible. Full scale testing rapidly followed at Salford and Worcester. This technique has proved highly successful and adaptable to a range of conditions.

Early sewers had been localised and frequently discharged waste directly to the River Don. It was not until the early 1880s that the first trunk sewers and treatment works were built.

Blackburn Meadows Waste Water Treatment Works (WWTW) was opened in 1886 and used the latest techniques for treating the effluent. Part of this site no longer needed for water treatment is now a local nature reserve. For many years the treatment of sewage in lime precipitation tanks was known as the "Sheffield Method". Blackburn Meadows was also the site of pioneering work by John Haworth, the works general manager, in 1916 when he introduced Bio-aeration plant radically improving treatment. This became known as the "Sheffield System". Two years previously experiments had been made to aerate the effluent with compressed air jets but this was not successful. Haworth devised a paddle system to agitate the effluent and so introduce oxygen which was successful and in succeeding decades widely adopted around the world.

Through the 1950s and 60s works were undertaken to improve the handling of the sewage sludge. In 1992 the treatment process was modified to remove ammonia using anoxic zones and diffuse air activated sludge treatment

From 1869 through to 1939 the council opened a series of slipper baths across the city to allow people to bathe. Some included wash-houses for laundry while some also had swimming baths and Turkish and other treatment baths. Glossop Road baths had originally been opened in 1836 a private undertaking but taken over by the council in 1898. Ponds Forge is a recent addition to these facilities.

In the 1890s the city adopted the powers it had under the 1875 Public Health Act to improve sanitary conditions. This included improving solid waste collection and disposal. From 1818 the Sheffield Improvement Commissioners had been empowered to clean the streets of the town (within ¾ mile of the Parish church) with the streets at least weekly. The first waste destructor was built in 1896 at Lumley Street. Domestic ash bins were introduced in 1903 and a waste separation and incineration plant built at Bernard Road in about 1932. This has been rebuilt several times with the latest energy recovery plant being completed in 2006. Sheffield introduced its first smoke controls following the 1878 Factories Act having introduced by-laws in 1854. However, only modest progress was made before the 1956 Clean Air Act. The first smoke control order was in place by 1959 and the entire city by 1982.

The sewage treatment works now process the effluent to very high standards. The treated water discharged to the river is very clean and contributes to the overall improvement in the quality of the water. The sludge that is produced undergoes advanced biological treatment to eliminate pathogens. The mesophilic anaerobic digestion enables the breaking down of biodegradable materials using micro-organisms under moderate temperatures. This generates methane gas which is captured to fuel parts of the plant. Spare heat from the works is also captured to sterilise the sludge which is combined with composted vegetation from municipal green waste collections. This produces an organic fertiliser for use in agriculture or horticulture.

The principal treatment works is Blackburn Meadows. The plant at Woodhouse Mill treats effluent from the south east of the city. This has recently been fitted with new sludge digestion facilities. Stocksbridge and Deepcar works, originally built in 1919, have been recently renewed, as has the works at Tankersley. The sludge being taken by tanker to Blackburn Meadows for further treatment. These are part of a programme to upgrade all wastewater treatment works to improve the quality of discharged water and operational efficiency.

When built in the latter part of the 19th century, the brick and masonry sewers were more than adequate for the amount of sewage. Since then, population growth and increased industrialisation have put enormous strain on the work of the original engineers. Many of the early sewers combine both the rainwater flow from roofs and the wastewater from lavatories, sinks, etc. This works well most of the time. However, at times of heavy rainfall the flow can be too large for the pipes to carry causing flooding of contaminated water.

Schemes are continuing to be built to improve the performance of the old sewerage system. In the early 1980s the Don Valley Interceptor sewer, a 5.5m diameter pipe, collects water from the city centre and lower Don Valley for treatment. This eradicated 200 storm outfalls to the river. Across the city additional very large storage tanks, such as at Millhouses Park, Abbeydale and Hillsborough have been built. Together these provide thousands of cubic metres of storm water storage capacity to further reduce flooding. These safely hold the sewage during times of flood flow preventing its discharge to the city's rivers. Once the storm has passed the water is allowed to safely continue its journey along the sewers to the wastewater treatment plant.

Even where foul and storm water are separated at source, flooding can still occur from heavy rainfall. The increased development of the city has "concreted over" large areas which prevents water permeating naturally into the ground. (It should be noted that the natural clay soils of much of the city are relatively impermeable anyway and so the area has always been prone to localised flooding at times of heavy rain.) This means that water has to flow over the surface or through the drainage system which can quickly become overloaded. Engineers are developing new drainage techniques such as Sustainable Drainage Systems (SuDS) that capture and filter or store water before it enters the drainage system, replicating in part the natural processes that would have occurred without the developments. This reduces the maximum flow through the pipes in time of storms and so reduces the risks of flooding.

River water quality has been dramatically improved recently from the very poor state that had arisen in the early 1970s. The Environment Agency is working with the diverse river owners and other authorities to reduce pollution, improve bio-diversity and mitigate flood risks. In the Living Don project Yorkshire Water, other river owners and Sheffield Wildlife Trust are working together to improve the biodiversity of the river. Many of the native fish species had become locally extinct. However, restocking of the river after habitat improvement has created a thriving coarse fishery. Since 2016, Salmon and Otters have been seen in the rivers of the city. This is a good indication of the health of the river system.

Large sections of the river are being improved to mitigate flood risk and improve habitat quality for our native wildlife. One of the biggest problems in doing this is the large quantities of alien plants such as Japanese knotweed. This notifiable species can be spread very easily and is difficult to eradicate once established.

Dredged silt containing the roots is classed as a special waste and very few landfill sites will accept it, greatly increasing transport and disposal costs.

Fish passes are being built at the larger weirs to allow migratory species to be able to swim upstream to the spawning gravel beds and non-migratory species to return to their home stretches of river if washed down stream in a flood.

The Don catchment is being used as a pilot area to understand the implications of implementing the EU Water Framework Directive. This includes modelling of the water quality as well as water flows and flooding potential.

The five mile reach of river from the city centre to Meadowhall has benefited from the Lower Don Valley Flood defence project. This was instigated after the 2007 flood which badly affected Meadowhall shopping centre, Sheffield Forgemasters Ltd and Gripple Ltd works. The seven year project was completed in January 2018 and cost £20.7M of which 90% was funded by the Environment Agency and DEFRA. Local businesses paid in £1.4M with a "Business Improvement District" having been established for the purpose – a national first. This has allowed the 500 businesses to once again access flood risk insurance cover at affordable prices. The risk of a flood has been reduced to an average of 4% per annum to 1%. This has been achieved by raising flood barriers and installing new walls and flood gates as well as carefully controlled dredging of the river channel. Five further schemes are in the planning stage by Sheffield City Council and their partner organisations affecting the Upper Don, Sheaf and Porter Brook rivers.

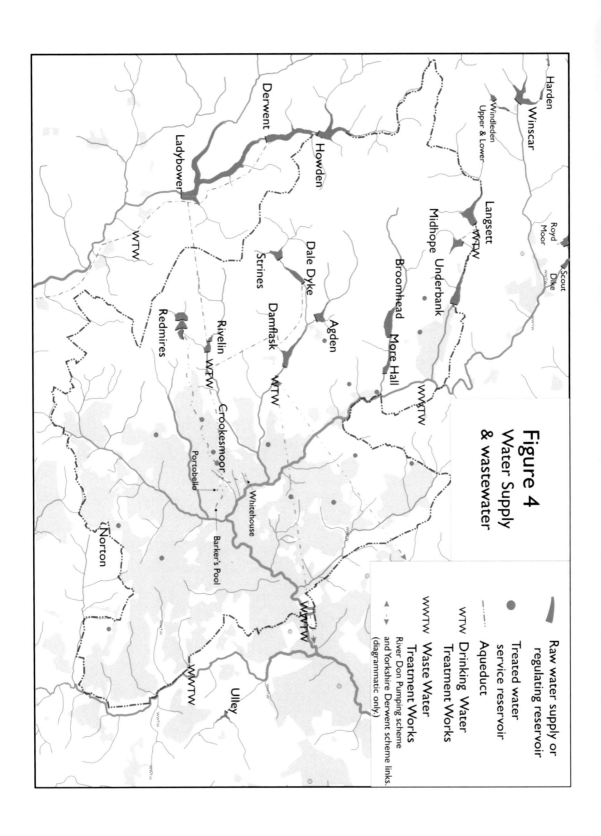

Figure 4
Water Supply
& wastewater

Sheffield's water supply reservoirs.								
Reservoir	Date	Engineer	Contractor	Height (m)	Length (m)	Impounded Volume (m³)	Supply Yield (Ml/d)	NGR
Upperthorpe (Whitehouse)	1737	Matthewman		~2-3	~10-39	60-300?	?	SK 338 888 No longer existing
Crookesmoor (Great Dam)	1782			~8?	160	100,000?		SK 338 874
Crookesmoor lesser dams	1782 1853			~2-4?	30-150?	200-2,500 =>6,000?		SK 33_87_ No longer existing
Redmires (middle)	1836	J. T. Leather		14	689	0.85 M	24.5 +6.6 Regulating	SK 265 855
Rivelin (lower)	1848	J. T. Leather		15	305	0.79 M		SK 276 867
Rivelin (upper)	1848	J. T. Leather		12	220	0.22 M		SK 271 869
Redmires (lower)	1849	J. T. Leather		15	579	0.63 M		SK 267 856
Redmires (upper)	1854	J. T. Leather		15	686	1.56 M		SK 260 855
Dale Dyke (original)	1864	J. T. Leather	Craven, Cockayne & Fountain	29	382	3.24 M		SK 246 918
Agden	1869	T. Hawksley		28	458	2.86 M	58.6	SK 261 923
Strines	1871	T. Hawksley		27	127	2.24 M		SK 232 905
Dale Dyke (replacement)	1875	T. Hawksley		25	280	2.21 M		SK 244 817
Damflask	1893	T. Hawksley		26	350	5.26 M	26.0 Regulating	SK 284 907
Midhope	1896	W. Watts		21	262	1.5 M		SK 224 997
Langsett	1905	W. Watts	S. Fox & Co.	36	352	6.39 M		SE 214 003
Underbank	1907	W. Watts	S. Fox & Co.	16	466	2.95 M	21.7 Regulating	SK 253 993
Howden	1912	E. Sandeman	DVWB labour	36	329	9.3 M	32.2 (For Sheffield)	SK 170 924
Derwent	1916	E. Sandeman	DVWB labour	35	338	9.8 M		SK 173 898
Broomhead	1929	T. & C. Hawksley	S. Fox & Co.	30	305	4.77 M	43.5	SK 269 960
More Hall	1936	T. & C. Hawksley	S. Fox & Co.	24	280	2.55 M		SK 287 957
Ladybower	1945	G.H. Hill & Son	R. Baillie	43	381	28.6 M	Regulating	SK 200 854

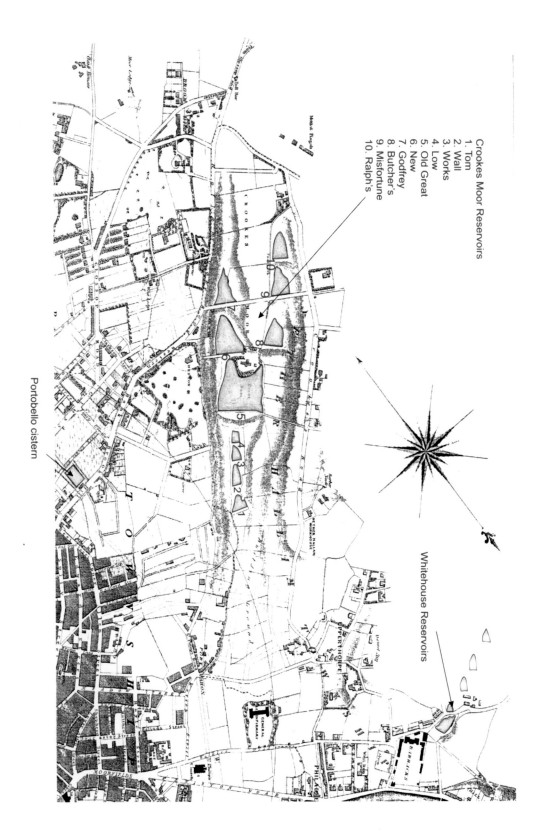

Crookes Moor Reservoirs
1. Tom
2. Wall
3. Works
4. Low
5. Old Great
6. New
7. Godfrey
8. Butcher's
9. Misfortune
10. Ralph's

Portobello cistern

Whitehouse Reservoirs

3.1   An extract of Taylor's map of 1835, showing the Crookesmoor water supply reservoirs. Reproduced courtesy of Sheffield City Archives and Libraries.

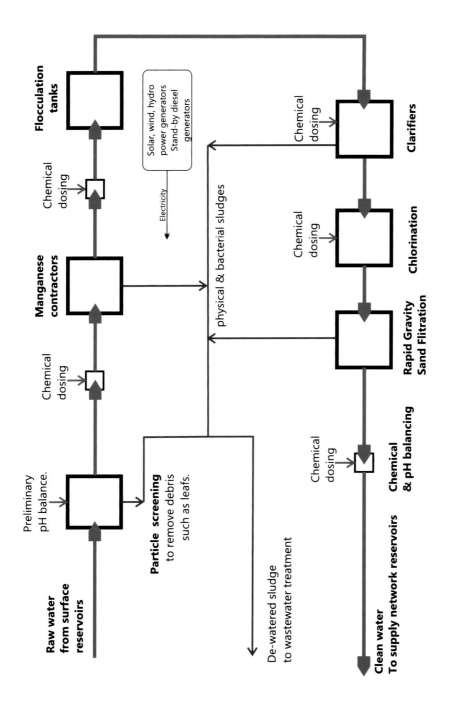

Water treatment process diagram.

All processes continuously monitored to ensure compliance with strict standards.

3.2   Raw water reservoirs in the North west of the city earn the area the nickname Sheffield's Lake District.

3.3   Once treated the water is stored in covered reservoirs to prevent contamination.

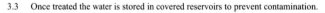

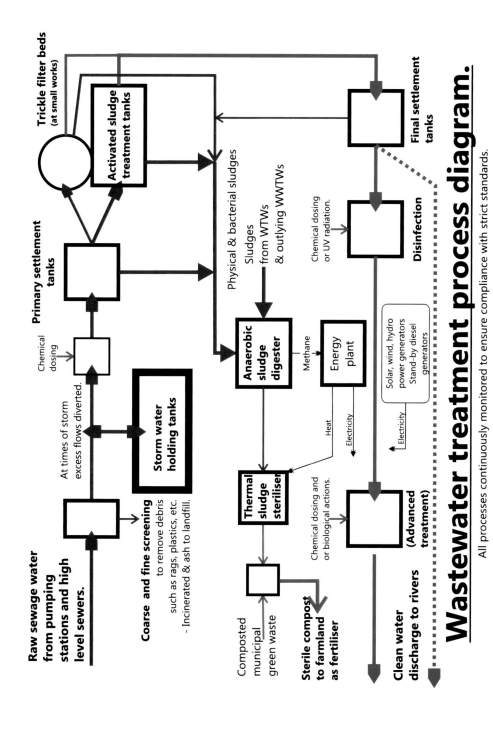

Wastewater treatment process diagram.

All processes continuously monitored to ensure compliance with strict standards.

Energy

The many wheels on the local rivers and sustainable harvests from the local woodland supplied much of the energy needed for Sheffield industry into the 19th century. The growing population and industrial processes required more energy. Coal came to dominate and gas was manufactured and distributed to homes and businesses.

Water and wind power.

Currently, only four of the many scores of water wheels remain able to be used for their intended purposes. The industrial museums at Shepherd Wheel, Abbeydale Hamlet and Wortley Top Forge occasionally demonstrate the water power in use at their sites. Sharrow Snuff Mill while generally powered by electricity has the capacity to operate the machinery by the old water wheel mechanism.

Until recently, very little was known of the men (and very occasionally women) who designed and built these early power generating sites. Thank to Christine Ball's researches we are now able to identify some of the people involved. The earliest known record of mill-wrighting in Sheffield dates to 1441 but generally what records that do exist start from the latter part of the 16th century. Regrettably many key records from the second half of the 18th century, when a lot of the wheels were being built, appear to have been lost.

In the 1580s George and Henry Swyft are recorded as working on many mill site for the lords of the manor. Notably, however, they were also consulting on schemes as far away as Herefordshire.

By 1611, William Vintin had arrived in Sheffield from Sussex. He founded a dynasty of professional millwrights active until at least the mid 18th century. John Hawkesley is also recorded as acting as a millwright on various schemes from 1634 onwards. After the disruption of the civil war the two families formed an enduring partnership. It is clear that the partnership advised and executed work on all aspects of mill and wheel construction from surveying sites, selecting specific trees for construction, building the dams, weirs and goyts, to constructing the buildings and machinery. In the breadth of their expertise they were clearly superior to almost all the other millwright in the area. The latter were essentially the skilled craftsmen who worked under the supervision of the likes of the Hawkesleys and Vintaines (the spelling of the family name varied) or carried out basic tasks. From the 1770s to 1860s local directories list some of these craftsmen. The number varies from year to year, being typically around ten. After the reconstruction work following the 1864 flood, it would appear that the industrial developments largely superseded the use of water power and mill-wrighting went into a decline. However, some sites such as Low Matlock Rolling mill and Shepherd Wheel continued well into the 20th century. Shepherd Wheel and Abbeydale Hamlet operate as part of Sheffield Industrial Museums. A working water powered corn mill can be found at Worsborough Mill Barnsley.

There is now the possibility that some more of the old water wheel site may be brought back into use as micro-hydroelectric generating stations. Jordan Wheel, near Blackburn Meadows and Kelham Island are proposed sites. Future generators may use an Archimedes Screw turbine (Jordan Wheel) rather than a conventional water wheel

(Kelham Island) or turbine. Archimedes Screws are relatively efficient, simple and with a low environmental impact. Water flows down a tube filled with a corkscrew blade causing it to slowly rotate. A new hydropower plant has successfully been installed down stream at Thrybergh weir east of Rotherham by Barn Energy and Yorkshire Hydropower Ltd. This uses an Archimedes screw to turn the generator and can supply enough power for 300 homes (1.2MW) for 10/11 months of the year depending upon river flows. A fish pass was installed as part of the works to aid the migration of fish, including salmon. A 1.2MW battery storage facility is on site which allows the power to be released to grid at the times when it is most needed and so most valuable.

Typically the mills on the Sheffield rivers were rated at 3 to 9 kW. Some were larger and some smaller than this. In all cases they were dependant upon an adequate supply of water and were not able to work continuously or necessarily throughout the year. This was particularly so in the mill higher upstream. The further downstream a site the larger the catchment area and so more reliable the flows. Hence storage ponds were less often built. The upstream site were also often a seasonal employment with agricultural work in summer and industrial activity in winter. The efficiency of the water wheel at harnessing the power of the river depended upon the design of the wheel and how the water flows through the mechanism. Early simple wooden undershot wheels were probably no more than 10-30% efficient. Smeaton's developments in the mid 18th century using overshot and low breast wheels improved the figure to 40-70%. Fairbairn's work in the early to mid 19th century developed the use of iron in the wheel which further improved efficiency and allowed larger wheels to be produced. Iron wheels are more durable when properly maintained. Efficiencies of up to 80% have been claimed. An Archimedes Screw mechanism will have an efficiency of 80% or more compared with a water turbine's 80-95%. However, Archimedes screws are more robust, need less maintenance and are less damaging to wildlife, but are only suitable for low head applications.

Historically, there were relatively few windmills in the area - the abundant water power being more reliable and convenient for most villages. However, windmills are recorded in Attercliffe, Beighton, Chapeltown, Eckington, Halfway, Handsworth Woodhouse, Norton, Mosborough, Thorpe Hesley, Wincobank and Woodthorpe. These wind mills will have had a power capacity of 2.5-7.5kW similar to the water mills. This was adequate for the work required. They were sited on hill tops to capture as much wind as possible. None of these survive. They were generally constructed as a masonry tower with a rotating timber cap holding the shaft for the sails. The cap usually had a mechanism to automatically turn the sails into the wind. However, Beighton, Eckington and Norton were post mills where only the ground floor was masonry and the main structure above housing the machinery was timber frames supported off a central timber post and could be turned to face the wind. This design is more common further south in the country in areas with less extreme winds.

The nearest surviving tower, to my knowledge, is at Wentworth. However, to find a working mill the nearest is probably at Heage, near Belper in Derbyshire. Heage has a 7.9m tall stone masonry tower up to 7.3m in diameter surmounted by a 3m cap with 9.1m long sails. The sizes of the local mills are unknown but will have been similar. The nearest surviving post mill is as Dale Abbey, near Derby.

There are no large scale wind farms in Sheffield - there is limited space between the built up area and the Peak National Park. There are wind farms north of Penistone and also south of Rotherham. E.on's Royd Moor array has 13 turbines generating a maximum total of 6.5MW of electricity. The Advanced Manufacturing Research Centre has a single turbine rated at 0.85MW and a smaller 225kW turbine. A number of local businesses and individuals have installed micro-generating units. Micro generation is classes as below 50kW rated capacity. Household turbine may be rated at 80W to 1kW typically while those found on poles on farms and small businesses are typically in the range of 1 to 15kW. A 10kW turbine would typically have a 12m tall steel tubular mast less than 1m in diameter supporting three blades up to 5m long. Britain has a thriving micro generation industry but the large scale turbines are mostly imported.

All wind turbines are dependant upon having wind blowing. Operational wind speeds are typically of the order of 5 to 25 m/s, that is from a breeze to a gale (Beaufort scale 4 to 9). The taller and larger a turbine the less it is affected by the reduction in wind speed at ground level due to the many obstructions that can occur and so can work when the general wind speed is low. Major wind farms may have the right wind conditions about 30% of the time. This reduces to 10-20% for the rural tall pole mounted turbines while in suburban areas this will be less than 10% and for small turbines in urban areas possibly only no more than 2% of the time.

The systems at the AMRC are linked to energy storage systems to provide some back up when the wind is not suitable. This is rare, but becoming more common.

Electricity

John Tasker, an engineering stores merchant of 29 Sheaf Street established the city's first permanent generating plant there in 1886. This had three horizontal compound steam engines each driving a British Thompson Houston dynamo creating 2kV for a 50 arc lamp series. The first customer is believed to be H. L. Brown jewellers. Tasker merged his existing telephone exchange business with this company to form Sheffield Telephone Exchange and Electric Light Company in 1888. The same year, Lodge Moor hospital is recorded as using electric lighting. The following year a 35kW 2kV single phase 100Hz Mordey alternator was installed to power incandescent lights. There were initially 20 customers each of whom had a transformer on the premises to step the voltage down to 100 volts. Every customer was visited twice daily by a company technician to check the apparatus. Supply was via overhead lines with the alternating current service operating from 7.00 am to 11.30 pm while the direct current service for the arc lighting ran from dusk to 11.00 pm. In 1892 the company obtained powers under the 1882 Electric Lighting Act to supply electricity to Sheffield. This required them to install cables buried in the streets of borough centre. The 2kV cables were paper insulated and lead covered laid through 7.5cm cast iron ducts. The Sheffield Electric Light and Power Company (SELPCo) was set up in 1892 when the telephone business was sold off to National Telephone.

A new generating station was opened on 17 March 1894 on Sheaf Street with four alternators. The records for the month of May that year show 7662kWh generated using 16.3kg of coal per kWh. The company went onto 24 hour generation. Additional plant was installed the following year to cope with rising demand and new company offices were opened on Commercial Street in 1896.

The city council bought out the SELPCo in 1898 for £290,000 with William Johnson continuing as company manager and chief engineer. On Johnson's death in 1900 S. E. Fedden moved from Edinburgh to take up the post of engineer and manager. That year he purchased a Parsons Steam turbine generator after it had been used to power the Paris Exhibition. The following year supply was changed to 200 V two phase 50 Hz as this was more appropriate for the increased usage for motors. The corporation started manufacturing their own transformers and in 1905 pioneered the use of Stalloy (a soft iron) for transformers.

A new power station was built at Neepsend opening in 1904 with 3MW capacity with linking inter-connector cables to Sheaf Street and the city substations. A third alternator was installed here in 1909 and a synchronous condenser at Sheaf Street to improve the efficiency and reliability of supply. A synchronous condenser is a large motor with a linked large flywheel connected to the supply that buffers the loading. Electric street lighting began in 1907 and Edgar Allen pioneered using electrically powered melting furnaces in 1910. There was very substantial growth in demand through the first world war as the factories of the city carried out vital war work. By 1916 it was clear that a new larger site would be required. Spare land at the Blackburn Meadows Sewage Treatment Works was selected and the necessary legislation enacted in 1917. This entailed changing the borough boundaries with Rotherham and exchanging land with various businesses and the Midland Railway Co. Construction did not begin until in 1918. In the meantime load shedding had to be introduced. The major users were linked to the control centre by dedicated telephone lines to co-ordinate the times of their peak usage. Each major user would have their supply cut at times to ensure adequate availability to the other key users when they needed it. Energy use had increased from 21.5 GWh in 1913 to 172.5 GWh in 1919.

The Blackburn Meadows plant opened in 1921 with 40 boilers feeding 8 generators producing 28MW of power. The dry weather flow of the river in itself was insufficient to provide all the cooling required and so 4 timber duplex cooling towers were built each capable of handling ½ million gallons of water per hour. Also in 1921 a link cable was laid to the Yorkshire Electric Power Company's operations in the West Riding. A link to Rotherham corporations undertaking was made in 1928. Even before the city boundaries were expanded to the south Dore, Norton, Dronfield and Beighton were included in the city supply zone.

In 1929 S. E. Fedden left to become a regional manager of the new Central Electricity Board and was succeeded by Ernest Morgan.

In 1933 a second generator set opened with a capacity of 100MW. This operated at a new high pressure (4.3Mpa, 450 °C) steam turbine system. Subsequently, the first of the hyperbolic concrete cooling towers was built, long since demolished. Towers no 6 & 7 - the famous Tinsley Towers - were built and commissioned in 1937-8, each capable of handling 4.5 million gallons of water per hour. They were 250 feet high of 165 feet girth and 5" thick. This form of cooling tower, with a hyperbolic paraboloid shape, was first developed in Holland in 1915. L. G. Mouchel & Partners led their development in the UK from 1925 onwards designing over 150 towers. The doubly curved shaped helped stabilise the very thin wall - comparable if not thinner in thickness scale to that of an egg shell.

From 1934 the major steel users started to require extra capacity and 33kV cables were laid to their premises with the first 33kV feed to the public network in 1935. The first 132kV link across the Pennines was laid in 1942.

The expansion of the Blackburn Meadows power station in the 1930s coincided with the completion of the first national electricity grid in 1932 and the subsequent large increase in power demand – a peak of 908 GWh in 1944. The electricity supply was nationalised in 1948 after the very severe winter of 1947 put extreme demand on the system which had changed very little since before the war. The pre-war expansion of capacity had allowed to the city to supply the necessary power at the time with continuous upgrading to the cabling to provide redundancy.

By the 1970s the Sheffield area was the most concentrated area of electrical load in Europe, if not the world.

The 132kV grid was supplemented with a 400kV super grid from 1965 reaching Sheffield in 1975. A key local link in the network is a trans-Pennine connector running through the Woodhead tunnels. The then disused Victorian railway tunnels were converted for use from 1964 to 1969 to carry the high voltage cables. This was followed by the construction of the very large coal fired power stations of the region, and nuclear power stations at various locations around the country. The National Grid manage the power being supplied minute by minute to ensure that it meets exactly with the fluctuating demand of consumers.

The Blackburn Meadows plant stopped generating in October 1980. A local trust was formed to convert these iconic structures into a contemporary art space. However, they could not raise the necessary money to fulfil their aspirations. The cooling towers were demolished in the early hours of 24 August 2008 watched by thousands of people.

E.on UK built a new 30MW bio-mass fuelled power plant at Blackburn Meadows. This became operational in summer 2014. It uses waste wood material as a fuel stock – material that currently goes to landfill. Waste heat from the plant will be able to heat nearby business premises.

Local farmers are increasingly growing crops specifically to fuel power stations. The large coal fired power stations, such as Drax, Eggborough and Ferrybridge now include bio-mass crops as part of their fuel. Drax is the largest user of bio-fuel in the UK. Cement manufacturers, such as Breedon at Hope in Derbyshire, are also using a blend of fuels to reduce waste and carbon emissions. Perhaps ironically, the demise of coal fired power stations is reducing the supply of pulverised fuel ash which is often blended with Portland Cement to produce a cementitious material with good durability and ease of use. Similarly the loss of steel making capacity is reducing the availability of ground granulated blast furnace slag which is also used for similar purposes.

Yorkshire Water built an anaerobic sludge digester plant at the Blackburn Meadows Waste water treatment works. This was completed in late 2014 and to become the largest single site plant of its type in the UK with an energy output of 1.9MW.

Gas

William Murdock, one of the engineering brains behind the major industrial enterprise of Boulton and Watt, had written a paper for the Royal Society on the topic of generating gas from the controlled combustion of coal in 1808, but there was no early commercial interest - his employers dismissed the idea! However, about a dozen towns, including Sheffield, started gas lighting between 1810 and 1820, Sheffield being the sixth, Nottingham having started work a couple of months earlier. The Sheffield Gas Light Company (SGLCo) opened its first gas works on Shude Hill in 1818 with the first 20 gas street light from Churchgate to Waingate being lit on 6 October 1819. Shude Hill near to Sheaf Bridge was selected for the works as conveniently close to, yet down wind of, the town centre to not require lengthy supply pipes and also close to the forthcoming canal wharf for ease of supply of the raw materials. These gas lamps replaced earlier oil lamps used since 1734 on a few streets in the town centre. From 1747 a lamplighter was employed to light the lamps. As late as 1809 there were only 599 oil lamps which were only lit on 100 nights a year between 19 September and 25 March and not on nights when an adequate moon was scheduled (regardless of the weather). The latter was a practice that persisted long after the introduction of gas lights. In these early days all gas undertakings were somewhat experimental as different materials and techniques were tried at the different towns. Initially the Barlow Bros. of London had been appointed engineer. However, within a year they had been replaced by John Grafton of Edinburgh, while Edwin Rawson was retained as sub-engineer. The works proved successful and expansion and improvements were necessary by 1829. New retorts by the, by then, eminent engineer George Lowe of Derby were installed along with a gas-holder by Joshua Horton of Brierley Hill.

In 1835 they were continuing to struggle to keep pace with increasing demand as the town grew. They were supplying 5,665-8,495m^3 daily from four gas-holders totalling 2,487 m^3 capacity. Partly as a result of a change of coal from the Newbiggin to Swallow seams they were experiencing excess ammoniacal liquor and hydrogen sulphide in the supplied gas. As a result a rival company "the Sheffield New Gas Company" was established with James Colquhoun as engineer. Their plant was situated on Effingham Street and constructed by Newton Chambers of Chapeltown. Colquhoun's early experience had been as a fitter with the SGLCo In 1818 but by this time had an extensive portfolio of schemes behind him including Mansfield in 1823, Lincoln, Nottingham, Leeds, Wakefield, Belfast and Newry.

The early 1840s was a period of depression in the economy and both companies struggled to be profitable in the face of their competition. As a result the two companies merged in 1844 to form the Sheffield United Gas Light Company. The price that gas was being sold had dropped from 8/- to 5/5 per 1000 cu. ft in this period, it had been 12/- in 1820, but leakage remained high at 37% in 1848! In that year this was partly as a result of the Highways board commencing to lay new sewers in the town following the Public Health Act and disturbing the gas pipes.

In 1850 the town council and some local businessmen were again dissatisfied with performance of the gas company and so incorporated the rival New Gas Consumers Company under a Board of Trade Licence with their Neepsend works opening in 1852. However, they did not have authority to dig up the town street to lay their supply pipes. As a result the farcical situation arose that they would dig a trench and they SUGLCo would fill it in before pipes could be laid! Unable to get parliamentary approval themselves the new gas company acceded to a merger with SUGLCo 1855 by Act of Parliament. The price they were charging for gas had now dropped to 3/6 per 1,000 cu ft.

In 1864 the Neepsend works were enlarged and altered, the original gas-holder having been demolished due to faults in 1855. Land at Grimesthorpe which had been purchased in 1862 was developed from 1865 but was plagued with problems as coal working were causing subsidence of the foundation of the new plant. By 1874 consumption had grown to 21.78M m^3 up from 4.25M m^3 in 1854 with the company supply an area stretching from Totley to Rotherham.

In the 1890s two gas-holders were successfully built at Grimesthorpe with a new production plant. However, the later proved faulty and the retorts at Neepsend and Effingham Street that were to be closed had to be restarted. Throughout the existence of the gas undertakings in Sheffield by products such as tar and coke and some organic chemicals had been sold. However, the market for some items such as sulphate of ammonia remained small. Nevertheless, a national report on the gas industry in 1895 showed that only Sheffield was profitable.

By the early 1900s sales of mantle gas lamps as opposed to open flame lamps, and fires and gas engines grew. In part, this was thanks to more creative marketing in the showroom in the company offices built back in 1874. The gas mantle had been invented in Austria in 1885 and produced a much better quality light using much less gas than the simple burner. However, it was expensive until around 1901.

A new 0.22M m^3 gas holder was erected at Neepsend in 1905 increasing capacity there to 0.39M m^3. By 1910 gas furnaces were becoming widely adopted by the steel makers of the area.

World War I was a challenging period for the undertaking. The Sheffield heavy steels industries were absolutely vital to the war effort and the demand for gas soared from 5.4M m^3 in 1913 to 130.4M m^3 in 1918. This was achieved at a time of severe labour shortage rising costs of materials and labour and the need to remove toluol and benzol from the gas for use in the explosives industry affecting the quality of the gas. In 1917 labour shortages were so acute, despite employing women where they could that they had to petition the government for assistance. At this time the company decided its long term future was as a distributor not a producer of gas with the intention of buying gas supplies from a network of local gas producers. Coke being an important material in steel production at the time many coking plants were being set up at local collieries. In order to satisfy the demand they had started buying gas from Tinsley Park and Orgreave collieries to feed Grimesthorpe purification station.

From 1932 the South Yorkshire gas grid was established to supply gas from coking works such as Orgreave, Tinsley Park, Nunnery and High Hazels together with the Thorncliffe coal Distillation Works. The Wincobank (Meadowhall) purification and storage works dates from 1932-8 and included the world largest gas holder of its type at the time at the time. By 1938 this local grid, the first in the country, had 56 miles of pipework feeding gas from the coking plants to the town supply system. The Sheffield supply network then covered an area of 315 sq miles using 1,233 miles of supply mains delivering 0.28M m^3 of gas to 184,000 customers. The demand from a single steel works could exceed that from towns as big as Blackpool or Salford. The grid allowed the closure of small in-efficient plants at Baslow, Eckington, Elsecar, Grimesthorpe, Hoyland, Killamarsh and the reconfiguration of operations at Matlock. At this time 2/3 of the supply was from the coking works. Gas that had hitherto been vented to the air as waste. Sheffield gas industry was probably the most sophisticated in the country and the company research department worked with its industrial customers to improve methods of production.

In 1916 new coke ovens replaced an earlier limited coking facility at Stocksbridge steelworks, using coal from the Hunshelf colliery which was also owned by the steelworks owners. When the seam became exhausted locally in 1950 the plant closed and Stocksbridge's gas came from the South Yorkshire Grid.

All gas undertaking were nationalised in April 1949.

The introduction of North Sea natural gas in the 1970s transformed the delivery of gas across the country with a new national grid. The local town gas production works were then closed. Every gas appliance in the country had to be altered. Coal gas contained typically 50% hydrogen, 35% methane and small amounts of other hydrocarbons together with carbon monoxide, carbon dioxide and nitrogen. Natural gas has a calorific value approximately double that of the coal gas it replaced.

The network of cast iron and lead distribution pipes is now being progressively replaced with welded polyethylene pipe-work. These are more resistant to any slight ground movements and less prone to leakage. In Sheffield there are over 1,000km of pipe-work, part of the 278,000km total in the UK, of which 7,600km form the strategic national grid. These pipes range in size from 63mm to 1.2m in diameter. These figures exclude the individual small property supply pipes.

Britain's native gas fields are now starting to become depleted and the country imports gas from overseas. This is either through gas pipeline inter-connectors to Norway, Ireland and Holland, where we are connected to the trans-European grid receiving gas from Russia, or in the form of liquefied Natural Gas (LNG) brought by tanker from much farther afield. Civil engineers are now constructing huge gas storage facilities at Milford Haven and The Isle of Grain to receive these supplies. In these the gas is cooled to -160 °C to liquefy it and so dramatically reduce the physical volume of material to be stored. There are also smaller storage facilities at strategic points in the national gas pipe network and large scale storage is possible by partial recharge of a depleted gas field in the southern North Sea. This "Rough" Storage facility via the Easington Gas Terminal is capable of holding approximately 3.2 billion m^3 (35TWh of energy) from summer to winter. There are plans to capture the carbon dioxide emissions from some power stations and feed them into some of the depleted North Sea gas or oil fields. If this technique can be developed to a commercial scale it will give Britain a world lead in Carbon Capture and Storage technology.

These are all in addition to the familiar the local gas-holders in most towns and cities, such as those at Neepsend, Effingham Street, Meadowhall and Stocksbridge. However, all of these locally have been de-commissioned as it is expensive to feed the gas at the right pressure to utilise them effectively.

Combined heat and power

Sheffield Energy Recovery Plant provides heating for much of central Sheffield. The system recovers heat from the incineration of municipal solid waste, producing steam which is used to generate up to 19MW of electricity to the National Grid and up to 60MW to the Community District Energy Network.

The plant is carefully regulated and monitored. This includes the incineration, waste reception and storage, waste-fuel and air supply systems, boilers, facilities for the treatment of exhaust gases, on-site facilities for handling and storage of residues and operations.

Connected buildings contribute an improved local air quality. When a connection to the District Energy Network is made, a building no longer uses fossil fuel to provide heating so precious resources are being conserved. The net effect of connecting each building is a reduction in carbon emissions, saving approximately 75% of previous carbon emissions. Businesses can also avoid the Climate Change Levy.

The equipment used to transfer the heat from the network takes up less than one quarter of the space of a conventional boiler plant, and does not need a chimney. This allows valuable space to be put to other uses.

The E.on Blackburn Meadows renewable energy plant can generate up to 29MW of electricity and up to 25MW of thermal energy which it distributes to local business including the Sheffield FlyDSA Arena and Sheffield Forgemasters steelworks.

Now energy comes from a range of sources - fossil fuels, nuclear, water, wind, solar, bio-mass and waste materials. The demand for electricity varies throughout the day. Now the energy available also varies less predictably. The amount of electricity entering the system has to match that being drawn out to maintain a stable voltage and frequency - essential for sensitive electronic equipment. This is managed by switching on and off various power supplies as needed. Hydroelectric plants can react quickly, thermal plants, that is all that burn some type of fuel, are slower to react as they have to warm up. Gas, coal and then nuclear each take significantly longer to react but once operating can produce electricity cheaply. A few hydroelectric plants have the capacity to go into reverse and store energy by pumping the water back up to the head reservoir. Increasingly batteries are being used for short term storage. The E.on renewable Energy Plant at Blackburn Meadows incorporates a 10MW lithium-ion battery facility contracted to National Grid to help balance and modulate the power demands across the grid and ensure a stable voltage and frequency.

Sheffield company Faradion was founded on the premise that sodium-ion batteries are cheaper and safer than lithium-ion, with a higher energy density and a wider operating temperature range than other batteries. It is the world leader in non-aqueous sodium-ion cell technology that provides cheaper, cleaner energy for non-portable applications. Where weight is a major factor lithium will still have the edge but for stationary application the abundance of sodium is likely to provide a competitive advantage.

Ensuring the right mix of energy supplies is available at the right time is a complex business for the engineers involved. It is teams of civil, mechanical, chemical, nuclear and electrical engineers that source, generate and distribute the energy upon which a modern society depends.

Sheffield businesses such as Sheffield Forgemasters are instrumental in creating the infrastructure and machines used in the large wind farms and most other power generators.

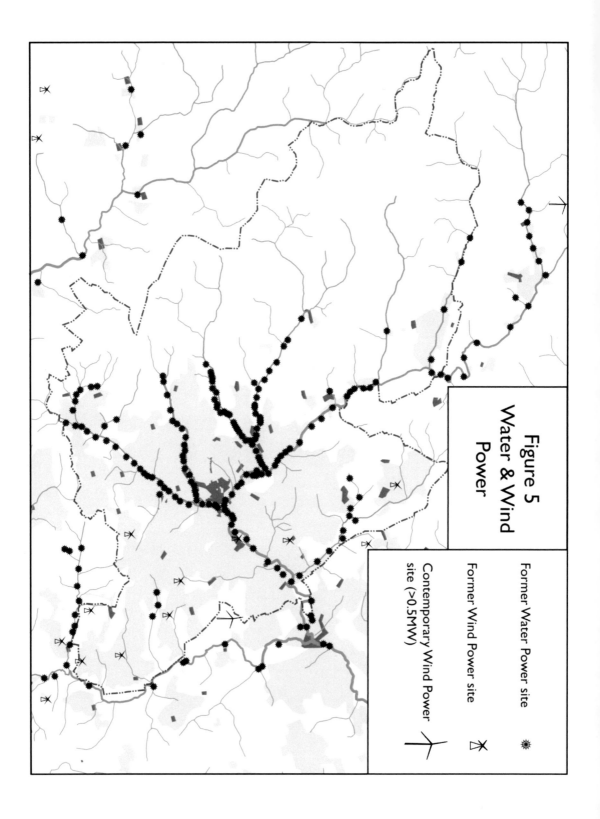

Figure 5
Water & Wind
Power

Former Water Power site

Former Wind Power site

Contemporary Wind Power
site (>0.5MW)

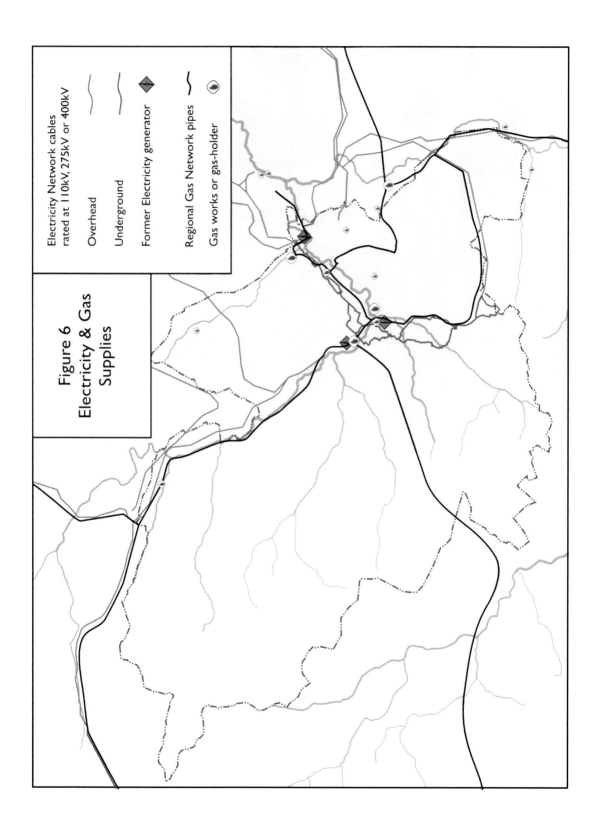

Figure 6
Electricity & Gas
Supplies

Electricity Network cables
rated at 110kV, 275kV or 400kV

Overhead

Underground

Former Electricity generator

Regional Gas Network pipes

Gas works or gas-holder

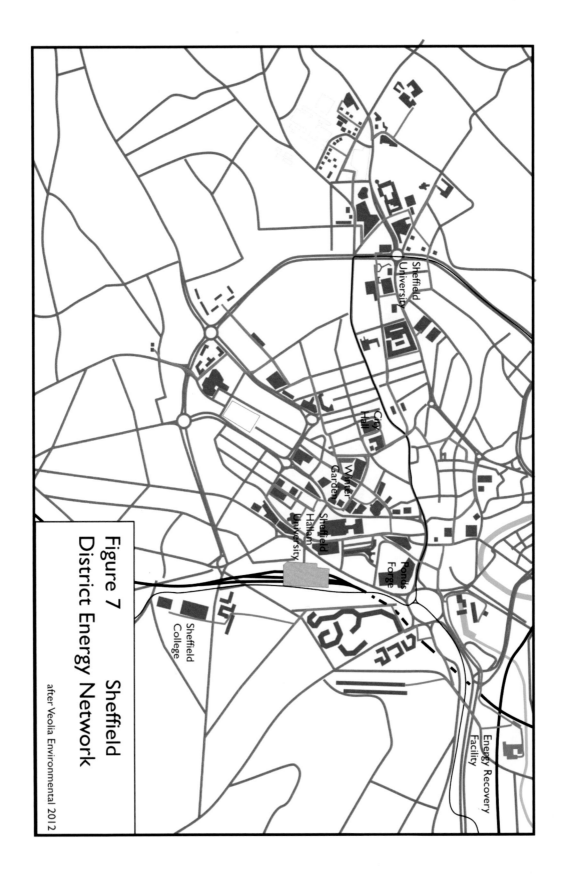

Figure 7   Sheffield
District Energy Network

after Veolia Environmental 2012

Sheffield University

City Hall

Winter Garden

Sheffield Hallam University

Ponds Forge

Sheffield College

Energy Recovery Facility

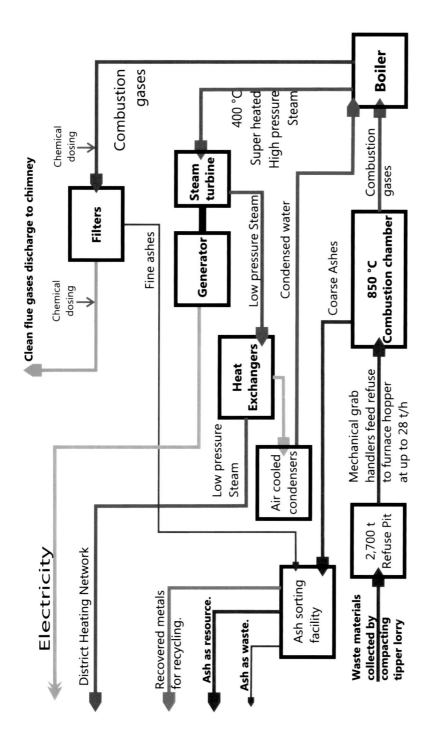

Energy Recovery process diagram.

All processes continuously monitored to ensure compliance with strict standards.

Labels within the diagram:

- Boiler
- Combustion gases
- 400 °C Super heated High pressure Steam
- Steam turbine
- Generator
- Clean flue gases discharge to chimney
- Chemical dosing
- Chemical dosing
- Filters
- Fine ashes
- Low pressure Steam
- Condensed water
- Coarse Ashes
- Combustion gases
- 850 °C Combustion chamber
- Heat Exchangers
- Air cooled condensers
- Low pressure Steam
- Mechanical grab handlers feed refuse to furnace hopper at up to 28 t/h
- 2,700 t Refuse Pit
- Electricity
- District Heating Network
- Recovered metals for recycling.
- Ash as resource.
- Ash as waste.
- Ash sorting facility
- Waste materials collected by compacting tipper lorry

4.1   Heage Windmill is the nearest working windmill and is similar in design to the local mills with the exception that Heage is unusual in having six as opposed to four sails. Most mills in the region had stone or brick wall supporting the floors and machinery with only the top section of wood and free to turn into the wind. A design known as tower mills.

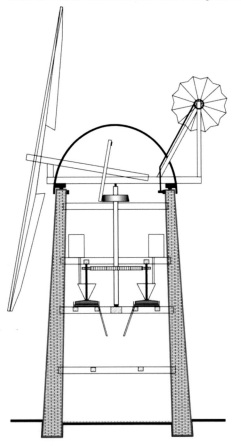

Typical cross section of a tower mill
such as that at Norton

4.2   Attercliffe Windmill. (Reproduced courtesy of PictureSheffield.com ref: s08097)

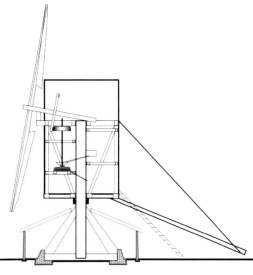

Typical cross section of a post mill
such as that at Eckington

4.3   Cat and Fiddle post mill at Dale Abbey near Derby is the nearest surviving mill of the type, which was more prevalent in the Midlands than the north of England. Beighton, Eckington and Norton were post mills.

Post mills were almost entirely made of timber and the entire mill was turned to face the wind.

© Sheila Harris

4.4   These modern turbines at Border View Farm each have a similar power capacity as a traditional windmill at 10-20 kW.

© Dave Pickersgill

4.5   Royd Moor wind farm near Penistone. 13 turbine each producing up to 0.5 MW from 37 m diameter rotors mounted at a hub height of 35 m above the ground.

4.6   Abbeydale Industrial Hamlet high breast water wheel for the tilt forges generates up to about 30 hp (22.5 kW).

(Reproduced courtesy of SIMT)

© Barn Energy Ltd and Yorkshire Hydropower Ltd

4.7   Thrybergh Weir Hydropower plant utilised an existing weir to create the operating head. It uses a pair of Archimedes Screws to extract the energy from the water flow and incorporates a fish pass. It is rated at 1.2 MW.

4.8   Tinsley towers, now demolished, were a famous local landmark by the M1 Motorway for many years. They cooled the water from the 100MW coal fired electricity generating plant.

© Highways England, Amey

4.9   E.on Bio Energy 30MW plant uses processed wood to produce both electricity for the national grid and heat for local businesses.

4.10   Effingham Street Gas holders temporarily store gas locally to provide a constant uniform supply pressure. A 6 M cu. ft gasholder would contain approximately 190 GWh of energy.

4.11   Bernard Road Energy Recovery facility generates electric and thermal energy from municipal waste. It is rated at up to 60 MW.

Communications

Roads

Little is known of the early road network in Sheffield. Undoubtedly there were primitive roads and trackways across the area from prehistoric times, possibly linking the settlements around the hill fort at Wincobank with those on the eastern fringes of the peak, such as Carl Wark. The Romans built a road from their fort at Brough, near Castleton to another fort at Templeborough. The exact route of this highway is uncertain. It is thought to have come over Stanage edge, passed Stanage Pole to cross Hallam Moor to Sandygate or Ringinglow and then towards the town centre passing the cathedral and crossing the River Sheaf, then probably along Cricket Inn Road towards Catcliffe and so to join a road heading south from Templeborough (the route of which is similarly a matter of conjecture) towards Whittington Moor and Chesterfield. It has been suggested that there may have been a Roman fortlet either near the cathedral or castle sites. However, to my knowledge no evidence has been found so far. However, in 2011 a Roman site was found at Whirlow Hall dating from the reign of Hadrian which is thought to be a trading post or estate centre due to the high quality materials found. A substantial metalled causeway was found running east - west through the excavation. The Roman remains appeared to be on top of earlier Iron Age material.

A significant route way passed through the city in early mediaeval times linking the kingdoms of Mercia to the South and Northumbria. The meeting of rival kings at Dore in 827 saw Ecgbert become king of all England. Again the route of this ancient trackway is uncertain. The main North - South routes or the region are to the East at Doncaster and Rotherham. The main East - West routes also tend to skirt the city, crossing the Pennines at Salters Brook and then on to Barnsley or Rotherham, or via Chapel-en-le-Frith and Totley Moss passing the city to the south. Some of the old routes, particularly to the west of the city have eroded into "hollow ways" on some hills. This is where the passage of feet and wheels of centuries or millennia carve a route into the ground. Of these, some are now just footpaths while others are quite busy lanes.

Lady's Bridge is the oldest known bridge over the river with the present structure dating back to 1486. However, sited as it is under the watch of Sheffield Castle some form of crossing be it a ford or timber bridge will have existed here since at least early mediaeval times. The Broad Street crossing of the Sheaf will also mark an ancient crossing point although nothing remains of the early structures. It seems probable that there was some sort of crossing of the River Don in the general vicinity of Wincobank or Tinsley in ancient times. The river may well have been wide and marshy at the time. However, this would potentially have facilitated the construction of some form of board walk across. Such structures are known elsewhere in the UK from 2,000 to 3,000 years ago. That said the river was clear enough to the used by canoe style wooden boats. The two need not be incompatible.

Originally, the local owner of the land was responsible for the upkeep of any roads that crossed over them. Later, land owners passed these duties to the local community as they became more independent of feudal control in the 14th and 15th centuries. Thus it was that the local civil parishes were responsible, with the county magistrates having overall responsibility over the parishes, for the upkeep of the roads in any district. This was enshrined in an act of parliament of 1555. However, parishes were often reluctant to bear the cost of maintaining roads or carrying out statutory labour, that did not directly benefit them. It was quite common for parishes to be indicted for not maintaining the roads. In which case a parish would be fined by the quarter session court. However, this would be remitted on presentation of a certificate showing that the road had been repaired. Generally, parishes did not employ engineers as their surveyors and the quality of repair was often poor as a result. This meant that many roads became impassible in bad weather, especially for wagons carrying goods. This was not helped by the geology and topography of the district that created a clay soil and steep hills and valleys. Early roads and packhorse trails tended to keep to the relative dry high grounds wherever possible. Little remains of the packhorse trails that is clearly identifiable today. However, there are five packhorse bridges in the valleys to the west and north of Sheffield. These generally date from the mid 18th century when earlier timber or primitive clapper bridges were replaced with stone arch bridges.

From the mid 18th century the magistrates were required to employ surveyors to both map the county and oversee, but not directly carry out, the maintenance of important bridges.

The state of disrepair nationally was restricting the economic development as the country started to industrialise in the 18th century. This may have been exacerbated by the mini-ice age affecting Europe at the time. Thus legislation started to empower turnpike trusts to build new roads or improve existing ones. In return for paying the cost of building and maintaining the highways they were allowed to levy a toll on users.

It would appear that the trusts tried to build rather cheaply. From the records currently available it would appear that professional engineers were not employed, although John McAdam was briefly employed by the Glossop Trust. The trustees of the trust were more concerned about achieving a low initial cost than an economical and effective solution for the whole duration of the trust. Instead, local brickyard or foundry men were employed who tended to use the waste materials from their own enterprises, without consideration or understanding of how they would perform when trafficked.

Notwithstanding the above, the new turnpikes greatly facilitated travel and long distance coaches were set up to allow travel by businessmen and other travellers between the towns and cities of the country. The Tontine Inn on the Haymarket became the centre for the many coach services operating to and from the city from 1785 onwards.

The numerous local turnpike trusts remained responsible for the roads they had built although there were several disputes with the local townships as to the liabilities for maintenance. Investors in the schemes often failed to receive the promised dividends as repair costs were high and tolls inadequate or subject to too many exclusions. The Cutlers' Company and large landowners or businessmen were investors in many of the turnpikes as they strived to improve the transport links for the district to allow them to export their wares more effectively. However, for many investors such as the Cutlers' Company and mine and forge owners, the main purpose of the investment was to allow them to transport their goods to market more quickly, cheaply and above all reliably. To this extent their investments paid off.

In addition to the turnpikes which acted as the arterial routes, local roads were built in the town as new housing and business areas were laid out. In the rural areas the enclosure movement of the 18th and 19th centuries were responsible for the construction of most of the byways. The local industrialists built new roads and river crossings to serve their factories as the town expanded along the river valleys and hills.

The Bridges act of 1803 updated the earlier statutes. This together with other 19th century legislation such as the Municipal reform Act of 1835 and the Public Health Act of 1875 expanded the duties of the surveyor and introduced borough surveyors. They were, by the end of the century, responsible for bridges, roads, lighting, drainage, sewerage, water supply and public buildings. The engineers became increasingly specialised and various professional bodies were set up from the 1870s to 1930s to regulate and promote good practice in the various fields of endeavour.

The town council took over responsibility for all roads in the area in 1884. However, some of the trusts had passed over responsibility for their roads in the preceding 3 decades.

The council remain responsible for all public roads except the motorways (including all of the Tinsley Viaduct) and the Stocksbridge A616(T) bypass which are the responsibility of the Highways Agency.

Until the early 20th century roads were either cobbled or surfaced with compacted crushed rock. There were some attempts to improve the weather resistance by incorporating tar, bitumen or asphalt prior to this. Notably, John Cassell of Millwall, London patented a system in 1834 for coating a macadamised road surface with pitch and sand. In 1902, Edgar Purnell Hooley, The County Surveyor in Nottinghamshire patented Tarmac where tar and aggregate are mixed and then spread and compacted as a road surface. This was following noticing the effect of a spillage of tar on the roadway. He founded a company to make the material the following year. This was of limited commercial success and was bought out by Sir Alfred Hickman of Wolverhampton and the Tarmac company was established in 1905.

However, it was not until the 1920s that asphalted roads became common. Bitumen, although naturally occurring in a few places world-wide, is generally a by-product of the distillation of crude oil to produce petrol and oils. Tar is a by-product of coal processing. The increasing oil production led to greater availability of bitumen to create asphalt surfacing just as road traffic increased leading to greater need for road surfacing. (The first UK oil production was in Hardstoft, Derbyshire in 1915, with significant development near Eakring, Nottinghamshire in the late 1930s.) Similarly pneumatic tyres became widespread in the 1920s with the development of synthetic rubbers. Reinforced concrete has also been used as a road paving material. It was first widely used in the UK for airfield construction during WWII. Its use has varied from time to time, largely depending upon the relative costs of concrete and bitumen.

At the turn of the 20th century there were, nationally, approximately one licensed horse drawn vehicle for every 1500 people, a figure that remained constant until about 1920 when it started the decline of the following two decades. In 1900 motorised vehicles were rare. However, by 1910 there were as many motorised commercial vehicles as horse drawn wagons. These grew in number so that by 1939 there was one commercial motor vehicle for every 120 people. A figure that has not changed greatly since. However, the size and weight have increased significantly and the population of the country has increased by over one third over the period, increasing the absolute number of lorries. Furthermore, the mileage covered by goods vehicles continues to rise as has the proportion of the lorries that are heavier.

Private motor vehicles ownership has nevertheless grown throughout the last century. During the 1920s the number of cars grew fivefold from approximately one for every hundred people at the start of the decade. The main growth of car ownership was in the latter half of the twentieth century, rising from the pre-war level in 1950, to one for every three people in 1980, and enough for half the population by the end of the century. Car ownership is of course not uniform with 1 in 3 households not having access to a car. Nevertheless, the growth in traffic has been huge and again there has been a rise in the distance people regularly travel. Together this has dramatically increased the volume of traffic on our roads and the wear upon them. The capacity of the roads may be mainly influenced by the increase in cars. However, the wear on the roads is dominated by heavy traffic. A typical car axle load of say ½ tonne produces less than a 10,000th part of the stress induced by a standard HGV axle of 8 tonnes. Thus the weight of lorries is strictly regulated.

Legislation was introduced from the 17th century onwards to regulate vehicle weight with a complex set of often local rules created through the turnpike legislation of the 18th and early 19th centuries. This was standardised nationally around the turn of the 20th century as motor vehicles were developed. The maximum axle load has only increased from 8 to 11.5 tonnes since then although maximum gross vehicle weight has increased from 12 to 44 tonnes by introducing additional axles. (The maximum normal vehicle size is now 2.9m wide and 18.65m long.) Better vehicle design – improved tyres and suspension have meant that the increased axle weight is no more damaging than the standard axle to the road pavement. Bridges, however, obviously have to carry the full increased vehicle weight. This meant that the introduction of 44t lorries in 2002 was preceded by a reassessment of the load carrying capacity of all of the country's bridges. Many were proved to be strong enough to carry the additional load without strengthening. Others were strengthened, replaced or made subject to traffic orders restricting heavy traffic from using them. In addition to the loads from normal vehicles many structures, especially on the principal routes around the city have to be capable of carrying exceptional loads. This is particularly so around the industrial manufacturing sites in the east of the city. These exceptional loads, such as special castings from the steel works or large prefabricated components for major structures, may weigh several hundred tonnes. They require police escort on the highways and are transported, on specially designed vehicles with many axles, along carefully prescribed routes. These vehicles will limit the axle loads to normal levels and the routes to structures that can withstand the extra overall loads. In some instances structures have to be temporarily strengthened to allow the passage of the load.

Through the latter part of the 20th century in response to this growth, the government, city council and development partners have worked to improve the road network. The aim being to improve access for businesses and the public. The most obvious new roads of the 20th century were the motorway network. The London to Yorkshire motorway (M1) was given the go ahead by the government in 1956 with the preliminary design of the Aston to Leeds section being given to the West Riding County Council highways department in 1959, being completed in 1962. Sir Owen Williams and Partners meanwhile were designing the Aston to Nottingham section.

The legacy of old abandoned mine workings and potential of subsidence from future deep mining were significant factors in the design and site investigation of the motorway. Many of the bridges in the West Riding section were specially designed to accommodate the settlement, rotation and displacements associated with the extraction of coal at depth below them. This created several innovative flexible designs. The span footbridges, Smithy Wood, Birdwell Quarry and Stainborough, which incorporate the principles of the Wichert Truss were the first bridges of their type to be constructed in concrete in this country, and the first use of concrete tri-hinges. Two of these have now been replaced by long span steel truss bridges. This has allowed the hard shoulder to be reopened around them. It had been closed to protect them from possible vehicle impacts.

Another notable design is that of the Needle's Eye Footbridge, Barnsley. This is one of the most eye-catching structures on the motorways in Yorkshire, if not England.

Furthermore, the existing heavily trafficked roads and limited available space were key factors in the stretch between Sheffield and Rotherham. Thus the two deck Tinsley Viaduct was conceived to carry the motorway and A631 Across the Don Valley. The viaduct was designed and built under a separate contract while the construction of the motorway was let under a series of contracts. Junctions 31-34 and 36-38 were won by Dowsett Engineering Construction Ltd, the M18 by Tarmac and French, 34-35 by Holland & Hannan & Cubitts Ltd, 35-36 by A. Monk & Co. Work started at Aston in July 1965 with that section being completed two years later. The remaining local sections were completed by Summer 1968 with the viaduct opening to traffic on 12 June.

The motorway carries far more traffic than originally envisaged and has often been congested at peak times.

The Highways England government agency recently successfully introduced "managed motorways" to 12 miles of the M1 in South Yorkshire from j32 to j35a. This followed the successful use of the technique on the M42 around Birmingham. This is an alternative, and cheaper, method of safely increasing traffic flow capacity within the existing highways footprint, as has been done elsewhere, such as south of junction 28 of the M1 in the East Midlands. In managed motorways the traffic is intensively monitored and traffic speeds adjusted accordingly to ensure a smooth flow of traffic without sudden large changes in speed. The monitoring also allows any incidents to be spotted very quickly and dealt with as safely as possible. On the M42 the hard shoulder was only opened to traffic as and when required to cope with the traffic flow. There are also frequent additional safety refuges and many sign gantries to inform the road users of the available lanes and speeds. The design in South Yorkshire involves permanent hard shoulder running. This is the first smart motorway scheme to use variable mandatory speed limits to manage both traffic and air quality requirements. The project was delivered through an integrated delivery team of the Highways England with designer WSP and Costain (Principal Contractor). They faced significant challenges including high traffic volumes, limited access and narrow verges which resulted in several innovative solutions to deliver the project on programme and to budget. The South Yorkshire Police had initially had significant safety concerns regarding the smart motorway concept as proposed here. However, these have now been largely allayed now the scheme is operational. The section from j28 to j32 has also been upgraded to managed motorways and have been delivered by the same integrated Delivery Team under a separate contract. It is proposed to continue north of j35a in due course.

The Stocksbridge Bypass was built by McAlpine to designs by Scott Wilson Kirkpatrick and opened in 1988. It was conceived as a section of the M67 motorway to form a second trans-Pennine motorway along the route of the Woodhead pass.

The A630 Catcliffe link road was designed and built by Sheffield City Council. It opened in 1974. This work included improvements to Sheaf Street, Exchange Place and Park Square. The A57 Handsworth bypass and Mosborough Parkway was conceived in the 1960s as an alternative link route to the motorway and access to the Mosborough area which had been planned for expansion of the city. However, the link road was not built until the 1980s.

The A6102 Sheffield Ring Road was designed and built in stages. Prince of Wales Road was laid out when the housing estates were initially developed from the 1930s. Bochum Parkway between Jordanthorpe parkway and Norton Avenue was added in 1981 to complete the link to the A61 south of the city. The section from Jordanthorpe Parkway to Meadowhead and on to Bradway had been built in 1974. The section through Darnall and the Don Valley was improved in 1990 prior to the World Student Games. The A61 Dronfield Bypass opened in 1975. At one stage there were proposals to complete the ring road around the west of Sheffield. This was soon abandoned due to the difficulty and cost crossing the hills and valleys and a perceived lack of demand.

Sheffield inner relief road has been built in phases from 1960 starting with the dualling of Netherthorpe Road. St Mary's Gate and Hanover Way were widened to dual carriageway in the early 1980s. Sheaf Street was improved again in the early 2000s leading to the improvement of the Sheaf Square - railway station area in 2006 and subsequently the links to the ring road at St Mary's Road up to 2009. The northern section of the inner relief road from Sheffield Parkway to Penistone Road was built in two phases following public consultation in the 1990s. The original 1970s proposal had long been abandoned as it would have destroyed important heritage assets such as Kelham Island and the canal basin. Phase 1a from the Parkway to the Wicker was completed in May 2000 and included bridges over the canal and River Don. This section was initially called Cutlers Gate but later renamed to coincide with the completed scheme naming. Phase 1b, Derek Dooley Way, from Wicker to Shalesmoor was completed in 2008. This includes a second river crossing and alterations to the railway viaduct and extensive remodelling of the Corporation street area. This completed a continuous loop of dual carriageway standard road clockwise from Granville Square in the south east to Sheffield Parkway in the east linking all main arterial routes to the city.

The improvements to Penistone Road took place in phases between 1974 and 1995.

The Exchange Place section has now been down graded to local access following the completion of the nearby ring road sections taking traffic around a little further away from the city centre. When the existing markets area is redeveloped it is intended to reduce the width of Exchange Place to make crossing easier and re-create the link from the city centre to the canal basin.

Most of the roads in the city remain largely as they were built, with only minor changes, and have not been designed to accommodate the demands that we now place upon them. The requirements of heavy traffic, cars, cyclists and pedestrians may often conflict and change over time and a difficult balancing act has to be achieved.

Sheffield City Council has developed its Streets Ahead Project to improve the quality of all the city's roads and maintain them to a high standard over the coming 25 years. The council will monitor the performance of Amey against 753 specified performance requirements. Payments will be withheld if requirements are not met. This will transform the city's roads from some of the worst maintained to the best. Amey was awarded the contract in the summer of 2012. In the first five years the majority of the city's highway network will be improved to a good standard in a phased zoned pattern. The zonal approach to the work is designed to minimise the disruption to road users throughout the process. Amey are committed to having a skilled work force and all staff, including staff transferred from SCC, are undergoing training and assessment to ensure work is carried out to a high standard. Every highway asset will be inspected by skilled and trained technicians or engineers. Where considered necessary, further investigation is done either by way of precision surveying and non-destructive testing or by sampling and laboratory analysis. All the carriageways and footways will be resurfaced and some will have more major strengthening during the 25 year contract. More than 40 bridges will be strengthened to current standards.

All the street lighting replaced with the latest high quality energy efficient technology. The new lighting will make Sheffield the first city in the world to be entirely lit with the highly efficient LED technology. This will result in an overall 40% reduction in Sheffield's street lighting electricity usage. The lights will be intrinsically more reliable than existing lamps. Every individual lamp will also be continuously monitored remotely by a central management system. This will allow light intensities to be altered as necessary for further economy or safety and any faults to be immediately identified. All the traffic signals and many traffic signs will be replaced over the 25 year contract with new efficient and easily maintainable systems. For instance, microwave and laser kerbside technology will replace magnetic coil sensors currently buried in the highway at traffic signals. Extensive drainage improvement works will be incorporated in the project including at 80 locations prone to flooding. The contract has determined a range of treatments appropriate to tackle the defects in the highways. Amey will continue an asset management approach. This means that they know the condition of the highways and structures and can intervene with the right action at the right time and not have to rely on an emergency response to failures. Once a road is resurfaced the road will be "protected" for a period of time such that the utility companies will only be able to undertake emergency interventions during this period. This should encourage the utilities to plan the effective management of their assets in the streets. Amey aim to recycle as much material arising from the works as possible. A special recycling plant was built in the east of the city to receive the old road surfacing material that is removed. This is then processed to create new surfacing and foundation materials for use elsewhere. This will reduce the need for new quarried aggregates and many miles of road haulage.

Sheffield's highway network comprises over 1,900km of carriageways & 3,400km footways. In addition there are 610 bridges, culverts and other structures, and over 75,000 street lights and illuminated signs. The 38,000 highway trees are also being carefully managed, including replacement of up to 50% of them with species more appropriate to a highway environment to ensure a long term sustainable landscape resource.

Sheffield has long had a commitment to high quality public transport services to serve the citizens of the city. It is now developing voluntary and statutory quality service agreements and contracts to improve the reliability of public transport through highway improvements, better buses and better staff training.

The city council and others are developing a network of walking routes and cycleway across the city which link into national long distance routes. These include the Sheffield Country Walk and Sheffield Round Walk, Upper Don Walk and Five Weirs Walk together with the Trans Pennine Trail and National Cycle Network routes. Many of the sites featured in this guide are accessible from this network.

Waterways

By 1719 the River Don was navigable to Aldwarke, and by 1751 to Tinsley. William Palmer and Joseph Atkinson assisted by Joshua Mitchell surveyed the Don in 1722 for the Cutlers' Company. The Doncaster - Tinsley Navigation act was passed in 1726 and that for below Doncaster the following year. The cost by 1731 being £12,000, £3,500 of which was met by Doncaster corporation. The River Don Navigation company was incorporated and appointed John Smith, engineer of Attercliffe, initially assisted by and then replaced by John Thompson of Sheffield, to oversee the completion of the works at a cost of a further £40,000. By the 1760s the toll income exceeded £6,000 pa. From here goods had to travel by road to and from Sheffield.

The Sheffield and Tinsley Canal was promoted by the Cutlers' Company of Sheffield but initially opposed by the Duke of Norfolk, the major landowner in the area and mill owners who were concerned about any loss of water from the river. A key problem to overcome was to find a suitable water source that would not interfere with the operation of the many wheels on the River Don. This was achieved by recycling waste water being pumped from two collieries and using two small brooks without wheels on them. There were 14 water powered sites between Lady's Bridge and Tinsley reliant upon the river. Any navigation along this length would not only have to by pass the weirs but also ensure there was an adequate flow of water retained to power the works. The Canal was finally granted approval in 1815 and completed in 1819 approximately 100 years after a navigation was first proposed. The locks are 19.5m long by 4.8m wide to accommodate the Yorkshire keel boats and the canal basin is 182.9m by 30.5m wide. William Chapman was the engineer.

In 1847 the canal was taken over by the newly arrived Manchester, Sheffield and Lincolnshire Railway company. It went into a steep decline in the early-mid 20th century, but is now enjoying a renaissance with the Quay being reopened in the mid 1990s. There are some fine examples of canal engineering to be seen, including the Worksop Road aqueduct.

The Chesterfield Canal was completed in 1771 having been first promoted in 1766 and gaining its Act in 1771. The intention was to provide a cheap means of exporting the coals from the area and to under cut the south Yorkshire colliers. It would also provide an alternative route for Peak District products to reach the Trent. In the 1840s it also carried stone from North Anston quarry for the rebuilding of the Houses of Parliament. The canal continued to prosper even under railway ownership until the Norwood tunnel collapsed in 1907, permanently severing the canal. Traffic continued on the lower reaches until 1962 and the canal maintained below Worksop as a cruise way from 1968. In 1976 the Chesterfield Canal Society was formed to endeavour to reopen the remainder of the canal, becoming the Chesterfield Canal trust in 1998. The section up to Kiveton Park was reopened in 2003.

They now have ambitious plans to restore the missing link through Killamarsh and revitalise the canal into Chesterfield. They also intend to make the River Rother navigable from there down to the Don. These proposals have all been assessed and approved by the British Waterways Board as being of national importance and achievable - subject to funding.

Railways

Sheffield collieries were in the forefront of the development of iron railways, being pioneered by John Curr in Sheffield Park Colliery in 1784. This system used plain wheels running on a flanged rail and it was adopted by the Butterley Iron works in 1790 and then all coalfield outside of the NE England. However, with the success of the Stockton & Darlington Railway, from the 1820s, the rival system came to dominate.

The first railway to Sheffield was a local line, the Sheffield and Rotherham Railway, which terminated near Spital Hill in 1838. This linked to the North Midland Railway services to Leeds and Derby at Masborough from July and May 1840 respectively. This section of the Midland Railway along the Rother Valley now serves primarily as a freight route.

The Sheffield, Ashton-under-Lyme and Manchester Railway (SAMR) arrived in 1845, initially with a road link around the Woodhead Tunnel section. Spital Hill tunnel was built to link the Wicker Station of the Sheffield and Rotherham Railway, now part of the North Midland Railway, with their Bridgehouses Station. At the same time the newly formed Sheffield and Lincolnshire Junction Railway (SLJR) started work in Darnall.

The Woodhead Tunnel was started within 6 months of the enabling act of May 1837 with Charles Vignoles as Engineer. Due to financial arguments with the board of the company Vignoles resigned and was replaced by Joseph Locke. Thomas Nicholson was the contractor for the eastern section and Richard Hattersley for the western, with five intermediate shafts being used to aid progress. It was opened in December 1845 as the world's longest tunnel at just over 3 miles. During construction 25 side accesses were built which facilitated the construction of a second bore from 1847 to 1852. Both were single line tunnels. From the 1930s there were plans to electrify this relatively steep line. Work started in 1936 but halted 3 years later to be revived in 1947. The old tunnels were replaced by a twin bore tunnel by 1954 which could accommodate overhead electrification. However, the line closed in 1981 and the tunnel is only used for trans-Pennine power cables.

The substantial Wicker Arches took 6 years to build, being completed in 1849. It linked the line to Victoria Station and the line to the East. The viaduct is 660 yards long with 42 arches and was the largest masonry viaduct in Europe at the time. (Sir) John Fowler was the engineer, Miller Blackie and Shortridge the contractors and Weightman Hadfield and Goldie were employed as architects to advise on the appearance of this prominent structure. The Beighton viaduct of the SLJR (now merged with the SAMR to form the Manchester, Sheffield and Lincolnshire Railway (MSLR)) was also completed in 1849 and the new Victoria Station opened in September 1851. There were various other small lines built in the lower Don Valley over the next 40 years to serve the expanding steel industry. Many plans for more substantial projects faltered due to difficulties raising finance and rivalry between the competing interests.

There had been many plans for a more direct link to London, but it was not until February 1870 that Sheffield truly joined the main line with the completion of the Bradway Tunnel to the Midland Railway line at Chesterfield. The current railway station on Sheaf Street, often still referred to as the Midland Station, was the principal station in this scheme. The railway line was designed by John Crossley, principal engineer to the Midland Railway Co. After much argument the scheme was granted its act on 11 July 1864. Work began one year later. The line from Chesterfield to Sheffield was let in several contracts. George Thompson of Cheltenham won contracts 2 to 4 from Dronfield to Beauchief including the 1,850m long Bradway Tunnel. Contract No 5 from Beauchief to Grimesthorpe including the main Midland station was won by Benton & Woodiwiss of Glossop (Note: Benton was originally from Dore) with Eckersley and Bayliss of Chaple-en-le-Frith winning the Chesterfield to Dronfield contract. Chadwick and Thirlwell of Masborough were principal subcontractors for the station. J. & E. Wood was the contractor for most of the local stations, including Dore & Totley built later in 1872. Between Pond Street and Grimethorpe Junction the line crossed the Don Valley on the 48-span 524m Attercliffe Viaduct. This includes the 24.6m skew span Norfolk Bridge over the river. This was built in 1868-70 and is a late example of cast iron bridge construction. The line opened on 1 February 1870. The section between Dore and the Sheaf Street station was four-tracked between 1899 and 1905 when the main Midland station was also extended. The four tracking was reversed in 1973 but the land retained. It has recently been intended to renew this widening to remove the restriction on the network capacity, subject to funding being available. It is not clear what priority this very useful scheme now has. It is my opinion that if Tram-trains are to be successfully deployed in South Yorkshire fundamental capacity constraints such as this must be addressed.

The Midland Mainline was due to be electrified from Sheffield to St Pancras by 2019, with ongoing improvement to the signalling infrastructure to improve reliability and safety while reducing running costs. This will reduce journey times and improve reliability of services on this route. However, this has been delayed and the northern sections of the route are only to be electrified in parts with the intention of having dual fuel locomotives switching between diesel and electricity as required. This remains unproven technology and the areas that will be the hardest to electrify are likely to the ones that would benefit the most from it.

It is also my opinion that it would be wise to improve the Sheffield to Doncaster (and on to Finningley) route by straightening bends and electrifying the line.

This would provide better links to the airport and both London to Yorkshire lines. Network Rail are already negotiating with Peel Holdings, the airport owner, to determine the feasibility of creating a railway station next to the airport on a realigned section of the East Coast Mainline. The Doncaster Sheffield line as with many railways in South and West Yorkshire were built in the mid 19th century primarily to carry heavy freight at low speed and needs significant investment to match the needs of the 21st century.

It is worth noting that the increased speed of rail travel had a profound effect upon the way people related to time. Prior to the railway age the clocks in a given place were set to the local passage of the sun at noon and so varied across the country – in effect every town had its own time zone. The railway companies soon realised that this made time-tabling very complicated. The Great Western Railway was the first company to introduce a standard time across its entire network, adopting London (Greenwich) mean time in 1840. Thus towns would have local and "Railway" times. It was not until 1880 that Greenwich Mean Time was adopted by law throughout the country. Prior to the industrialisation of the country time was a fairly imprecise concept for most people working the land. The introduction of factories and strict hours had introduced a much more rigid concept of time keeping governed by the factory clock.

In 1897 the MSLR changed its name to the Great Central Railway (GCR). Over the next 10 years it carried out various improvements to the local lines, notably to Victoria Station. The MSLR had ambitions to rival the Midland Railway company and wanted a direct access to London for products of South Yorkshire, Derbyshire and Nottinghamshire. It therefore developed plans for a line from Beighton through the Nottinghamshire and Derbyshire coalfield to Nottingham and Loughborough and onward to London. This line was originally known as the London Extension. The company changed its name to reflect its new geographical reach. The line was later routed through Mansfield. It was the last major railway line to be built in the UK until HS1 was built from London to the Channel Tunnel. The GCR Sheffield to London through line closed in 1966. The old MSLR trans-Pennine section closed to electric passenger services in 1970, becoming a freight only line serving Stocksbridge. The tunnels finally closed in 1981, but the spur from Sheffield as far as Stocksbridge remains in use.

For many years a more direct and flatter route between Sheffield and Manchester had been promulgated. It was not until 1893 that the completion of the Dore and Chinley line, with the Totley and Cowburn Tunnels occurred. It had been granted its enabling act on 28 July 1884 to a design by Edward Parry of Nottingham and Story of Derby. A ventilation shaft was included near the centre of the tunnel's length in the engineer's initial design and so was also included in the enabling act of parliament. However, the land owner objected to the intrusion on the nature of the moor. The tunnel was therefore initially built without this shaft. The eastern section of the line was built by Thomas Oliver of Horsham with P. Rickard as Resident Engineer while the western part was by J. P. Edwards of Chester with G. E. Story as Resident Engineer. The Totley Tunnel is 5,697m long. It is the longest not under the sea or estuary in the UK. Despite its length the only intermediate shafts during the construction of the tunnel were within 1,100m of the eastern portal. Excavation started in September 1888 and the headings met on 23 October 1892. The lining was completed on 4 August 1893. At about this time it became clear that the No 5 shaft was necessary and work commenced on sinking this. The permanent way was laid by 2 September 1893 and the tunnel opened for good traffic on 6 November 1893. However, the first passenger service did not start until 16 May 1894. Considerable quantities of water were encountered with up to 10,200m^3 per day being extracted from the Totley heading and up to 34,000m^3 per day from the Padley heading. Compressed air pumps and machine drills were used extensively, a novelty at the time. The shafts can be seen around Totley Bents but the tunnel itself is not visible from publicly accessible land in Totley. It is best viewed at the Grindleford Station end.

It is now planned to improve the Dore to Chinley line, which is congested, by introducing passing loops and an additional line and platform at Dore Station. This is part of the Northern Hub programme of rail improvements. This is aimed to improve services both passenger and freight between Liverpool and the Humber focusing largely on Manchester and Leeds. There are also early stage investigations into improving the Sheffield – Doncaster – Lincolnshire route.

The government are currently proposing the construction of a new high speed rail line, HS2, through South Yorkshire. It is intended that this would provided a faster passenger service to London via this entirely new route via Birmingham. If the scheme goes ahead as planned it will open here in 2033. The route will follow the M1 motorway from Nottingham and then the M18 to junction 1 thence northwards through Mexborough to South Kirkby and Ryhill towards Leeds. To service Sheffield and South Yorkshire it is intended that a spur line will connect through to the Midland Main line station in Sheffield. While this is not geographically in the centre of south Yorkshire the station already serves as the regional rail hub and so will provide the best rail connections. However, it is currently proposed that this will be achieved by running on the Midland Main line track between Clay Cross and South Kirkby. It remains unclear how this can be achieved while providing the necessary improvements to train reliability, frequency and speed. The planned improvements to the signalling and electrification of the main line southward of Sheffield will no doubt help in this respect, but further works will be required, especially to improve the links between Sheffield and Leeds and Doncaster. The scheme is currently mired in controversy as to its costs and benefits, especially benefits to the regions as opposed to London. Time will tell what the outcome will be.

Trams

The 1872 Sheffield Tramways Act empowered the Sheffield tramway company to provide 5 routes in the city. By 1877 these horse drawn services included Lady's Bridge to Attercliffe, Carbrook and Brightside, Moorhead to Nether Edge and Heeley and Snig Hill to Hillsborough Bridge. The Corporation took over the company in 1896 and from 1899 started electrifying the routes from a steam powered generator set at Kelham Island. The routes were linked through the city centre, linking with Rotherham in 1905 and extended to the suburbs. In 1914 the electricity supply for the trams was integrated with the city's general supply and the Kelham Island generator closed down. The last horse drawn car ran in 1902 while the first enclosed car was in 1911 with air brakes being introduced in 1924 and padded seats in 1926. The last tram of this generation ran in October 1960.

By the late 1970s plans were being drawn up to introduce a new high quality mass public transit system to the city. Work on the scheme finally got under way in 1991 with the first section being opened in March 1994 and the last part of the 3 line network opening in October 1995. Of the 29km long network 50% is on street. This entailed laying 60 km of track and 30 new structures were required. On street the rails are bedded into a reinforced concrete track bed using an elastomer resin. This helps insulate the system and reduce track noise. The design of the overhead system tried to minimise the visual intrusion. Notable features of the scheme include the Commercial Street bowstring arch bridge and parkway viaduct.

Sheffield has now launched the first UK use of Light Rail (Tram-trains) on the main rail network, initially from Sheffield to Rotherham and Parkgate. This would allow the Supertram network to reach Rotherham, and Stocksbridge with minimal additional investment in new track. It will provide greater capacity by using the tram track at intervals between existing tram services while avoiding the busy main line as much as possible. The new tram trains have to be able to accommodate the differing platform heights and more importantly the power and signally arrangements of the tram and conventional rail systems. The wheels also had to be specially designed to cater for the differing rail designs.

Air Travel

Following its use in the first world war by the Royal Army Flying Corps, there were plans to use a site between Norton and Coal Aston as an airport in the 1920s. However, these came to nothing. Over the years various other sites were considered including Redmires, Todwick, Hardwick and Laughton Common near Rotherham. The hilly nature of the city being a major limiting factor. By the 1980s Sheffield was the largest city in Europe without its own airport. A feasibility study by Scott Wilson Kirkpatrick in 1988 identified Tinsley Park as potentially viable if contributions to the initial costs could be found such as by commercial coal extraction, and use of adjoining land as a business park. Almost all airports rely upon either subsidy or commercial activity to fund their operations.

Opposition to plans to include part of the Tinsley park Golf Course within the airport site restricted the runway length. In 1990 an agreement was signed between Sheffield City Council, Rotherham MBC, Sheffield Development Corporation and AF Budge Ltd. This allowed for the clearance of the former Tinsley Park Steelworks and extraction of 1.5M tonnes of coal and the creation of a 50 acre business park. The agreement allowed for the purchase of the airport land for a nominal sum if the airport was not viable after 10 years operation.

The restriction to the existing works site made the airport unsuitable for general jet aircraft. The 1,211m runway could only accommodate planes capable of short take off and landing, in a similar way to London Docklands city airport. Tight noise limits were also imposed. This effectively limited the aircraft choice to the Bae 146 jet or turboprop aircraft of around 50 seat maximum capacity, although notionally the licence allowed 107 seat aircraft and 300,000 passenger per year.

The Sheffield City Airport opened in 1997 and was handling 1000 aircraft movements per year by 2002. The bankruptcy of Budge saw the airport operator and developer, Peel Holdings, take 50% ownership of the airport. Although there were regular flights to London, Dublin, Amsterdam and Brussels, amongst others, there was never enough traffic to make the venture a commercial success. The last commercial flight was in 2002 and the licence withdrawn in 2008. The default clause was implemented and the site has been turned into a business park. However, part of the site operated as a heliport and was the centre of operations for South Yorkshire Air Ambulance and South Yorkshire Police helicopter surveillance unit, until 2014 and 2016 respectively.

The much larger former RAF Finningley air base near Doncaster has now been developed by Peel Holdings as Robin Hood Doncaster Sheffield Airport (DSA) offering a range of commercial and freight flights. The runway is capable of handling the largest aircraft now flying. The Finningley and Rossington Regeneration Route now provides direct access off the M18 motorway. Studies into the improvement of the rail link are on going. Finningley formerly had a station on the Great Northern and Great Eastern Joint Railway and lies only a few miles from the East Coast Main Line at Doncaster. There is a proposal to divert the East Coast mainline to an alignment adjoining the airport to allow a station to be built with direct access to the airport.

Although Sheffield no longer has an airport within the city boundary the skies above us are part of the air navigation corridors used by all major civil flights. Bamford, Froggatt, Oughtibridge, Stocksbridge and Wickersley are all home to air navigation waypoints along these corridors. Most aircraft now use global positioning satellite networks to navigate. However, a system of radio beacons are maintained to provide navigational aid for all aircraft. The ones covering this area are at Manchester Airport, and near Carsington, Todmorden and towards Spurn Point.

Coal Aston 5½ miles south of the city with a small grass landing strip is the closest airfield for light fixed wing aircraft. Finningley DSA is the nearest major airport at 20 miles distant, followed by Manchester, Leeds-Bradford and East Midlands at 28 to 39 miles distant by air. Retford and Huddersfield also have small airports.

Telecommunications

Sheffield had one of the first telephone exchanges in the world, with the system starting in 1879 only 18 months or so after the world first in New York. Tasker, Sons & Company were one of the most successful pioneers of this industry with 343 lines within 7 years. They were visited by the British Association for the Advancement of Science and chosen by the Queen to install exchanges at Windsor and Balmoral. In 1888 the Sheffield Telephone and Electric Light Company, as it had become, had its telephone operation taken over by the more financially powerful National Telephone Company of London. By 1926 self dialling became possible with new exchanges being built. Over 35,000 lines were connected 10 years later. Subscriber Trunk Dialling came-in in 1966.

There are now approximately 206,500 residential telephone lines and 10,500 business lines served by the 17 telephone exchanges across the city. BT is currently rolling out their Infinity Project across the city's exchanges. This extends the fibre optic cable network from purely a trunk system between exchanges to local kerb side boxes, with only the last few hundred metres of cabling to a customer being in copper wires. This significantly increases bandwidth and data carrying capacity at relatively modest cost compared with a full fibre optic system. Broadband download speeds of up to 40 Mb are achievable. In a few parts of Sheffield and the vicinity now have Openreach full fibre connections to the customer. These are mainly in the Don Valley and all of the Advanced Manufacturing Park at Waverley.

The 1984 liberalisation of cable television allowed cable operators to show non public service broadcasts for the first time. This created an opportunity for the network to develop. Nationally, by 1990 large parts of the towns and cities of the country were within franchised cable areas operated by numerous different companies. However, less than 1 million homes had access to the new network and of these around 15% subscribed. The cable network grew in the early 1990s but large areas of the city remain beyond this network. The diverse companies were not profitable and unable to finance the debts incurred in constructing the cable network. As a result they merged down to two companies nationally by 2000. These then merged six years later to eventually become Virgin Media. Virgin announced in the autumn of 2010 the roll out of an improved network, with a capacity of up to 100 Mb, across the country.

Virgin and BT are the only national cable telecoms suppliers, although small local companies exist in Hull and the Isle of Wight. Community groups are also coming together to bring fibre optic broad band services to remote rural communities.

The first public mobile phone coverage for the city was in 1975 served by a central transmitter covering much of Yorkshire with a capacity of approximately 200 callers in total. Cellular phone were licensed in the UK in 1982 and the network reached Sheffield and the M1 in April - June 1985. This technology allowed very many more people to access mobile phone technology. By the end of the following year, 80% of the UK's population were reported to be covered by a signal. However, geographical coverage was poor. The network became digital in 1993. By 1996, UK population coverage had increased to 98% using a common European standard. The 3G system was rolled out after 2002 allowing more data as well as voice transmission. This new system required separate transmitters to be installed world wide.

There are now several hundred mobile telephone transmitters across the city from around 10 m high to approximately 40 m high. O2 and Vodafone have formed a project called Cornerstone, whereby both operators share new and existing mobile phone base stations. This will allow an improvement in network coverage for customers, whilst minimising the number of new sites required. The network operators' focus, at present, is on improving network coverage to cities, large towns, and other urban areas. The mobile phone network across the city was again further upgraded to accommodate the latest mobile telecommunications technology from 2012. Naturally, this concentrated on areas of high demand first, but now includes most rural areas of the city. What is known as 4G provides more capacity in each telecommunications link. Computers and phones will be able to download at speeds of typically 8Mb but potentially up to 20 Mb, comparable with much fixed line broad band capacity. Mobile phone manufacturers are now testing the next generation of technology "5G" with speeds potentially 40 to over 100 times that of 4G. This is likely to start coming to market after 2020.

The first experimental radio broadcasts in the UK took place in 1920 in London by General Electric and Marconi company broadcasting as a station called "2MT ". Two years later the British Broadcasting Company was set up with a 1.5kW transmitter in London with call sign "2LO". By 1924, the BBC was established with similar transmitters in Manchester, Bristol, Cardiff, Glasgow and Bournemouth. Sheffield had a 100W relay transmitter. All the broadcasting was by Amplitude Modulation on the Medium Wave band. Long wave broadcasts started from the Daventry site in 1926 with a 25kW transmitter. The Moorside Edge transmitter near Huddersfield, was built in 1931 to replace the Manchester and Yorkshire relay service. In 1954 the transistor radio was invented allowing reliable commercial portable radios to be produced. The following year Frequency Modulation broadcasts on the Very High Frequency band started in the UK allowing much higher quality sound to be received, albeit over shorter ranges. In 1973, commercial radio stations were licensed for the first time, with Hallam FM starting in October 1974. The 1980s saw the introduction of 50W transmitter licences allowing small community stations to broadcast. However, most of these micro stations were unlicensed. Digital Radio broadcasting started in the UK in 1999 three years after Virgin commenced an internet radio service. Local radio digital multiplexes were rolled out across the country between 2007 and 2015. The former date also saw the introduction of the DAB+ system that allows higher data rates and so better quality audio to be transmitted. Both DAB and DAB+ remain in use together with the AM, and VHF FM broadcasts. There has been talk of shutting down VHF FM. However, a great many people still use it as their preferred means of reception. Increasingly, people are using internet streaming as their alternative through smart phones or computers.

The history of television stretches back to 1909 when Alan Campbell Swinton wrote a technical paper proposing broadcast by synchronised scanning of cathode ray tubes. However, the earliest demonstration of working technology was by John Logie Baird in 1925 with public broadcasts from 1929. The BBC started broadcasts in August 1932 using Baird's 30 line system and the existing radio transmitters. In November 1936 the BBC initiated a competition between Baird's 240 line system and General Electrics Marconi's 405 line system, both broadcast on Very High Frequency radio channels. Baird's system stopped transmission the following February. Broadcasting stopped for the duration of WWII. In 1949 EMI experimented with 1001 line system, but this was not taken up commercially. In December 1950 the first high power transmitter was opened outside London. Holme Moss was operational from 12 October 1951 to serve the north of England. Emley moor being built in 1956. The year 1964 saw the introduction of 625 line Ultra High Frequency transmission, initially in London. The following year the first satellite relay from America took place with the Intersat 1 "Early Bird" satellite. Colour television started on the UHF service in 1967. The VHF television service finally ceased in 1985. Sky were broadcasting via the Astra satellite in 1989 allowing reception via a small dish antenna and so more modest cost. The BBC started their *iplayer* internet service in 2007 and Freesat including HD channels was launched in 2008 and Freeview HD in 2010. The switch over to digital broadcasting was completed in 2014 at which point the analogue transmitters were decommissioned.

The main television transmission for South Yorkshire is from the 330m high transmitter on Emley Moor, in West Yorkshire. However, there are 8 radio and television transmitters within the city to provide the necessary coverage to the area. Emley Moor is the tallest free standing structure in the UK being a slip formed concrete tower built in 1970 to replace the 385m guyed mast that collapsed in an ice storm. Emley Moor also serves most of Yorkshire and parts of Greater Manchester. The tower consists of a circular concrete shell 274.3m tall tapering from 24.4m diameter at the base to 6.5m at the top with a wall thickness of 0.53 to 0.35m. This concrete section houses a lattice steel access tower and is surmounted by a lattice steel mast clad in a fibreglass shell 55.7m tall supporting the aerials. Careful attention was paid to ensure the tower and mast would be safe under wind and ice loads with helical strakes fitted to the top section to control vortex shedding which can set up damaging vibrations in a structure! The mast section was built up in sections and lifted into the concrete tower where the aerials and associated equipment were fitted prior to the whole assembly being jacked up through the top into position. The new tower was commissioned by the Independent Television Authority and designed by Ove Arup. The main contractor was Tileman & Company Ltd. Despite the spectacular views from the location the client brief specifically excluded provision for public viewing platforms in the tower.

The local transmitters range from small low power community radio to the 57m tall lattice masts at Crosspool serving a variety of broadcasters to much of the city. This mast was commissioned in 1967 when BBC Radio Sheffield was launched. Radio Sheffield was one of the first local radio stations to be opened by the BBC. The valleys of Sheffield have always meant that some people have had poor television reception. Hence the various local transmitters provided to improve coverage.

The 225m high guyed lattice steel mast on Holme Moss provides the region's principal radio transmissions. This, the most powerful transmitter in the UK, serves an area from Anglesey to Skegness and Birmingham to Hartlepool and a population of 11 million people. It was built in 1951 by British Callender's Construction Ltd, part of British Insulated Callender's Cable Co Ltd, to BBC specifications. The mast is designed to safely accommodate 125 mph wind and icing of the structure. A depth of 3.6m of peat had to be removed to find a suitable stratum to secure the mast foundation and stay anchorages. There are sets of three carefully tensioned steel wire ropes radiating out from the mast to provide stability at four points up the mast up to 12.2m from it apex.

Some parts of the city are also served by the 352m Belmont transmitter in North Lincolnshire for radio and television signals. This was the third tallest transmitter in Europe and is a modified twin of the collapsed Emley Moor Mast. With the switch over, a new antenna was installed in 2010. This was heavier than the preceding aerial. In order to ensure the continued safety of the mast it was decided to reduce its height by removing the top 36m of lattice and associated guys. The alternative would have been a comprehensive strengthening of the structure. With the reduction in height this transmitter is now the second tallest in the UK after Skelton in Cumbria and only 14th tallest in Europe. (The 646m tall Warsaw radio mast of 1974 was the tallest in Europe until it collapsed during maintenance work in 1991. The concrete Ostankino Tower in Moscow at 540m is currently the tallest structure in Europe.) All these local and regional transmitters are operated by Arqiva. Arqiva is a British telecommunications company having its origins in the BBC and ITA and IRA transmitters network operations. It provides infrastructure and broadcast transmission facilities in the United Kingdom and the Republic of Ireland, along with commercial Wi-Fi.

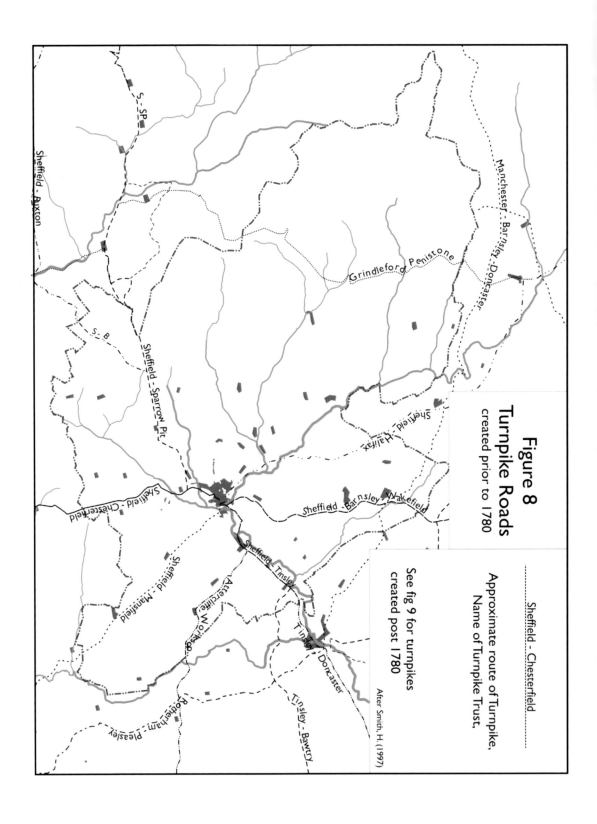

**Figure 8
Turnpike Roads**
created prior to 1780

Sheffield - Chesterfield
....

Approximate route of Turnpike,
Name of Turnpike Trust,

See fig 9 for turnpikes
created post 1780

After Smith, H. (1997)

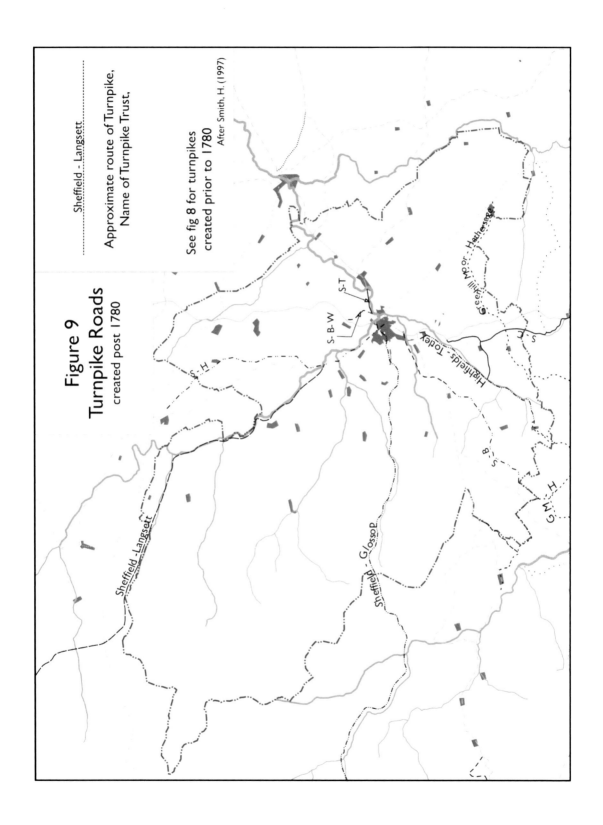

Figure 9
Turnpike Roads
created post 1780

Sheffield - Langsett

Approximate route of Turnpike,
Name of Turnpike Trust,

See fig 8 for turnpikes
created prior to 1780

After Smith, H. (1997)

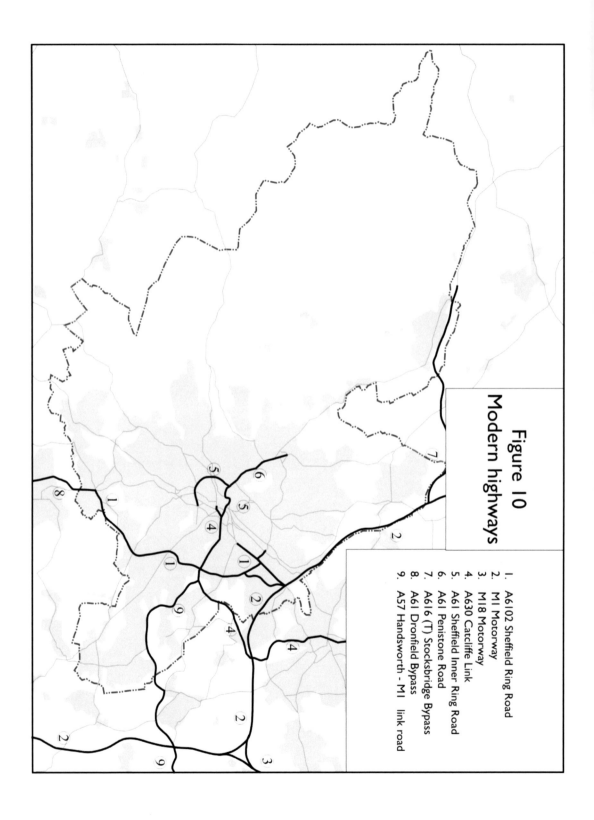

Figure 10
Modern highways

1. A6102 Sheffield Ring Road
2. M1 Motorway
3. M18 Motorway
4. A630 Catcliffe Link
5. A61 Sheffield Inner Ring Road
6. A61 Penistone Road
7. A616 (T) Stocksbridge Bypass
8. A61 Dronfield Bypass
9. A57 Handsworth - M1 link road

Year turnpike established	Turnpike Trust	Length (miles)	Year tolls ceased
1726	[in the Don Navigation Act] Sheffield to Tinsley not built until 1759, new trust formed 1849.	3	
1756	Duffield (Derby), Chesterfield and Sheffield	32	1875
1757	Sheffield, Barnsley and Wakefield	22	1876
1758	Sheffield and Sparrow Pit	23	1884
1758	Little Sheffield, Fox House, Hathersage, Castleton, Chaple-en-le-Frith + Grindleford & Eyam, Tideswell, Buxton.	26	1884
1760	Tinsley and Bawtry	18	1879
1764	Tinsley, Rotherham, Conisborough and Doncaster	15	1873
1764	Attercliffe, Handsworth, Anston and Worksop	16	1881
1764	High Moors Trust – Linking existing roads	15	
1771	Penistone, Strines and Grindleford	16	Post 1807
1779	Sheffield, Mosborough and Mansfield	20	1867
1781	Greenhill Moor, Owler Bar and Hathersage	33	1880
1795	Sheffield Chesterfield (re-routed from Coal Aston to Old Whittington following valley through Dronfield and Unstone)	22	1880
1803	Goosegreen, Highfield and Totley	13	1880
1803	Owler Bar and Baslow	5	1880
1805	Sheffield and Langsett	5	1875
1812	Sparrow Pit Trust (re-routed at Dore Moor and Mam Tor)	12	
1818	Sheffield and Glossop	24	1875
1825	Greenhill Moor and Gleadless	3	1880

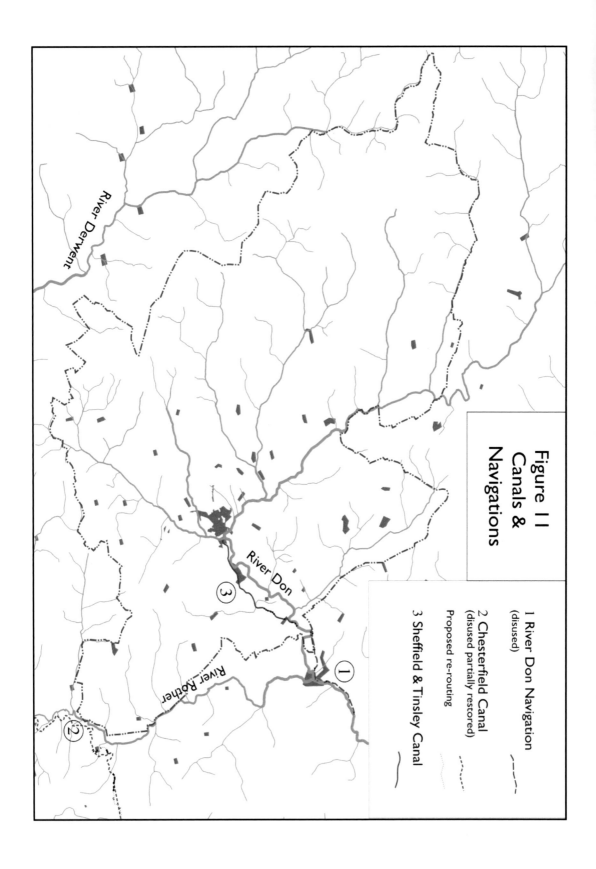

Figure 11
Canals &
Navigations

River Derwent

River Don

River Rother

1 River Don Navigation
(disused)

2 Chesterfield Canal
(disused partially restored)

Proposed re-routing

3 Sheffield & Tinsley Canal

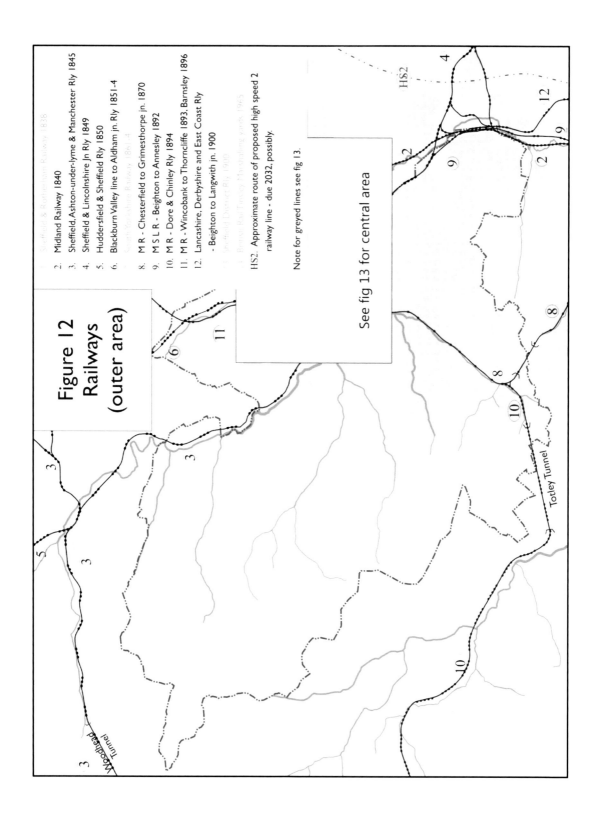

Figure 12
Railways
(outer area)

1. Sheffield & Rotherham Railway 1838
2. Midland Railway 1840
3. Sheffield, Ashton-under-lyme & Manchester Rly 1845
4. Sheffield & Lincolnshire Jn Rly 1849
5. Huddersfield & Sheffield Rly 1850
6. Blackburn Valley line to Aldham jn. Rly 1851-4
7. South Yorkshire Railway 1861-4
8. M R - Chesterfield to Grimesthorpe jn. 1870
9. M S L R - Beighton to Annesley 1892
10. M R - Dore & Chinley Rly 1894
11. M R - Wincobank to Thorncliffe 1893, Barnsley 1896
12. Lancashire, Derbyshire and East Coast Rly
    - Beighton to Langwith Jn. 1900
13. Sheffield District Rly 1900
14. Brightside Tinsley Marshalling yards 1965

HS2. Approximate route of proposed high speed 2 railway line - due 2032, possibly.

Note for greyed lines see fig 13.

See fig 13 for central area

HS2

Woodhead Tunnel

Totley Tunnel

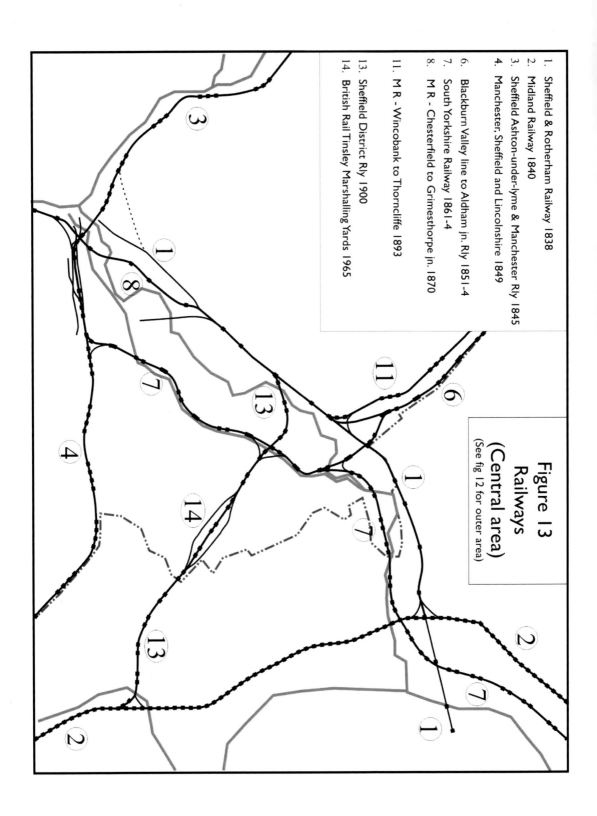

Figure 13
Railways
(Central area)
(See fig 12 for outer area)

1. Sheffield & Rotherham Railway 1838
2. Midland Railway 1840
3. Sheffield Ashton-under-lyme & Manchester Rly 1845
4. Manchester, Sheffield and Lincolnshire 1849
6. Blackburn Valley line to Aldham jn. Rly 1851-4
7. South Yorkshire Railway 1861-4
8. M R - Chesterfield to Grimesthorpe jn. 1870
11. M R - Wincobank to Thorncliffe 1893
13. Sheffield District Rly 1900
14. British Rail Tinsley Marshalling Yards 1965

Railway Company	Date Opened	Approximate number of features	Approx. distance *(miles)	Route
Sheffield and Rotherham Rly	31 Oct 1838	12 bridges	5	Wicker to Rotherham Westgate.
North Midland Rly	July 1840	7 tunnels, 200 bridges, 1 aqueduct	72	Derby to Leeds via (locally) Chesterfield, Eckington, Killamarsh, Treeton and Rotherham Masborough.
Midland Rly	1 Feb 1870	1 Tunnel, 1 viaduct, 32 bridges	15	Tapton jn to Grimesthorpe jn via Dronfield, Dore & Totley, Beauchief, Millhouses, Heeley, Sheffield (Pond Street) and Attercliffe Road.
Midland Rly	1894	3 tunnels, 2 viaducts, 19 bridges, 1 aqueduct	21	Dore jn to Chinley via, Grindleford, Hathersage, Bamford, Hope and Edale.
Midland Rly	1896	1 tunnel, 14 bridges	4+8	Wincobank jn to Thorncliffe, extended to Barnsley via Ecclesfield, Chapeltown, Wentworth, Elsecar and Wombwell.
Sheffield Achton-under-Lyme & Manchester Rly	22 Dec 1845	3 tunnels, 3 viaducts, 62 bridges	42	Manchester Piccadilly to Sheffield via (locally) Dunford Bridge, Penistone, Wortley, Deepcar, Oughtibridge, Wadsley Bridge, Bridgehouses.
Sheffield and Lincolnshire Junction Rly	February 1849	2 tunnels, 3 viaducts, 60 bridges including a 110m two span river crossing	33	Sheffield to Gainsborough via (locally) Sheffield Victoria, Darnall, Beighton, Kiveton Park, Shireoaks.
Manchester Sheffield and Lincolnshire Rly	1852?	1 tunnel, 8 bridges	6.5	Penistone to Barnsley Branch via Silkstone and Dodworth.
Huddersfield and Sheffield Junction Rly	July 1850	6 tunnels, 25 bridges	13.5	Huddersfield to Penistone via (locally) Denby Dale, Shepley.
South Yorkshire Rly Blackburn valley to Aldham jn	1854	1 viaduct, 14 bridges	11	Wincobank jn to Aldham jn via Grange Lane, Ecclesfield, Chapeltown, Westwood, Birdwell, High Royds, Wombwell.
South Yorkshire Rly	1864	9 bridges	3	Tinsley, Broughton Lane, Attercliffe, and Woodburn junction.
Manchester Sheffield and Lincolnshire Rly	1892	2 tunnels, 2 viaducts, 31 bridges	22	Woodhouse jn to Annesley, via (Locally) Beighton, Killamarsh and Eckington.
Lancashire Derbyshire and East Coast Rly	1900	1 tunnel, 19 bridges	12	Beighton to Langwith jn via (locally) Spink Hill.
Sheffield District Rly	1900	1 tunnel, 18 bridges	3.5	Brightside jn to Treeton jn via, West Tinsley and Catcliffe.
British Rail	1965			Tinsley marshalling yards.

Companies group as blocks that merged.

* distance excludes sidings and minor branches

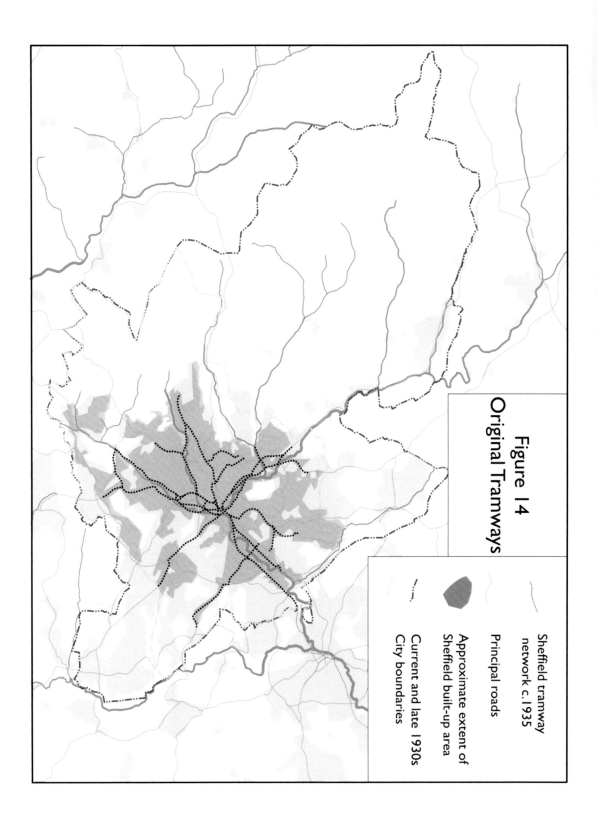

Figure 14
Original Tramways

Sheffield tramway
network c.1935

Principal roads

Approximate extent of
Sheffield built-up area

Current and late 1930s
City boundaries

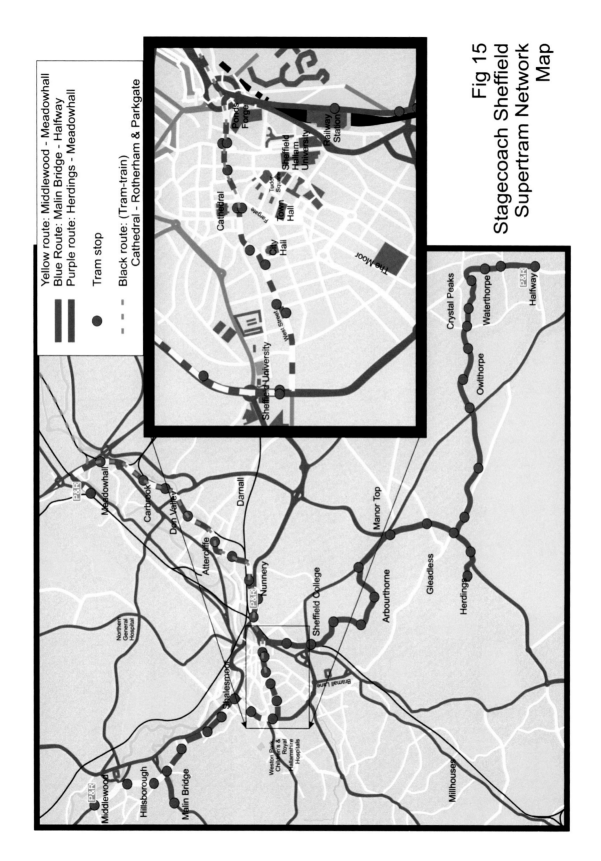

Fig 15
Stagecoach Sheffield
Supertram Network
Map

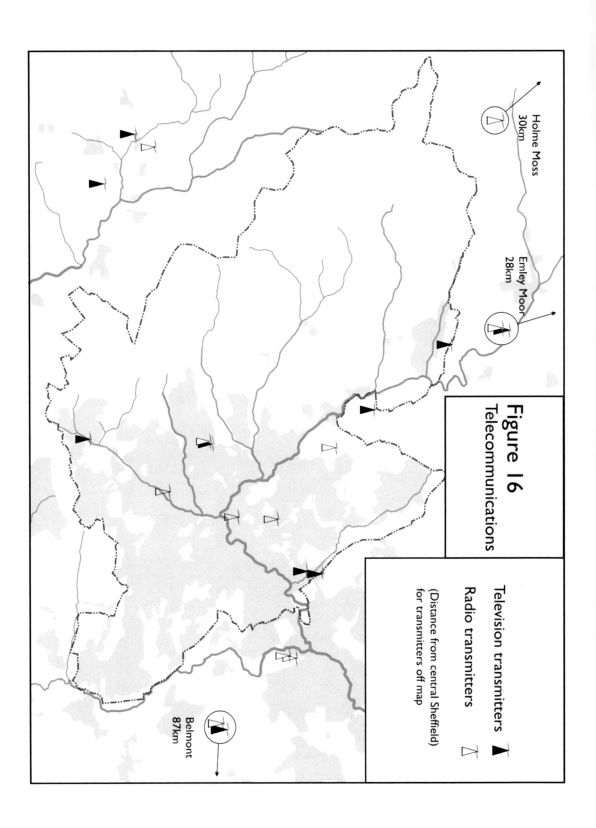

Figure 16
Telecommunications

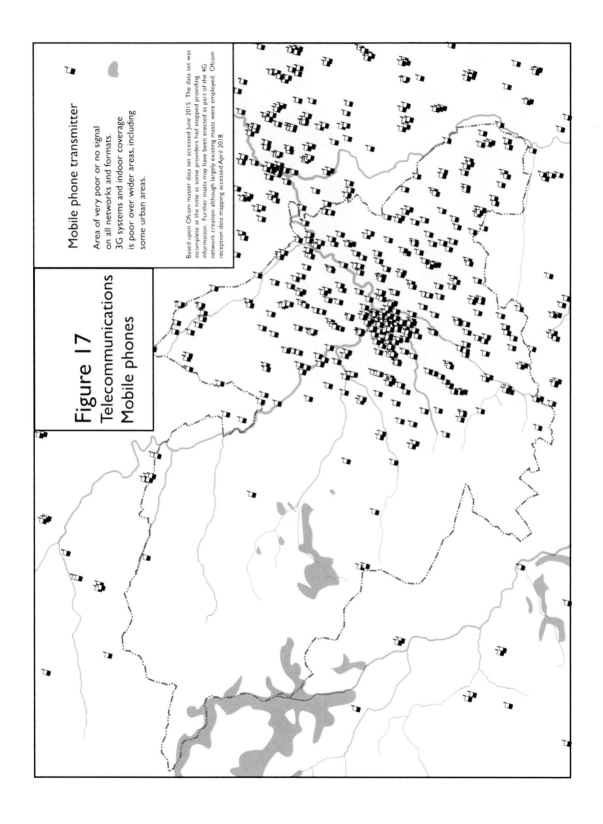

Figure 17
Telecommunications
Mobile phones

Mobile phone transmitter

Area of very poor or no signal
on all networks and formats.
3G systems and indoor coverage
is poor over wider areas, including
some urban areas.

Based upon Ofcom master data set accessed June 2015. The data set was
incomplete at the time as some providers had stopped providing
information. Further masts may have been erected as part of the 4G
network creation although largely existing masts were employed. Ofcom
reception data mapping accessed April 2018

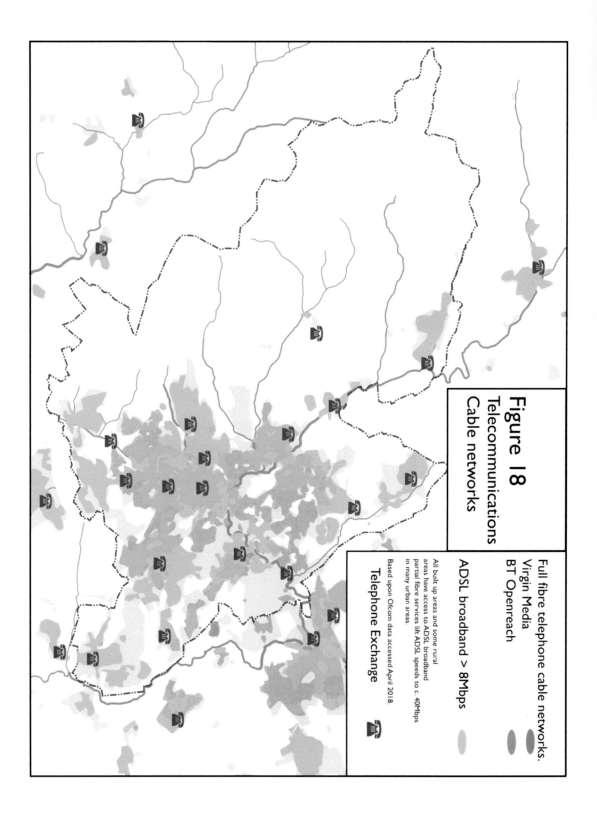

Figure 18
Telecommunications
Cable networks

Full fibre telephone cable networks.
Virgin Media
BT Openreach

ADSL broadband > 8Mbps

All built up areas and some rural areas have access to ADSL broadband partial fibre services lift ADSL speeds to c. 40Mbps in many urban areas.

Based upon Ofcom data accessed April 2018

Telephone Exchange

5.1 Any crossing of the River Don in the Iron or Bronze Ages may well have been in the form of boardwalks through marshes and fords. A boardwalk may have looked something like this reconstruction of the Sweet Track in Somerset. The original 3,400 year old structure was preserved in the peat. Split rather than sawn logs would have been used.

Ancient trackways continue in use today as bridleways or public lanes. Sometimes they have naturally cut themselves into the slopes of hills forming hollow-ways. The passage of feet and wheels over centuries or even millennia can erode even a hard stone surface by well over a metre.

cc-by-sa/2.0 - © Richard Webb- geograph.org.uk/p/5650438

5.2   The Willow bridge near Oxspring is thought to date from the mid 17th century. The elegant packhorse bridge is grade 2 listed and now carries a part of the Trans-Pennine Trail over the River Don.

5.3   The packhorse bridge near Burbage dates from the mid 18th century, a period when many such bridges were renewed. This example has lost its parapet walls.

5.4 Tinsley Viaduct across the Don Valley carries both the M1 motorway and the A631 across the River Don, Sheffield and Tinsley Canal, two railway lines, the Tram-train link spur, the Tinsley Bus Rapid Transit link road and access roads.

5.5 Sheffield Inner Relief Road required major bridges under the railway and over the river.

5.6   Streets ahead LED lighting give white light on the highway with limited overspill creating a darker sky.

5.7   Streets ahead reconstruction of worn out roads.

© Highways England, WSP

5.8 & 5.9 The M1 motorway has been widened to four running lanes within the existing highway footprint. Frequent overhead signs help motorists drive safely.

© Highways England, WSP

5.10 The Tinsley Bus Rapid Transit link road is carried of the River Don and Rotherham rail line used by the Tram-train services. It provides traffic relief to the busy Tinsley Viaduct south junction.

© Dave Pickersgill

5.11   Sheffield Canal Basin full of barges in the 1880s.

5.12   Straddle Warehouse converted to offices at Victoria Quays.

5.13   Double decker trams were common in the first tram system.

5.14   Super trams are single deck and longer allowing more people to be carried and to get on and off more quickly in safety.

5.15   The Tram-trains superficially look like supertrams but can accommodate differing platform heights, power supplies and signalling systems.

5.16   Sheffield City airport could only service aircraft capable of short take off and landing. Thus 107 seat aircraft serving the UK and near continent were as much as it could accommodate.

5.17   Typical 4G mobile phone mast.

5.18   The valleys of Sheffield required supplementary transmitters, primarily the one at Crosspool.

5.19 & 5.20   Television and radio transmitters at Emley Moor and Holme Moss are record making structures serving the north of England at 330m and 225m tall.

Techniques

Measurement.

Weights and measures legislation goes back as far as we have records of law making in this country. The Magna Carta of 1215 was one land mark in this. Standards were governed by the counties and for some measures were not uniform across the country until the 1824. The improvements in the transport network over the preceding decades had increased long distance trade and so the need for consistent measurement. However, this act was of limited scope. The need for uniform components required greater standardisation of measurement. Nevertheless, complications arose from the adoption of the metric system across Europe, particularly in those countries that had been part of the French empire and so subject to their rationalisation of measurements. From 1864 both the British Imperial system and metric system were permitted to be used in the UK. The Ordnance Survey introduced a metric grid to their mapping in the 1930s although they were still reproduced to an imperial scale until 1974. In 1959 the British Imperial measures were redefined against the International Metric standards. The UK's National Physical Laboratory is one of the key institutions defining and safeguarding measures world wide as our need for ever more accurate measurement grows. Modern precision engineering can manufacture components to a level of accuracy unimaginable a short time ago. This allows us to have more reliable, efficient and cleaner machines of all sorts.

Prior to the renaissance, design was by rules of thumb and there was little need for sophisticated measurement. Quite adequate accuracy could be achieved with a measuring rule, dividing compasses and set square together with plumb line and a knotted long length of cord and occasionally a magnetic compass. Copernican ideas on astronomy were brought to Britain by Leonoard Digges in the 1550s who wished to apply them to navigation. He wrote a landmark treatise on surveying in 1556. Christopher Saxton from Sowood, in Calderdale created the first accurate mapping of the counties of England and may have been the first to use triangulation in the process using a theodolite built by Thomas Digges. A theodolite is an instrument consisting of a telescope mounted on a frame that allows the measurement of vertical and horizontal angles. Triangulation is a means of measuring the postion of things by determining the angles to them from two known fixed points and so is similar to plane table surveying, but applicable over much larger areas and gives greater precision. William Gasgoigne from Rothwell, Leeds made significant improvements to the design of such instruments to greatly increase the accuracy available in 1639. However, it was Jesse Ramsden from Salter Hebble, near Halifax who in 1767 developed a technique to manufacture surveying instruments to a very high level of accuracy and/or also at reasonable costs. He was awarded £300 from the Longitude Prize fund in 1777 for his method of producing marine sextants allowing the navy to be equipped with accurate equipment. He was also responsible for creating "the great theodolite" for William Roy's survey of 1787.

In the mid 18th century the mapping of the country had hardly advanced from the work of Saxton. Consequently, The Royal Society for the encouragement of Arts, Manufactures and Commerce offered a prize for accurate county surveys at a scale of one inch to one mile in 1762. Peter Burdett started a survey of Derbyshire the following year and completed his work to the RSA's satisfaction five years later. Thomas Jeffery completed his maps of Yorkshire in 1771, and John Chapman, Nottinghamshire in 1774. This was also a period where the government started to map parts of the country. Following the Jacobite rebellion, the highlands of Scotland were mapped over 8 years to allow the construction of the military roads into the area. The French revolutionary turmoil led to fears of invasion and so the mapping of the south coast of England. These were the foundation of the Ordnance Survey. Notwithstanding the political antipathy with France the Royal Society from 1784 worked with their French counterparts to carry out a geodetic survey to link the observatories at Greenwich and Paris. This allowed a better understanding of the overall shape of the planet and meant that the world mapping by the two countries could be related to one another. This was completed by William Roy in 1791. The first Ordnance Survey (OS) map offered for sale was of Kent in 1801. Their one inch series for the entire country was not completed until 1870, by which time many areas had been surveyed several times as they developed! The Sheffield area was first surveyed by the OS in 1837-9 and published the following year with the most up to date revisions possible as the railways changed the landscape. At a local level, the family of Fairbank produced many surveys in the Sheffield area for many purposes.

If a surveyor wanted to accurately position an object it would either be measured off another object of known position or located from the 6500 triangulation stations erected by the Ordnance Survey from 1935 to 1962. These replaced a triangulation carried out across the country in the first half of the 19th century. By accurately measuring the angles between the stations and then any object between it is possible to precisely locate it in space. The initial survey was established during the Napoleonic wars to determine how best the south coast of England could be defended against invasion. It subsequently mapped the entire country and was part of an international scientific exercise to measure the shape of the planet. The triangulation stations are found on hill tops and vantage points where many miles of country could be viewed. The familiar concrete pillars largely date from the mid 20th century resurvey. These were all made by hand with the men carrying all the materials and tools themselves to these often remote heights. The primary survey stations at Margery Hill and Harland South (Beeley Moor) were erected in 1936. The second and third order pillars that fill in the detail from 1948.

In the last two decades these have become obsolete as new technologies such as precision aerial photography, radar and laser scans and Global Positioning Satellite (GPS) systems have taken over. Aerial photography was first used in WWI and adopted for civilian use shortly thereafter, including for archaeological surveys. However, it was not widely used until the latter part of the 20th century outside of the military. It is only the increasing power of computers that has allowed the extensive use of photographic and scanned imagery to be used for mapping. Lidar is a similar technique to radar but used light (from UV to infrared) instead of radio waves. GPS systems work by calculating the range to the network of satellites orbiting the earth. Generally, the American satellites are used although other countries are now creating rival systems. The distances are measured by comparing the time on extremely accurate clocks on the satellites. A GPS devices needs to "see" at least four satellites in order to make its calculations. A single GPS receiver is able to locate it self to within about 5-20m. However, by combining the information from two receivers, one in a fixed location, accuracies of a few millimetres can be achieved. The position of the fixed receiver needs to be known for a survey to produce an absolute location otherwise a relative survey is created. Information is passed from the base station to the mobile survey equipment by radio. Since 1999, the Ordnance Survey have established a national network of over 90 reference stations in all parts of Great Britain - the active stations of the National GPS Network, known as OS Net. The active stations are deployed such that any point in Great Britain, will be within 75 km of the nearest active station and in many areas much less. The nearest active station is at Hoober Reservoir. A few of the old trig points, such as Harland South, and the Fundamental Bench Mark at Broom Head Moor are in use as some of the 900 or so passive reference stations in the OS GPS network.

On many building and structures around the country you can see an arrow symbol of a vertical line and two inclined lines topped by a horizontal bar all a few centimetres long carved into the stone work a short distance above the pavement. This is an Ordnance Survey benchmark and was used until the recent introduction of satellite based surveying to measured the height of anything in the vicinity. The Ordnance Survey has a database of the precise level of the top bar element above their datum level in Newlyn and shown on large scale maps. By comparing the level of the bench mark to the object of interest the precise level of the object can be determined. These benchmarks are to be found across the entire country. They are on many of the abutments of the local bridges and many major buildings existing in the mid 20th century including the Cathedral, Town Hall, Old Town Hall, Howard Hotel, Sheffield Waterworks offices and River Don and Templeborough Works. The first national level survey commenced in 1841 using a level datum in Liverpool. Like the triangulation points, the bench marks are now less used and are frequently lost in redevelopment.

Construction technologies

Improvements in transport and mining technologies during the 18th century reduced the real terms cost of coal which made the manufacture and distribution of bricks more affordable. From then on bricks have been the material of choice for almost all housing construction. Previously, only very important buildings were built with anything other than what was available locally. The local sandstones in Sheffield readily break into pieces suitable for rough walling and in some cases roofing stone. A few outcrops are more massive in nature and suitable for dressing and carving into regular blocks for a finer finish.

The woodlands of the area were managed for many centuries. However, there were competing uses for the timber through out. The predominant species was oak, a tree that takes 100 - 150 years to reach normal maturity. Oak is noted for its strength and durability. Its foliage and nuts were used as fodder for animals, its bark for tanning leather, twigs and small branches for fire wood, charcoal or as whitecoal. Only the largest sections can be used as building material and needed careful selection. The trees growing on the north facing sides of the valleys grow more slowly but this conveys greater density and strength to the timber. The south facing sides of the valleys would suit the rapid grow for coppice timber harvested every 8-20 years for poles and wood coals. Foresters would often manage individual trees, growing them with a particular usage in mind, even when they may not be harvested for another generation or more. For large and complex structures, such as roofs, it is necessary to join several sections of timber together to achieve the required length. From the earliest times, lap, scarf, and mortice and tenon joints were held together with wooden dowels. The new market hall at Penistone is an excellent place to witness the product of traditional carpenter's skills. Other woodland tree species are more suited to uses such as the making of tools and furniture.

Contemporary political improvements made trade with the Baltic easier. This allowed Sheffield to import high quality iron ore from Sweden. The Cutlers' Company of Hallamshire had been granted a monopoly on the import of this ore. Moreover, it also facilitated the import more generally of timber. The slow grown soft wood trees yielded timber eminently suitable for construction with long straight trunks. This supplemented the dwindling supply of native timber, mainly oak, of a quality suitable for structural use at a time when the demand for construction materials was growing with rising population and wealth. Fast grown soft wood UK sourced timber became widely available in the mid 20th century. This requires preservative treatment to achieve the durability of the earlier timbers. Metal fastenings are now routinely used. Now a wide range of imported timbers is also used together with engineered wood products such as plywood and various wood particulate boards and glu-laminate timbers. The ability to build up timber sections out of multiple smaller sections glued together has made it possible to remove defects such as knots and create large timber sections economically. This opens many structural possibilities as is shown at the Winter Garden. Joining timber sections remains a complex business often using stainless steel plates.

The advent of the railways allowed the long distance transport of heavy building materials and so non-local materials were increasingly used. Perhaps the most obvious manifestation of this was the introduction of slate roofing tiles in place of sandstone flags, clay tiles, thatch or very occasionally sheet lead.

Cavity wall construction was developed in the late 19th century in the wetter parts of the country including the West Riding of Yorkshire. I do not currently know when the technique was first used in Sheffield specifically. It became widely adopted in the large scale rebuilding in the second quarter of the 20th century onwards. Some drier parts of the country did not adopt the technique for a further two or three decades. By the 1970s energy conservation became a higher concern with rising fuel prices and insulation started to be introduced within the cavity. The purpose of the cavity is to resist rain permeating the wall during a storm. A clear cavity is still needed in exposed locations to achieve this so be careful before filling your cavities! Expert advice should always be sought before altering the structure of a building.

Through the 20th century concrete has been increasingly used for components or even entire framing of housing. The 1970s onwards saw increasing use of plastics in various forms most notably uPVC windows frames and doors. There has also been advances in glass technology to provide more thermal insulation and better light control and structural performance.

Steel is a vital part of the civil engineering industry. Although some significant structures have been built entirely without the use of iron or steel - Stonehenge and the Egyptian Pyramids, iron and steel tools, be it the carpenter's axe or masons chisel, have been an essential part of all construction since they first became available, from 3000 years ago. Sheffield has been a world centre for the manufacture of steel tools since at least the 16th century. The great westward expansion of America in the 19th century was largely achieved with tools shipped from Sheffield.

Ditherington Flax mill near Shrewsbury (owned by English Heritage, but not currently normally open to the public) is generally regarded as the world's first iron framed building. It has cast iron beams and columns supporting a "fireproof" floor of shallow brick jack arches between the beams. Overall strength and stiffness of the building, however, are provided by the substantial external masonry walls. The Crystal Palace of the Great Exhibition in Hyde Park London of 1851 marks another landmark in the use of cast and wrought iron frame construction. Designed by Joseph Paxton, the gardener-cum-engineer at Chatsworth House, it used simple repeated modules to allow rapid construction of the vast building and wrought iron bracing at strategic point to stabilise the building. Five years later the London Museum of Science and Art used an iron frame and corrugated iron sheeting as a cladding, much to the disgust of elements of the architectural press. In 1860, John Brown and Company rolled the world's first steel girders for use in a London Bank. 1871 saw the world's first iron frame shop in Derby, three years later the Cockayne building on Angel Street was built with iron framing. However, this was imported from Belgium as this was cheaper than locally made items. This was a situation causing enquiries in parliament. In 1886, Dorman Long converted their rolling mill at Scunthorpe to the production of steel girders. Two years later the Frodingham steel works in Scunthorpe followed suit. By this time Dorman Long had produced the first design manual and section book for steel. It took until 1904 for a national standard to be established in the UK for steel production, a decade later than the US. However, within a decade the UK compliance far exceed that in the US where a vast multiplicity of apparently similar section of differing strengths were still produced.

Chicago in the 1880s and a decade later New York saw the development of iron and steel fully framed building up to 12 stories high. The Skyscraper was born! The opening of the Manchester Ship Canal in 1894 and the consequent development of Manchester and Salford docks saw the introduction of steel framed building to Britain and American methods of rapid construction - quadrupling production rates of some building trades. Meanwhile, the 1891 construction of the Royal English (Savoy) Opera House in London for Richard D'Oyle Carte set a new benchmark in theatre construction with substantial steel cantilevered balconies providing an excellent experience for theatre-goers.

The year 1906 is considered to be when fully framed steel construction entered the general construction idiom. The Pickering Cardboard Warehouse at the junction of Charter Row and Young Street is a notable early example from 1908. The steel framed building allowed the architect to create an ornamental facade unencumbered by the need to support the building, while providing a robust open fireproof working environment within. The body of the warehouse was demolished but the facade was retained in the new office building a few years ago.

With the introduction of the Bessemer Converter and later the Siemens Open Hearth Furnace several Sheffield steel companies were able to make large quantities of steel rail for the world expansion of the railway systems. They were producing much of the rail used to cross America, much of the Empire and large sections of Europe. Major steel bridges around the world also have components made in Sheffield, from New York's Brooklyn Bridge of 1883 to the Tsing Ma - Lantau Bridge, Hong Kong of 1997 and beyond.

Today, Sheffield still produces important equipment for the civil engineering industry. DavyMarkham Ltd produced the cutting heads for tunnel boring machines used in some of the greatest and most challenging tunnelling project around the world. Forgemasters with their world leading capacity supply components for bridges, power generators of all kinds and many more applications.

Obviously, steel is a major structural material used in its own right in many structures and has been so since the development of the Bessemer - Mushet process in Sheffield. Bulk steel making of these has now largely moved away from Sheffield, with only specialist suppliers remaining. However, structural steel framing represents a major part of the construction industry, with 70% of multi-storey buildings and almost 100% of single storey industrial buildings using the material. It is also widely used in bridges and other building structures. Steel can offer rapid and safe on site construction, and at the end of life substantial reusability or potentially 100% recyclability. The British steel construction sector is highly successful world wide and arguably the most technically advanced with on going investment at all levels.

Early design guidance was developed by the steel manufacturers with limited regulation through building regulations such as the 1909 London County Council Act. The Institution of Structural Engineers published recommendations in 1927 and the first British Standard in 1932. As knowledge grew, and steel properties subtly changed this was periodically revised. The introduction of a completely new design standard occurred in 1985, mirroring the changes in design ethos used in other materials. In the early 2000s design standards across Europe were being harmonised and a new British Standard published as a result in 2005.

Steel, often stainless, is also a vital component in most timber, masonry and glass structures, tying components together. Sheffield businesses, such as Ancon, produce some of the specialist fixing to attach cladding and components to buildings and transfer loads.

Stainless steel is a family of corrosion and heat resistant alloys of steel containing at least 10.5% chromium and often other elements. Harry Brearley of the Firth-Brown research laboratories in Sheffield discovered these properties in 1912 and patented the material the following year. His successor W. H. Hatfield went on to patent "18/8" stainless steel in 1924 which is the most widely used form of the alloys. One of the first significant structural uses of stainless steel was in the repairs and strengthening of the dome of St Paul's Cathedral in London in 1925 where stainless steel replaced rusting iron reinforcement carrying the tension forces in the base of the dome. Stainless steel is widely used in conservation projects. The corrosion resistant properties mean that it is the material of choice when in a corrosive environment or maintenance would be difficult. However, it also has other properties of use to the designer. It is more stable than normal carbon steel at both high and low temperatures and highly ductile. The latter means that it is safer in locations that may be subject to blast loads for instance.

Steel is also a major component of a concrete building, representing perhaps 3-5% of the mass of the structural frame. Although the Romans used a form of concrete, occasionally reinforced, it was a different material to modern concrete. John Smeaton while designing the Eddystone Lighthouse in 1750, developed hydraulic lime the forerunner of modern concrete. In 1824 Joseph Aspdin patented a method for making Portland cement. J. C. Loundon's Encyclopaedia of Cottage, Farm and Village Architecture of 1830 includes a proposal to construct roofs made from cement with embedded iron rods. In 1854, William Wilkinson patented a method of constructing fireproof floors based on concrete reinforced with steel strands. However, early work with the technique was plagued with a lack of understanding of the materials and poor quality control. In the 1890s, two Frenchmen, Coignet and Hennebique did much to develop the necessary theoretical and practical understanding. Through that decade the technique spread widely with Mouchel bringing it to Britain in 1897. There was no national standard for the design of reinforced concrete until 1948, although a code of good practice had been introduced in 1934. Prior to this design was carried out to various patented techniques. The design standards have been reviewed frequently since as research has improved our understanding. Major changes took place in 1972 and 2004.

The rotary kiln was developed in 1875 by Frederick Ransome. This made cement manufacture, by roasting limestone, both cheap and consistent. Cements have also been made from ground blast furnace slag - quite commonly used locally in the 1930s. Now Ground granulated blast furnace slag and pulverised fuel ash, a residue from coal fired power stations, can be carefully manufactured and are important components in some concretes. By blending the different cementitious materials the properties of a concrete can be regulated to suit the conditions in which it will be used. Concrete use expanded throughout the 20th century, perhaps achieving a zenith in the 1960s modernist architectural movement. In reinforced concrete high strength steel bars are tied or welded into a cage or grill in a carefully determined pattern and the wet concrete placed and compacted around them to protect them and share the loads. In some circumstances small steel or plastic fibres are also added into the mix. In pre-stressed concrete the steel is stretched before the external load is applied to the structure. This has the effect of compressing the concrete and enhancing the load carrying capacity.

The earliest recorded example of concrete framed construction that has been found so far is the Eldon Ward of the Royal Hospital constructed in 1910. This has since been demolished.

Breedon cement works at Hope in Derbyshire originally opened in 1929 and has received much development since to incorporate the best technologies. It now produces 1.3Mt of cement each year. Much of this is delivered by rail through Sheffield. The company, and its predecessor Lafrage, has recently invested £20M improving its rail connection allowing nearly 7,000 extra lorry journeys to be removed from the local roads. The plant, the largest and arguably the best in the UK, supplies much of the country particularly the SE of England. Much of the cement used in Sheffield comes from Hope. The Hope works has the lowest dust emissions of any cement plant in the UK. It has also reduced other pollutants. For instance, nitrous oxides emissions have reduced by 30% by burning chipped waste vehicle tyres.

Steel, often stainless, is also a vital component in most timber, masonry and glass structures, tying components together. Sheffield businesses, such as Ancon, produce some of the specialist fixing to attach cladding and components to buildings and transfer loads.

In addition to steel and concrete, masonry and timber new materials such as glass and carbon fibres and plastics are developing niche markets sometimes as additives to concrete and sometimes as distinct components. It is now possible to make bridges capable to taking HGV loads out of fibre reinforced recycled plastic, for instance.

Regeneration and development.

Our built environment is in a constant state of flux as structures reach the end of their useful life they are reused, replaced or simply abandoned. This means that wherever man has been active for some time a legacy of the past is left to the future. Engineers are central to the effective redevelopment of the land.

Until the mid 18th century Sheffield remained a small town. Most buildings were of timber or rough stone. The earliest brick building is thought to be the Upper Chapel on Norfolk Street, built in 1700. However, brick was not widely used until the latter part of the 18th century. The land south of Norfolk Street was the first to be systematically laid out and incorporated brick buildings and a regular road pattern. As the town grew rapidly in the 19th century this general pattern was repeated.

Sheffield used to have many collieries and quarries. The abandoned workings can leave instability in the ground and potentially collapse under future developments. The ground has to be carefully probed to locate old workings. These are then usually filled from the boreholes with gravel and grout to make them safe. This happened with many of the buildings on the Sheffield Hallam University City campus, for example. If the workings are very shallow it is sometimes easier to simply dig through them, as has happened in some of the Don Valley redevelopments. As the old workings had to leave a lot of coal to support the roof it is sometimes economical to opencast mine these. This was done at the airport and Orgreave for instance. When this is done the ground has to be carefully put back to minimise settlement of the fill material. The new structures built on top of the workings may also have some additional strengthening to further reduce the risks of unknown underground hazards.

Another potential problem is quantities of old filled material on site. This sometimes contains unpleasant material. When this is suspected a rigorous programme of sampling and analysis takes place before, during and after treatment to ensure that the land is fit for its intended purpose and the workforce and neighbours are safe at all times. How the land is treated will depend upon many factors - what is where, what form it is in, can the critical components naturally move, what is the proposed use for the area. Techniques are being developed all the time to make land remediation safer, quicker and cheaper. The many former industrial sites across the city have undergone these treatment methods.

Old building can often be brought back to life with new uses. Examples include the warehousing around the canal basin, Aizlewood's Mill on Nursery Street and the Cornish Place redevelopment. Sometimes even when the original use is retained, the changes in how a building must function may require significant changes to the structure. The redevelopment of the Lyceum Theatre illustrates this. However, there are cases where the changes needed are too great to be accommodated within the existing structure, but nevertheless the visual appearance needs to be retained. Here the outside walls may be preserved and carefully supported while the whole of the remainder of the building is demolished and rebuilt from the basement up. The old facades are then carefully secured to the new structure. Examples of this are the shops on the corner of Fargate and Norfolk Lane and the Leopold Street redevelopment of the former education offices.

Whenever an old structure is altered a rigorous assessment has to be made of how it will respond to the changes and how the alterations can be safely brought about. The structure is carefully monitored during the works to ensure that all movement that does occur is as expected and that changes can be made if any thing untoward occurs. The design engineer and contractor must work closely together to ensure a safe and efficient process. Especially on historic structures that have been altered in the past the behaviour of a structure to new changes can be very complex.

Nevertheless, the reuse of old structures as opposed to wholesale demolition not only preserves the aesthetic character of a location, it also retains all the energy used in the original construction. This is increasingly important consideration as we strive to continue development with minimal expenditure of precious natural and energy resources.

6.1   Ordnance Survey Benchmark.

These marks were carved into buildings, bridges and even gate posts across the country by the Ordnance Survey in the 19th century as it accurately mapped the entire country. Although now superceded by precision satellite technology, it still maintains a record of the precise elevation of these marks which were used to allow any surveyor to measure the altitude of nearby features.

6.2   Triangulation (Trig) point.

These were built by hand at over 31,500 locations across the country in the mid 20th century. They were used by the Ordnance Survey to re-triangulate the survey of the country to accurately determine the location of every feature. At least two other trig points will be visible from each station.

6.3   This antique theodolite is now used as the Institution of Civil Engineers Yorkshire and Humber Region Award. a prize given annually to recognise excellence in the concept, design and execution of works of civil engineering.

People

From Tudor times local magistrates, on behalf of the crown, would appoint surveyors on an *ad hoc* or part time basis to oversee the maintenance of important bridges and other strategic assets. The term "county surveyor" was recognised in law from 1803. The Municipal corporations act of 1835 and Local Government act of 1888 radically altered how the country was governed and administered at local level. In 1864, Sheffield Borough Council adopted powers granted to them under the Public Health Act of 1848, Local Government Act of 1858 and Highway Act of 1864.

These laws together with various other legislation required local government to be responsible for providing services for the community. The legislation made the borough or county engineer the person responsible for ensuring these provisions were met. Thus by the end of the 19th century local engineer was responsible for roads, sewers and sewage disposal, drainage, flooding, lighting, tramways, clean water, electricity and gas supplies and major public buildings such as hospitals, libraries and housing schemes.

County surveyors for the West Riding of Yorkshire.

April 1743 - April 1757	John WATSON (snr) of Hobroyd and Robert CARR of Horbury
April 1757 - April 1761	John WATSON (jnr) of Hobroyd and Robert CARR
April 1761 - August 1771	John WATSON (jnr) and John CARR (son of Robert)
August 1771 - April 1773	John BILLINGTON of Foulby and John CARR
April 1773 - July 1774	John BILLINGTON and Robert CARR (brother of John)
July 1774 - April 1777	Jonathan SYKES of Oulton and Robert CARR
April 1777 - July 1793	John GOTT of Woodall (with Jonathan SYKES as supernumery)
July 1793 - Jan 1797	William GOTT
Jan 1797 - April 1819	Bernard HARTLEY
April 1819 - April 1834	Bernard HARTLEY and Bernard HARTLEY (II, son)
April 1834 - August 1855	Bernard HARTLEY (II)
August 1855 - October 1882	Bernard HARTLEY (III, son of II)
October 1882 - 1914	J. VICKERS EDWARDS
1914 - 1921	F. G. CARPENTER
1921 - September 1945	Herbert Raikes HEPWORTH CBE MICE
September 1945 - 1949	Harold A. HOSKINGS MICE
1949 - 1970	Col. Stuart Maynard LOVELL MICE
1970 - 1976	John A. GAFFNEY MICE

Borough or City Surveyor / Engineer for Sheffield.

1864 - 1874	Samuel Furness HOLMES AMICE
1875 - 1878	P. B. COGHLAN CE
1879 - 1888	Robert DAVIDSON AMICE
1888 - 1915	Charles Froggatt WIKE AMICE
1915 - 1937	Walton John HADFIELD CBE MICE
1937 - 1941	R. NICHOLAS MICE
1941 - 1954	John Marr COLLIE CBE MICE MIMunE
1954 - 1961	Henry FOSTER MA MICE MIMunE
1961 - 1970	Clifford R WARMAN BSc MICE MIMunE MTPI
1970 - 1973	A T THREAPLETON CEng MICE MIMunE
1973 - 1974	post vacant.

With the 1974 local government reorganisation Sheffield abolish the post of City Engineer and create directors of Works and Planning. Subsequently there have been numerous changes to the management structure of the council.

1974 - 1977	Works: J EDWARDS FIOB FIMunE AMBIM Planning: Bernard F WARREN FRIBA MTPI
1977 - 1984	Works: J EDWARDS Planning: J WINTER Dip Arch RIBA DipTP FRTPI
1984 - 1986	Works: J EDWARDS Environment, Land & Planning: J WINTER Design & Building: A J WOOD Dip Arch RIBA
1986 - 1989	Works: D F GREEN CEng FICE Environment, Land & Planning: J WINTER Design & B: A J WOOD
1989 - 1993	Works: D F GREEN Environment, Land & Planning: R JONES MRTPI Design & B: A J WOOD
1993 - 1996	Operations:D F GREEN Works: J D WIDDOWSON Planning & development: R JONES Design & B: A J WOOD
1996 - 1997	Works: J D WIDDOWSON Planning & development: JOHNSON BA DipTRP DipM MIMgt Design & B: A J WOOD
1997 - 1998	Works: J D WIDDOWSON Design & B: I R STUBBS ARICS

1998 - 2000   Exec Director Development Environment & Leisure: John
MOTHERSOLE
Dir. Planning Transport & Highways: N R BAJARIA BArch DipTP
MRTPI   Dir. Design & Property: I R STUBBS

2000 - 2002   Exec Director Development Environment & Leisure: J MOTHERSOLE
Dir. Planning Transport & Highways: David CURTIS BA DipTP MRTPI
FIHT
Dir. Design & Property: I R STUBBS

2002 - 2003   Exec Director Development Environment & Leisure: J MOTHERSOLE
Dir. Planning Transport & Highways: D CURTIS
Dir. Design & Property: I TAYLOR

2003 - 2004   Exec Director Development Environment & Leisure: J MOTHERSOLE
Dir. Planning Transport & Highways: D CURTIS
Dir. Design & Property: I TAYLOR
Dir. Streetforce: John CHARLTON

2004 - 2008   Exec Director Development Environment & Leisure: J MOTHERSOLE
Dir. Planning Transport & Highways: D CURTIS
Dir. Streetforce: John CHARLTON

2008 - 2009   Exec Director Development Environment & Leisure: D BRENNAN
Dir. Planning Regeneration & Development:: Les STURCH
Dir. Streetforce: John CHARLTON

2009 - 2013   Exec Director Place: Simon GREEN
Dir. Planning Regeneration & Development:: Les STURCH
Dir. Streetforce: John CHARLTON

2013 - 2016   Exec Director Place: Simon GREEN
Dir. of Regeneration & Development Services: David CAULFIELD

2016 - 2018   Exec Director Place: Laraine MANLEY
Dir. of Development Services: Nalin SENEVIRATNE
Dir. City Growth: Edward HIGHFIELD
Dir. Culture & Environment: Paul BILLINGTON

Engineers of note associated with Sheffield.

Vintaine Family.

Although details are sketchy we can fairly confidently say that the Vintaine family came to Sheffield from Sussex around the end of the 17th century. They proved themselves particularly skilled in the trade and profession of mill-wright. There are records of them being called upon by the leading land and mill owners across the country. The family business thrived for at least 150 years. The Vintaines were able to command significantly higher fees than the jobbing millwrights they supervised and are thought to have been highly respected members of the Hallamshire community. John Vintaine was contracted in 1731 by the county magistrates to carry out repairs to Brightside Bridge.

John Smith.

Little is known of the early life of the two engineers named John Smith of Attercliffe, father and son. The father is first mentioned in extant records in 1731 when he took over from Palmer and Atkinson as engineer on the River Don Navigation. Later he is recorded working for his son on schemes for the Ouse, Nene and Wear river navigations. He died in 1767. The son is thought to have been born around 1725, but is first recorded from 1752 working for his father on design and build contracts for Ouse and Nene navigations. He worked on numerous river navigation improvement schemes. He died sometime between July 1782 and June 1784. For his Ure navigation scheme he initially built a timber bridge to carry the Great North Road over the canal cut at Boroughbridge. This was soon replaced by a bridge of iron beams. This has been attributed to John Smith and would make it one of the first iron bridges in the country. However, the attribution and date of the replacement are as yet unconfirmed.

John Carr

© National Portrait Gallery (4062)

John Carr was born in Horbury the eldest of six sons of Robert Carr a mason and bridge-master for the West Riding.

John Carr, his father and John Watson recorded the state of all the West Riding of Yorkshire county bridges in 1752-3 in his Book of Bridges, now in the West Yorkshire Archives. This document was commissioned by the then Bridgemaster; a position held jointly by Robert Carr and John Watson snr. On Robert's death in 1760 John Carr took over the post until 1772 when he resigned to become Bridgemaster for the North Riding. John Carr in parallel with his work on bridges developed a successful career in architecture to become one of the foremost architects of the late 18th century. One of his first commissions was Huthwaite Hall, Thugoland but he worked extensively throughout the north of England and further afield – including in Portugal. Notable works amongst a large catalogue include, Ferrybridge, the Buxton Crescent and Harewood House. He was also responsible for parts of Cannon Hall, Tankersley Park, Wentworth Woodhouse and Norton Hall amongst many others. The second bridge he had built at Ferrybridge can still be seen next to the former A1 road crossing. He surveyed and enlarged Lady's Bridge and also was involved in alterations to the parish church in Sheffield.

He married Sarah Hinchcliffe in 1746 and died without issue in 1807 and is buried in Horbury, having rebuilt the village church to his own design at his own expense.

John Curr

John, the son of another John Curr is thought to have been born in Kyo, a village near Lanchester, County Durham in 1756. The family was associated with the Buddles of Kyo arguably, the foremost mining consultants of the time. He is mentioned in Sheffield as a coal viewer at the age of 21 in 1777, in the papers of the Duke of Norfolk's estates. However, he may have arrived earlier as in 1797 he writes of introducing rail roads to the Sheffield Collieries 21 years before. These were originally of wood but by 1784 he had invented a system of iron rail to form a track to carry the coal trucks or corves. These were lengths of L shaped iron with a flat bed and outer kerb up to six feet long set in oak sleepers to a gauge width of two feet. Following a favourable report in 1787 by John Buddle the system was widely adopted both below and above ground. Jessop and Outram of the Butterley iron works exploited the design. Curr advised mine owners in the Midlands and South Wales. This led to his system being widely used in all parts of the country, but with the lowest take up being his native North East. Curr also patented numerous other inventions to improve the efficiency of mines, from flat rope to a corf raising machine and the automatic operation of ventilation doors within mines. In 1794 he wrote The Coal Viewer and Engineer Builder's Practical Companion. A report of 1796 described a six-fold improvement in output as a result of these techniques. In 1790 he built an improved Newcomen engine at Attercliffe colliery and 2 years later had a foundry building components for his rails and engines, of which he became a leading builder. In 1801 he invested in the Queen's Foundry on Duke Street, Sheffield to manufacture the flat rope he had invented 3 years earlier. This may have coincided with him losing his job as coal viewer for the Duke of Norfolk. Despite his improvements the preceding decade had been a difficult one for the local coal industry generally and the Duke's estate was not satisfied as the collieries were still losing money. Later that year trade improved and the Duke was able to buy out several rivals thanks to the greater efficiency of his operation instigated by Curr.

His system of flanged rails was superseded in the mid 1820s by the bull head rail and flanged wheel used so successfully by George Stephenson on the Stockton and Darlington railway.

The patent on flat ropes expired before he could fully exploit the technology and he sold out his business to Farley of Gainsborough, his original manufacturer of the ropes. In 1814 he is recorded as having an interest in an iron foundry in Norwich and built an early paddle steam boat. However, the venture did not develop.

His home Belle Vue, near Norfolk Park Road was sold in 1820 when he moved to France for his health. He returned 2 years later and died in 1823 and is buried in the RC cathedral. The house was demolished in the later 20th century.

John Towlerton Leather.

John was born, in 1804, into an engineering and mining Leather family of Beeston near Leeds. At the age of 25 he set up his engineering office in central Sheffield and a year later was appointed as an engineer to the newly formed Sheffield

© Leather Family

Waterworks Company, becoming chief engineer the following year. Over the next 35 years he built 8 reservoirs for the company, including two over 29m high, the second highest then built in Britain.

In addition to his responsibilities for the water works he had part of a successful railway contracting business with a brother and John Waring. Among the contracts delivered by them were the Chesterfield and Erewash sections of the North Midland Railway, part of the Birmingham and Derby Junction Railway and Leeds Extension railway. Leather also was the sole contractor for a major Admiralty contract, the 1.6 mile long Portland breakwater in Dorset. He used a temporary timber pier constructed of piles screwed into the sea bed guided by divers. The rock was dropped into the sea from railway lines on the pier. The breakwater included large circular forts to protect the harbour. He also worked for the admiralty on the sea forts at Spithead and Portsmouth Dock works from 1861 to 74.

His other interests include Inverness Suspension bridge and works on the River Nene and the Middle Drain near King's Lynn. He successfully completed the construction of the former in 1855 after two other contractors failed to progress the scheme. In the latter case he was able to mobilise large resources at short notice to repair a breach in the embankment within one tide, in 1864, thus saving many people from prolonged severe flooding. Leather also owned collieries near Leeds and latterly an engine works at Hunslet. The colliery management was described in a report of 1845 as "good with benevolent paternalism extended by the proprietors".

The inquiry into the failure of the Dale Dyke Reservoir, on 11 March 1864, blamed the construction of the dam but without a conclusive explanation. Although his design for the similar Agden reservoir was approved and successfully built, his later very successful career was almost entirely as a contractor. His work for the admiralty on the South coast brought him much approbation. It is understood that he spent a considerable part of his income privately providing assistance to families affected by the Great Sheffield Flood. He died in 1885.

Joseph Locke.

Joseph was born at Attercliffe, on 9 August 1805, the sixth of seven children, of William Locke, colliery manager. The precise location of the house is uncertain. From the evidence available it may well have been the house named Prospect Cottage on the 1850 Ordnance Survey Map. This was demolished around 1860 to make room for new terrace housing associated with the new steelworks in the area. These themselves have been demolished, the site being to the north of Janson Street nearly opposite the end of Bold Street.

© Institution of Civil Engineers

Five years later he moved with his family to Barnsley. After attending the town's grammar school, from the age of 13 he started various training positions before taking a pupilage with George Stephenson in Newcastle at 18. Two years later he was acting as resident engineer on the Black Fell colliery line in Co. Durham. He co-authored, with Robert Stephenson, a report on locomotive power in 1830. Locke surveyed for George Stephenson from 1830 for a number of routes including from Manchester to Sheffield via Stockport. From 1833 he became engineer-in-chief for the Grand Junction Railway as Stephenson was then too busy but was himself also engaged on many other projects. At this time he established a strong working relationship with John Errington who later came to be a partner.

In 1839 Locke was appointed as Chief Engineer of the Sheffield, Ashton-under-Lyne & Manchester Railway replacing Charles Vignoles who had fallen into dispute with the board. The Woodhead Tunnel was proving a formidable challenge, taking up to 800 men 6 years to build with many accidents. Locke reorganised the work and appointed new contractors and improved the supervision to the tunnel and other sections of the line. Locke was notable for ensuring the designs were build-able and reliable when built. He tended to avoid tunnels in most of his projects if he could as there were always great uncertainty as to how easy it would be to construct. He also ensured that competent contractors were employed, not just the lowest tenderer and that work packages were of a size to attract the best contractors. By these means he consistently provided his clients with projects that achieved their goals at an agreed budget and often delivered early while allowing the contractors to make a reasonable profit in the process.

Locke was invited to Paris to build several railways from the late 1830s onwards. Because of the inadequacies of French engineering at the time English contractors built the lines and English rolling stock had to be imported. The rapid progress achieved saw Locke decorated with the Legion d'Honneur in 1859.

Throughout the 1830s, 40s and 50s he was responsible for many railways across Britain and into western Europe. He was elected a member of the Institution of Civil Engineers in 1830, a Fellow of the Royal Society in 1838 and president ICE 1858-9. He died suddenly in Scotland in 1860 and is commemorated by statues in Locke Park in Barnsley and Barentin, France.

Thomas Hawksley

Thomas was born at Arnot Hill House, Arnold, Nottingham on 12 July 1807, the son of John Hawksley, a manufacturer, and his wife Mary Whittle. It is thought that John Hawkesley was a scion of the Hawkesleys of Owlerton, the Sheffield family of Millwrights. The Hawkesleys like the Vintaines were active throughout the 17th and 18th centuries in the design, supervision and construction of waterpower sites throughout South Yorkshire.

© Institution of Civil Engineers

Thomas was educated at the old Nottingham Grammar School, where he showed a particular interest in mathematics, geology and chemistry. At the age of 15 he was articled to Edward Staveley, architect and surveyor of Nottingham, and subsequently became a partner in this business, known as Staveley, Hawksley & Jolland, and he continued as the senior partner (after Staveley's death) until he left for London in 1852.

The distribution system that he installed in Nottingham in 1830 was the first to be successfully designed so that the pipes were constantly charged under pressure, thus allowing consumers to draw water at any time. Such a system was generally considered impracticable then because of the difficulty of designing fittings that did not leak seriously, and the usual practice was to charge the pipes for a short time each day (or even once in two days) in order to fill cisterns. Hawksley undertook the design of better fittings that could easily be repaired or replaced.

The report of the 1844 government inquiry into the Health of Towns had an immediate effect on his reputation, raising him from the status of a local engineer to a nationally eminent one, and numerous authorities responsible for water supplies started to approach him for advice. For the Sheffield Water Company, Hawksley was responsible for the reconstruction of the Dale Dyke Dam near Bradfield, west of the town, after it had collapsed in 1864 (causing a heavy loss of life), and made three more impounding reservoirs in the vicinity. He acted as engineer to the Sheffield company until 1887, when the Corporation took over and he became their consultant.

Hawksley constantly emphasised the necessity of decent housing for working families. As late as 1892, he gave evidence to a Royal Commission on London's water supply, and advocated using the Thames as a source. He installed gasworks in several towns. He gave advice on water supply schemes abroad, and received decorations from several foreign governments.

He died on 23 September 1893. Thomas Hawksley was a leader in his profession. He was President of the Institution of Civil Engineers in 1871-1873, President of the Institution of Mechanical Engineers in 1876-1877, and was elected a Fellow of the Royal Society in 1878. He was one of the founders of what became the Institution of Gas Engineers, and was its President in 1864-1867.

Sir John Fowler.

© Institution of Civil Engineers

John was born on 15 July 1817 at Wadsley Hall, the son of John Fowler a land surveyor. The grade 2 listed Georgian farmhouse is dated 1722 but is not open to the public or readily visible from the road (OS ref: SK 328 903). However, it was visible in 2002 and photographed as part of the Images of England project. This can be viewed at www.imagesofengland.org.uk using IoE Number 458129. After education at Whitley Hall School, at 16 he became a pupil of John Towlerton Leather civil engineer to Sheffield Waterworks. Through Leather, Fowler gained experience of railway engineering at an early age and by his mid twenties was acting as design engineer and had a team of assistants. His early work tended to be in Yorkshire and Lincolnshire, but he soon was working both nationally and internationally. By the early 1860s he was working on 70 major schemes a year. Fowler was consulted on schemes on all the continents, notably in India, Egypt and Australia.

In Sheffield his most notable structures were the Wicker Arches viaduct Europe's largest masonry viaduct and Sheffield Victoria Station, with a 24.4m span roof, both completed in 1849. At the time he designed, using wrought iron, the Torksey viaduct for the Manchester, Sheffield and Lincolnshire Railway. This proved controversial at the time and lifted him to national prominence. The two 39.6m span box girder structure pushed the boundaries of the analysis of structures and materials at the time. This bridge was opened in 1850.

He designed the first sections of London's underground, the Metropolitan line in 1853. This proved a great technical and commercial success. Fowler was widely consulted upon many of the other underground railway schemes designing much of the Metropolitan and Circle lines and giving opinion on most successful schemes. Fowler worked with Greathead on the City and South London Line - the world's first electric tube line, setting the pattern for most subsequent underground lines.

However, he is probably best known for his work, with his protégé, Benjamin Baker, in the design and management of the Forth Railway Bridge, one of the first major bridges to use Bessemer steel as opposed to wrought or cast iron. Fowler worked on this project from 1883 to 90 having helped develop the science of the analysis of continuous span bridges and the new material of steel over the preceding years. He notably pioneered the use of Portland cement for the foundations on the Forth Bridge. Five years later he was investigating the use of reinforcement for concrete slabs.

Throughout his career he promoted the need for good education and training of engineers. His ability to attract and nurture the talents of his assistants together with his great managerial ability were hallmarks of his career.

He was elected MinstCE in 1844 and became the youngest president of the institution in 1865, knighted in 1885 for his survey work in Egypt and Sudan. He was given a baronetcy in 1890 upon completion of the Forth Bridge. Fowler died in November 1898 at the age of 81 having remained active in engineering throughout his life.

His obituary notice in the ICE Minutes of proceedings summarised his life thus: "An independent professional career, commencing before the railway mania and extending some years beyond the completion of the Forth Bridge, is indeed a notable record, and it is scarcely possible that one quite like it will ever occur again. It lifts its author out of the ordinal category of engineers, and puts him among the few who have written their names in broad characters across the face of the nineteenth century. During the whole of the period he was in the forefront of the struggle in subduing the great powers of Nature in the service of man and whenever the difficulties were greatest he was certain to be found."

Professor Joseph Husband

Joseph Husband was born in Rotherham and educated at the Sheffield Central Science School and took his degree and a medal at Royal College, Dublin before returning to Sheffield. In 1892, at the age of 21 he was the first lecturer in civil engineering at the Sheffield Technical school. He was awarded the ICE James Watt Medal and Telford Premium in 1900.

He was the inaugural head of the department of Civil Engineering in 1917 of the University of Sheffield. This was a post he held until retirement in 1936, the last 16 years as professor. Upon retirement from the university he founded his own consulting practice Husband and Clark with his son, Charles, and Antony Clark, retiring a few years later. He was elected as the president of the Institution of Structural engineers in 1937-38. In addition to diverse engineering interests he took an

© Institution of Structural Engineers

active interest in the Council for the Preservation of Rural England being on its executive and he was also active in the Hunter Archaeological Society. He died in 1961 at the family home on Elmore Road. It is thought that the only work attributable to him in Sheffield is the Steel mast of the Barker's Pool war memorial.

Sir Donald Coleman Bailey.

Donald was born on 15 September 1901 in Rotherham the son of a commercial cashier. Bailey read engineering at the University of Sheffield graduating in 1923. After a short spell in York he returned to Sheffield and the offices of the London Midland and Scottish Railway and then the city engineer's department. However, in 1928 he left to join the War Office Military Engineering Experimental Establishment as a civil engineering designer.

© National Portrait Gallery x87182

He had his idea for transportable bridges in 1936. However, at the time the War Office preferred the design of Charles Inglis. He developed his ideas in his own spare time. In February 1941 Inglis' design failed under test and Bailey's design was taken up. By early May a prototype was ready and production units were reaching the forces before the year end. The bridge consists of standard welded rectangular truss units which could be bolted together as necessary and could be lifted by 6 men and fit in a standard 3 ton lorry. The component design allowed many small engineering companies to produce them. Over 2000 were used in Europe during WW2 and afterwards. Many remain in use today. There is an example over the River Don on the Five Weirs Trail.

Bailey was appointed OBE in 1944 and knighted in 1946. That year he was also awarded an honorary Doctorate in Engineering by the University of Sheffield. He has been described as 'a benign influence on the modern scientist - soldier' working on many technical solutions until his retirement in 1966. He died in Bournemouth on 5 May 1985.

Sir Charles Husband

© Institution of Structural Engineers

Charles was born in Sheffield in 1908, the son of Joseph Husband. He was educated at King Edward VII grammar school prior to taking his degree at Sheffield University. His early experience was with Barnsley Water Board, Henry Boot & Sons Ltd and the First National Housing Trust Ltd. In 1936 he formed the firm of Husband and Clark with his father and Antony Clark, becoming senior partner the following year. The company worked on a wide range of projects at home and overseas. From 1943 to 45 he was an assistant director for aircraft production at the Ministry of Works, and in 1946 designed the first high altitude testing plant for jet engines. He designed the 250 foot diameter Jodrell Bank radio telescope for the university of Manchester, completed in 1957. He subsequently designed various other large radio telescopes and antennae, including at the Satellite communications station at Goonhilly Down, Cornwall. The Institution of Civil Engineers awarded him the Benjamin Baker Medal after he presented a paper on this achievement. He was also involved in a number of bridge projects, including the reconstruction of the Robert Stephenson Britannia Bridge to Anglesey for which he was awarded the ICE James Watt medal in 1976. He was awarded the Institution of Structural Engineers Yorkshire Branch prize in 1957 and 62 for his papers on bridge work and the cantilever stand at Sheffield Wednesday.

In 1964 he was appointed CBE and given an honorary DSc from the University of Manchester, the following year he received the Royal Society's Queen's gold medal and subsequently the Wilhelm Exner medal from the University of Vienna (1966) and an honorary DEng from the University of Sheffield in 1967 and the gold medal from the Institution of Structural Engineers in 1974. He was knighted the following year. He held fellowships of several engineering institutions. He followed his father and became president of the IStructE in 1964-65, the only father and son to be presidents of the institution. He died in 1983.

Dr Wilfred Eastwood

Bill was born in Ackworth in 1923, where his father had been a miner. He grew up in several West Riding towns before leaving Rothwell Grammar School. He took a degree at Sheffield University during the war, graduating in 1944. A year later he became the youngest person to pass the Institution of Structural Engineers entrance examination. However, he had to wait a further five years before becoming chartered due to the minimum age limit. On graduation, he enrolled in the Royal Engineers and was seconded to the Road Research Laboratory where he researched airfield construction.

© Institution of Structural Engineers

After military service, from 1946, Bill undertook hydraulics research at Manchester University under Professor Jack Allen, whom he followed to Aberdeen University the following year and then became a lecturer there. He moved to the University of Sheffield in 1955, and eventually became Professor of Civil Engineering after the retirement of Norman Boulton in 1964. He held this post until 1971, during which time the department expanded notably. He resigned to become a partner in Husband and Partners, but left that company a short time later to set up his own practice, incorporating as Eastwood and partners in 1972. He retired in 1996.

He was always closely associated with the Institution of Structural Engineers, both locally and nationally. He became their President in 1976-77, and was later President of the Council of Engineering Institutions in 1981-82. In 1983 he was presented with the Lewis Kent Award by the Institution of Structural Engineers in recognition of his outstanding achievements to the profession of engineering in the field of academia and engineering consultancy.

In his spare time, he was a devotee of cricket and football. He died in September 2014.

Other people, although not civil engineers, but who are closely associated with engineering include:

Fairbank family

The Fairbank were a leading family of land surveyors based in Sheffield and active in the adjoining counties. William (I) 1687-1759 is said to have come from the Halifax area and worked on local land estates and some industrial schemes. His son William (II) 1730-1801 extended the areas of work to land enclosures and roads, working on many of the turnpikes in Derbyshire.

His son William (III) 1771-1846 continued the practice with his brother Josiah 1777-1844 including public works in their portfolio.

William (III) had been appointed surveyor to the Sheffield to Glossop Turnpike Trust in 1818. However, the difficulties he had with this project to build a road in unforgiving terrain led to his dismissal in 1821 in relation to the construction works. However, the practice remained as surveyor to the trust throughout the life of the trust. Loundon McAdam, the son of the renowned John Loundon McAdam oversaw the completion of the works later in 1821. William (III) successfully worked on several other turnpikes and his sons helped survey prospective lines for several railway ventures.

William Fairbank Fairbank 1805-1848 and his brother John Tertius Fairbank 1809-1875 continued their father's practice. It is thought that the latter turned to architecture in later life after the death of the former.

We are fortunate that a very extensive archive of the family company's papers have been preserved in Sheffield Archives. This gives a researcher astonishing detail of the working of a surveyor in an industrialising area over the period 1743 to 1848.

Benjamin Huntsman

Benjamin was born in 1704 in Epworth, Lincolnshire. He was apprenticed to a clock maker at the age of 14 and seven years later he was a watch and clock maker on his own account in Doncaster. Seeking to improve his products he experimented with re-melting steel to create a more consistent watch spring. To do this he "borrowed" technology from the Catcliffe Glassworks to create crucibles capable of withstanding the high temperatures needed. A clock dated 1740 incorporating his new steel is to be seen at Kelham Island Industrial Museum. He established his steelworks at Handsworth in 1742 at which point he ceased watch making to concentrate on his new steel manufacturing business. The works moved to new larger premises off Worksop Road in Attercliffe Common in 1751, building Huntsman's Row in 1770. His family lived there until 1899.

From Huntsman's Row he supplied special steels to Boulton and Watt in Birmingham and was well regarded throughout Europe and America by the end of the Century. By the early 1760s his process had been "borrowed" by many other local steel manufacturers. His pioneering work on tool steels was taken up by Mushet and allowed the creation of the complex machines integral to the development of the industrial revolution. His work established Sheffield as the foremost centre for quality steel production in the UK. The local cutlers did not initially embrace the new steel as it was harder to work. However, it was not long before the Sheffield cutlers were widely using the crucible steel. He died in 1776 and was buried in Attercliffe chapel yard (now known as Hill Top cemetery).

[It may be coincidental, but John Harrison the now world famous clockmaker, was able to build his marine chronometer to sufficient accuracy only in the late 1750s achieving success in 1761 with the introduction of high quality metal components as well as numerous technical innovations. It is highly likely that Harrison and Huntsman were acquainted.]

Sir Henry Bessemer.

Henry was the son of Anthony Bessemer, engineer and born on 19 January 1813 in Chalton near Hitchin, Hertfordshire. Inventive from an early age he had over 100 patents to his name and other successful inventions kept secret within the family business. When trying to find a harder metal for use in ordinance, he observed the effect of air blast when trying to fuse cast iron with crucible tool steel. Four years later, after many set backs, in 1858 Bessemer established his own works in Sheffield, partnered by William Galloway, a Manchester engineer. As he perfected his process he licensed it to other Sheffield firms like John Brown (1860) and Charles Cammell (1861). This resulted in a huge expansion of steel production with over 200,000 tons being produced by 1870 which transformed the city's and country's economy.

HENRY BESSEMER ESQ.

© National Portrait Gallery x45593

Ten years later Sidney Gilchrist Thomas, a London Police court clerk with an interest in applied chemistry, developed the basic reduction steel furnace. This alteration to the Bessemer-Mushet and Siemens Open Hearth processes allowed a much wider range of iron ores to be used in steel production. As a result, steel production world-wide grew rapidly and other areas took over from Sheffield in the production of basic steel.

Bessemer, in 1843, also invented a form of float glass, casting the glass on a bed of liquid tin. However, it was not commercially viable. It was not until 1959 the Sir Alistair Pilkinton successfully developed a system for the mass production of float glass.

Bessemer was awarded the Telford Medal by the Institution of Civil Engineers in 1859 and in 1879 he was elected FRS and knighted. He died in London on 15 March 1898.

Robert Forester Mushet.

Robert was the son of David Mushet of Midlothian and born in Coleford Gloucestershire in 1811. Although he never came to Sheffield himself he had a significant influence on the development of the steel industry. It was he who discovered the benefits of alloying steels to blown steel. His patent of 1856 lapsed and so he never benefited from the success of the Bessemer-Mushet process. Nevertheless, his work with other alloys were successfully patented. Self hardening tool steels were developed known as Robert Mushet's Special Steels (RMS) in a non patented process retained in the family. Key parts of the process were carried out in secret by the family. In 1871 he joined with Samuel Osborn, a Sheffield steel maker, to mass produce the special steels through very carefully controlled processes, still in secret by his sons who went on to join the Osborn company.

Osborn's Clyde Steel and iron works were on the Wicker the offices fronting onto the street. They are now the SADACCA centre. Mushet received a royalty from Osborn for every ton produced and also had an annual income of £300 from Bessemer in (private) recognition of his contribution to his process. Mushet's role in the emerging steel industry was partly recognised at the time - The Iron and Steel Institute awarded him its Bessemer Gold Medal in 1876. Robert Mushet died in 1891.

Sir John Brown

© The Company of Cutlers of Hallamshire

John Brown was born in 1816 in Favell's Yard in Fargate to Samuel, a slater, and his wife Anne. He only had a modest education and was apprenticed to the cutlery firm of Earl, Horton and company at the age of 14. By the age of 21 he was able to buy a partnership in the firm and continued to act as a traveller for them for a further 7 years. He was then able to cease working as a salesman and expand into steel making on his own account.

Four years later he successfully invented and manufactured the conical spring buffer for railway wagons. In 1855 he, like many other important steel makers, moved from the cramped city centre site to new premises in the lower Don Valley, now serviced by the railway as well as the canal. By 1858 he was employing the puddling process for making steel. This allowed the manufacture of steel in quantity for railway rails and armour plate. Only two years later he became the first manufacturer to use the Bessemer-Mushet process for steel manufacture which he applied to rail making. This meant that by 1865 the company was the world largest rail producer supplying half the UK demand at the time of the railway boom and many overseas markets.

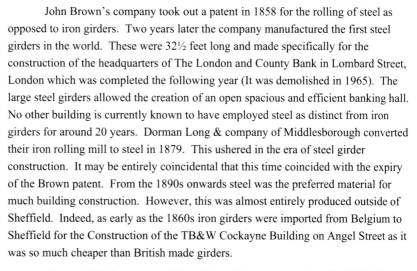

John Brown's company took out a patent in 1858 for the rolling of steel as opposed to iron girders. Two years later the company manufactured the first steel girders in the world. These were 32½ feet long and made specifically for the construction of the headquarters of The London and County Bank in Lombard Street, London which was completed the following year (It was demolished in 1965). The large steel girders allowed the creation of an open spacious and efficient banking hall. No other building is currently known to have employed steel as distinct from iron girders for around 20 years. Dorman Long & company of Middlesborough converted their iron rolling mill to steel in 1879. This ushered in the era of steel girder construction. It may be entirely coincidental that this time coincided with the expiry of the Brown patent. From the 1890s onwards steel was the preferred material for much building construction. However, this was almost entirely produced outside of Sheffield. Indeed, as early as the 1860s iron girders were imported from Belgium to Sheffield for the Construction of the TB&W Cockayne Building on Angel Street as it was so much cheaper than British made girders.

Also, in 1859, he pioneered the rolling of iron armour plate. By 1867, three-quarters of the British navy was clad in Brown armour and the Atlas Works was rolling the world's largest armour plates. Three years later the firm employed 4000 workers and had a turnover of around £1 M.

However, to finance this expansion Brown had gone into partnership with Bragge and Ellis, two Birmingham based industrialist in 1859 and further shareholders, notably Pochin and Whitworth from Manchester from 1864. From this time Brown had less involvement in the company - he had been largely sidelined by the other shareholders - and left entirely in 1871. Brown did not have a controlling interest in the company once Bragge and Ellis joined. The other shareholders balked at the costs of the rolling mills for armour plate and chose not to develop a steel girder rolling mill.

Subsequent investments by John Brown were unsuccessful and he did not reap the lions share of the returns of his ideas. He withdrew from public life from 1881 following the death of his wife of 42 years, Mary. He had been mayor in 1861 & 1862 and Master Cutler in 1865 & 1866. His significant contribution to the country's security through the armour plate manufacture had earned him a knighthood in 1867. He left Sheffield for Kent in 1892 and died at Christmas 1896.

Sir (Charles) William Siemens

Karl Wilhelm was born in 1823 at Lenthe, Hanover. Although he never lived in Sheffield his inventions profoundly affected the development of the city's industry. He came to England in 1843 with his brother to sell their electroplating methods. In 1856 he patented his regenerative furnace which allowed the melting and reheating of steel using cheaper fuel more economically. By 1866 the Siemens process was used to melt wrought iron with ore to form steel in an open hearth. By 1896 in Britain, 2.4 million tons of steel were produced by the process as opposed to less than 2 million by the Bessemer process.

© National Portrait Gallery 2632

He was also active in the family business of electrical engineering, that produced electrical generators, telegraphs and cables. He was the president of, amongst others, the Society of Telegraph Engineers (later to be the Institution of Electrical Engineers), and awarded the Howard prize of the Institution of Civil Engineers in 1883. He was knighted the same year and yet died shortly afterwards.

Henry Clifton Sorby

Clifton was born at Woodbourne, Attercliffe in 1826, the son of a successful edge tool manufacturer. He was educated at Collegiate School and from the age of 15 by a private tutor in diverse scientific fields. He excelled at mathematics and soon was determined to pursue a career in science. Eschewing university as there were no courses at that time purely dealing with science and those available would not have helped his career it was thought. His father died when he was 21 leaving a substantial legacy allowing him to pursue his own scientific enquiries unfettered by employers or institutional constraints. He set up a laboratory in his home at Broomfield off Glossop Road, near what is now the Royal Hallamshire Hospital. In 1849 he pioneered a new branch of geology -"Microscopical Petrography" the microscopic examination of very thin sections of rock under both normal and polarised light. Although, he did not invent the technique he made it an accepted branch of science. He carried out pioneering theoretical and practical experiment on rock crystal formation and rock deformation.

From this he went on to be interested in meteorites and so to iron. He developed a means of microscopic examination of iron by polishing it to a mirror finish and controlled etching with acids as it is not possible to examine by the thin sections he had been using for minerals and animal and plant materials. This directly transformed our understanding of the structure of metals. The crystalline nature of steels and how this was affected by the chemical composition and manufacturing processes became apparent. This led to the development of the science of metallurgy, upon which the modern steel industry is founded and at which Sheffield excels.

He also had an interest in spectroscopy and discovered four elements. Another field of interest was marine biology studying the north sea from his yacht which was, of course, equipped with a laboratory of his own design. His work, in 1882, included 240 days studying the effect of sewage drainage into the River Thames for the Royal Commission on the drainage of London. This work laid the foundation of our knowledge of pollution of the seas.

He also studied archaeology, architecture, old churches, mediaeval art, illuminated manuscripts, Egyptian hieroglyphics. He also painted in water-colours as a hobby. He was an active member of the Sheffield Literary and Philosophical society throughout his life and was involved in numerous learned societies locally, regionally and nationally. He was instrumental in the setting up of Firth College, the fore-runner of the university.

He was elected a fellow of the Royal Society at the age of 31 due to his work on rock deformation. He was given the Wollaston Medal of the Geological Society in 1869, the Gold Medal of the Dutch Society of Sciences in 1872 and the Gold Medal of the Royal Society in 1874. He was also made an honorary Doctor of Laws at Cambridge University. He was president at various times of the Royal Microscopical Society, the Mineralogical Society, the Geological Society and the geological branch of the British Association. Sheffield presented him with his portrait and bust in 1898 in recognition of his achievements.

The Sorby Natural History Society was founded in 1918 in Sheffield as the Sorby Scientific Society in his honour and now is "A forum for naturalists of all ages and abilities to meet, enjoy natural history, collect, store and disseminate information, explore the Sorby Study Area and promote conservation of wildlife and geology."

For the last five years of his life he was confined to his bed following an injury but continued his studies. He died in 1908. He left £10,000 directly to Sheffield University to endow a professorship in Geology and another £15,000 to the Royal Society to endow a fellowship at the University of Sheffield. He is buried at Ecclesall Church.

Harry Brearley

Harry was born in 1871, the son of an expert steel smelter. He started work at the age of 12 with his father. However, he quickly moved to be a bottle washer in the laboratories of Thomas Firth and Sons. By 1891 he had an apprenticeship as a laboratory assistant. He progressed rapidly and after spells with other companies became the first director of research at the merged Brown-Firth research Laboratories at the age of 36. In May 1912 he tried a low carbon steel with chromium alloy for potential armament use. This failed to achieve the intended properties at the time. However, the scrap pieces showed corrosion resistance properties. Brearley gave samples to friends in the cutlery trade across the city. This rapid adoption prevented stainless steel being patented in England, but Firths and Brearley took out numerous patents world-wide.

In 1920 Brearley was awarded the Bessemer Gold Medal by the Iron and Steel Institute. He died in 1948.

Numerous other people have worked on corrosion resistant steels, some in Germany and America using chromium at about the same time as Brearley. However, Brearley is widely accepted as the inventor of, at least, martensitic stainless steel.

As early as c. 1820 Michael Faraday carried out pioneering work on alloying steels to improve corrosion resistance. Initially working at the Royal Institution laboratories in London, he later sent prepared samples to Sanderson's Works on West Street Sheffield for melting and treatment. The range of elements available for alloying was limited at the time. The rarer metals either not having been discovered or been very hard to acquire until sources in South America were opened up. He had limited success with an alloy with silver which was adopted for a while by some cutlers. Other local steel makers produced "meteoritic" and "peruvian" steels in the 1830s alloyed with secret minerals to improve performance.

The grade 2 listed research laboratory buildings were taken over by English Pewter Company Ltd as a factory when the labs moved elsewhere with the consolidation of the local steel manufacturing industry. The laboratory building can still be seen on Blackmore Street and Princess Street and are included in Historic England's list of the top 100 Irreplaceable Building in England.

Stainless steels – there are numerous types – are now ubiquitous in modern life. Razor blades; almost all cutlery and much kitchen equipment, both domestic and commercial; machine parts for many things large and small from mobile phones through cars to jet engines and nuclear power plants; building cladding fixings and reinforcement; medical implants and also sculptures are all made from stainless steel.

One of the first people to coin the term Civil Engineer was a Yorkshireman, John Smeaton, in 1768. In many ways he embodies the blend of practicality, creativity and scientific/technical knowledge that still are the hallmarks of an engineer today. The Institution of Civil Engineers (ICE) was formed in 1818 by a group of engineers, and granted a royal charter in 1828, to promote the cause in 'directing the great sources of power in nature for the use and convenience of man', and coincided with the expansion of both population and industrialisation. Today ICE has over 80,000 members in 150 countries and provides a voice for civil engineering, continuing professional development and promotes best practice throughout the industry. For over 100 years there have been strict standards of education and training for professional engineers.

Both Joseph Locke (1857-59) and Sir John Fowler (1865-67) when president of the Institution of Civil Engineers worked to promote the better education of civil engineers. The first university degree course in civil engineering was established at King's College, London in 1838, with Glasgow and Trinity College Dublin following in 1840 and 1841, respectively. In the two decades after Fowler's initiative there was a large expansion of specialist engineering education.

Originally any engineering for non military purposes was considered civil engineering. As knowledge progressed and so became more specialised then a range of institutions and societies developed to cater for the needs of the diverse engineering and scientific specialists. These people work together to create, maintain, protect and improve the environment in which we all live as a civilised society.

Civil Engineering companies of national-international significance.

(There are numerous other excellent civil engineers in Sheffield working locally and regionally.)

AECOM

AECOM was set up in 1990 in Kentucky, becoming a publicly traded company on the New York Stock exchange in 2007. Its headquarters are now in Los Angeles, USA. Throughout its life the company has grown with many mergers and acquisitions of engineering companies, some of which date back to the early 1900s. In the early 2000s AECOM took over Maunsell who had previously merged with Balfour Consulting Engineers. The latter had an office in Paradise Square and later Bell's Court from 1971 to 1998. AECOM now has an office in Chesterfield office, where there are approximately 300 staff.

The company has been responsible, world-wide, for numerous significant projects including the London 2012 Olympic and Paralympic Games, London Gateway Port, Royal Bank of Scotland World Headquarters, Spartak Stadium, Moscow, Russia, Kai Tak Development, Hong Kong, and the One World Trade Center, New York.

AECOM joined the Advanced Manufacturing Research Centre in April 2017 and will provide industry training and insight to research staff at the University of Sheffield. Under the membership agreement, AECOM and the University of Sheffield will also pursue research and development opportunities in the construction and other sectors. The research will focus on areas that meet industry's needs and help drive forward the Northern Powerhouse agenda in Sheffield.

AECOM is a global network of design, engineering, construction and management professionals, with approximately 87,000 employees. The company had revenue of approximately $18.2 billion during fiscal year 2017.

AECOM was ranked number one in transportation and general building in Engineering News-Record's 2018 'Top 500 Design Firms'. AECOM was shortlisted for NCE global consultant of the year in 2014 an award it won in 2015. It was 16th overall in the 2016 (inaugural) NCE 100 Awards and 6th for World View assessment. In 2017 it remained in 16th place overall with shortlisting for Technology Trailblazer, Low Carbon Leader, Diversity Champion and Collaborative Firm.

The NCE 100 Awards were created to champion the best companies to work for and with -assessing "the focus on technical excellence, the exploitation of future technologies, taking a world view, driving the equality agenda and seeking to develop the engineers of the future".

Project of note include the following.

One World Trade Center. At 541.3m (1,776 feet) tall, One World Trade Center (WTC) is the tallest building in the Western Hemisphere. In 2004, AECOM Tishman was selected to provide preconstruction and construction management services for the 104-story One World Trade Center. As the builder of the original Twin Towers in 1973, AECOM Tishman has been working at the WTC site since 2001, assisting with the 9/11 clean-up efforts and managing more than 11 million square feet of new construction.

San Roque Multipurpose Dam. AECOM provided engineering, procurement and construction for the San Roque project located in a remote region of North Luzon in the Philippines. The principal features of this $1.2-billion project include a 200-meter-high earth and rockfill dam, one of Asia's tallest, a 345-megawatt powerhouse and 7 kilometres of tunnels and shafts. Work sprawled over 18 square kilometres and included the construction of all infrastructure facilities necessary to support the project.

London Gateway Port. AECOM delivered a range of multidisciplinary planning, design, engineering and environmental services for London Gateway, the UK's first 21st Century major deep-sea container port and Europe's largest logistics park. Covering more than 1,800 acres (728 hectares), the project has transformed a former oil refinery into a modern, fully automated, multi-modal container terminal capable of handling some of the largest ships in the world.

AECOM, Royal Court, Basil Close, Chesterfield, Derbyshire S41 7SL

01246 209221   chesterfield@aecom.com
                                                                                      www.aecom.com

Amey

Amey began in 1921 when William Amey set up a quarrying company in Oxfordshire. During the Second World War we helped with the construction of RAF bases and involvement with the highways market began in 1959 with our supply of gravel for the M1, between London and Birmingham.

In 1972 it was taken over by Hanson, with the company being renamed to Amey Roadstone Construction. In 1989, the company returned to private ownership and became known as Amey again. In 1995, the company went back to the stock exchange having decided to focus on the provision of support services.

The 2003 acquisition by Ferrovial, the Spanish infrastructure services company, provided a sound financial base to develop. In 2002 it won the largest Public Private Partnership (PPP) in Europe, Tube Lines. Tube Lines was a company responsible for the maintenance, renewal and upgrade of the London Underground infrastructure on the Jubilee, Northern and Piccadilly lines. Amey sold the Tube Lines company to Transport for London (TfL) in May 2010. Amey continues to act as a contracting partner to TfL in the upgrade of the London Underground network. Significantly improving reliability, capacity and passenger comfort.

In 2006 Amey took over engineering consultancy Owen Williams, who were responsible for, amongst other things, the design of the motorway in much of the east midlands. Amey Consulting took over the independent Design and Building Services section of Sheffield City Council in 2012.

Four million people live in areas where the local highways or street lighting are maintained by the company. This includes Sheffield where under the Streets Ahead project they will be bring all the local highway assets up to a good standard and maintaining them in that state until 2037. Amey also are responsible for 100,000 railway structures as sole supplier for civil engineering examination to Network Rail.

The company offers a range of support services and specialises in transportation engineering on both highways and railways. They also provide waste management, facilities management and structures management and design consultancy services.

Amey are able to help clients such as Heathrow Airport Ltd maintain and maximise their spaces, making movement around airports safer. Amey have specialist knowledge of asset management and airport infrastructure to help airports perform better today, and prioritise investments for the future.

Amey, with a turnover of £2.2 bn, employs 20,000 people internationally with a focus on the UK, but with businesses in Australia and America. Amey is committed to developing the skills of their workforce with 2% of employees in apprenticeships or formal training agreements and has been voted among the top employers to work for in a recruitment poll. It has a £1M fund to develop employee ideas for innovation.

In 2015 Amey in conjunction with Sheffield City Council and Ferrovial set up the Sheffield Smart Lab programme. After a year nine innovative urban solutions were chosen from 50 entries from across the world for development in a Sheffield context for either "Energising the city centre" or Helping people live independently" with support from the city's universities.

Amey Consulting was the NCE consultant of the year in 2010 and short listed in 2011 & 2013. It was 57th overall in the 2016 NCE 100 Awards. It has 4,110 staff of which 3,852 are civil or structural engineers .

Charlotte Carroll, an Environmentalist at Amey's Sheffield Design Hub, was shortlisted for the Best Young Woman Award in the Women in Construction & Engineering Awards 2015. Of the 100 design staff within the Sheffield Design Hub, 30 are female.

The Sheffield Streets Ahead office is currently home to 583 employees, a number of whom have been responsible for projects including the purchase of electric vehicles and installation of 21 charging points at both depots in Sheffield; upgrading Meers Brook underneath the carriageway of Chesterfield Road at Heeley, as well as piling 170m of retaining wall whilst designing and building an inbound bus lane in partnership with Sheffield City Council and SYPTE; and in partnership with a developer, designing and installing porous paving incorporating a sustainable drainage system within the adopted highway on Scotland Street, Sheffield.

Amey Sheffield, 1st Floor, Distington House, 26 Atlas Way, Sheffield, S4 7QQ

www.amey.co.uk

Arup

In 1946, Danish born engineer Ove Arup set up his consulting engineering business in London. Over the twentieth century the firm made its name as the designer and engineer behind some of the world's most ambitious structures. In the more than 70 years since its founding, Arup has grown into an international consulting firm of worldwide scope and reach.

An independent firm of designers, planners, engineers, consultants and technical specialists, Arup works across every aspect of today's built environment. The company's goal is to shape a better world; solving technical challenges and turning exciting ideas into tangible reality through creative strength and independence of mind. Today, Arup employs more than 14,000 people across 34 countries – in a culture still underpinned by Sir Ove Arup's aims and values.

The first to open outside of London, Arup's Sheffield office started as a site office for the iconic Park Hill Housing development back in 1957. Arup's new Sheffield office, which has been awarded a SKA Gold rating for excellence in sustainable design and construction, today employs 140 people and stands in the core of the city. Arup is deeply embedded in the continued regeneration of Sheffield, and has been working with the Council to help deliver the redevelopment of the Sheffield Retail Quarter, now known as the Heart of the City, since the scheme's original conception. Arup is also committed to developing a greener future for the Steel City, providing specialist energy consulting roles on projects such as the flagship renewable energy plant at Blackburn Meadows.

Arup's long-standing relationships with Sheffield Hallam University and the University of Sheffield are a key element of the firm's activity in the city. Notably, Arup were the engineer behind the University of Sheffield's award-winning Diamond Building, and helped to deliver Sheffield Hallam University's state-of-the-art Collegiate Crescent Campus.

As a firm, Arup is recognised as an industry leader, as indicated by its ranking first and second in 2017 and 2018 respectively in the NCE 100 Awards.

The Sydney Opera House is one of the most famous buildings in the world and its history is inextricably linked with Arup. Ove Arup was involved in the original design, which began in the 1950s, and the firm continues to play a pivotal role in the building's long-term development and preservation plan. Danish architect Jørn Utzon won an international competition for the project in 1957. As the industry's eminent concrete designer, Ove Arup's contribution was sought early on, and he began to turn Utzon's freeform sketches into an architectural reality. Arup's team confronted an engineering challenge that has since become one of the profession's epic tales – the design and construction of the building's enormous, precast concrete shells.

The firm's portfolio today is both specialist and wide-ranging.

Arup, 9th Floor, 3 St Paul's Place, Norfolk Street, Sheffield S12JE

0114 272 8247

sheffield@arup.com
www.arup.com

Eastwood & Partners

The company was founded by Dr Wilfred Eastwood in 1972 being incorporated as Eastwood and Partners in 1973.

It grew steadily in the Sheffield premises, and branches were later set up in Huddersfield and London (both now closed), and also Fleet. It has a varied mix of clients, both public and private. Jobs included steelworks construction in this country and overseas, sports stadia (including stands at both Sheffield football clubs), hospital buildings, geotechnical and water projects, residential developments and many others.

Eastwood & Partners have a long association with the steel industry and have a particular expertise in the design of heavy foundations and structures. They have designed casting pits and platforms, hammer foundations, furnace foundations, rolling mill bases, together with various specialist heavy machine foundations. They have also been involved with the superstructures and heavy craneage associated with heavy industry. They have carried out the structural design for complete continuous casting plants at Llanwern, Ravenscraig and in Malaysia, India and Canada. They have also recently designed a new Primary Mill and Melting Shop extension in Rotherham.

Projects of note include the following. Eastwood & Partners have designed the structure of the 5 new 10 and 18 storey buildings of the Capital East project at Royal Victoria Dock London. This involved some of the largest piles in the UK.

Eastwood and Partners carried out the structural checking on the 'Shard of Glass' building in London, which is one of the UK's tallest building. The completed structure is 302 m high, on a total of 74 floors. The structure has a 13.5 m deep basement and is supported on piles up to 50 m deep. A mix of composite steel and post tensioned concrete frames was employed.

Eastwood & Partners have designed the steel framed processing and 10,000 tonne storage facility for Pulverised Fuel Ash (PFA is used as a cement replacement material) at Aberthaw power station in South Wales. Typical of their long expertise in steel and cement industries.

The Castle College Sheffield project involved the construction of five buildings of up to ten storeys with a seven storey glazed atrium, in steel and concrete framing on the site of the existing Castle South Campus. Eastwood & Partners designed the foundations and structural frames on all five buildings, together with the external works, retaining walls and drainage.

Current projects include a number of multi-storey buildings in Sheffield at various stages of design, the design of new car showrooms across the country for major marques including Jaguar Land Rover and Audi and recently work on the redevelopment of the Olympic Park in London now that it is being turned into a residential area.

They are also heavily involved in the design of roads and sewers, foundations and superstructures for most of the major house builders in the region. These projects often start with the ground investigation and land appraisal.

They have been involved in several development projects at Hope Cement Works in Derbyshire - from alterations to existing structures to multi-million pound redevelopment works. They have also been involved in several schemes for processing pulverised fuel ash (pfa) for use in the cement industry.

Eastwood & Partners has 96 staff of which 81 are civil, structural or geotechnical engineers. It was ranked 38th overall in the 2016 NCE 100 Awards and in the top 10 for diversity champion assessment. Subsequently, rankings of the awards beyond the top ten have not been specified. Eastwood and Partners have been in the NCE100 leading companies listing since the award inception.

Eastwood & Partners, 23 Kingfield Road, Sheffield, S11 9AS

0114 255 4554

mail@eastwoodandpartners.com
ww.eastwoodandpartners.com

Mott MacDonald

The Mott MacDonald Group was formed in 1989 when transportation engineers Mott, Hay & Anderson merged with Sir M MacDonald & Partners, who were leaders in water-related projects. This was one step in a series of mergers. In 1992 the company took over Husband & Co. which had been established in Sheffield in 1921 by Joseph Husband.

Today, Mott MacDonald is a £1.3bn turnover international, multidisciplinary engineering consultancy of approximately 16,000 staff, half of which are civil or structural engineers.

Internationally, the company has been responsible for numerous notable projects including large sections of London Underground, Egypt's Aswan Dam, the Channel Tunnel, Hong Kong International Airport and the connecting Tsing Ma Bridge and Lantau Link, and the Bay Area Rapid Transit metro system serving Silicon Valley in the USA.

The Tsing Ma suspension bridge is part of the Lantau crossing to Honk Kong Airport. With a 1,377m main span the dual deck structure was opened in 1997. It carries both road and rail traffic and was design to withstand the severe typhoons that occur there. It remains the longest span bridge carrying a railway line.

Mott MacDonald's association with Sheffield goes back over 80 years and during its time in the city has developed long-lasting relationships with a wide range of clients and been responsible for projects including Jodrell Bank radio telescope, and grandstands at both local football clubs. The 3,200t Jodrell Bank telescope was designed to be fully steerable, so that it could be pointed to any part of the sky. This was designed by Husband and Company and opened in 1957.

Working out of an office in Arundel Gate, Mott MacDonald continues to work on projects of local and national significance across the transport, buildings, and water sectors. Current and recently completed projects include the Sheffield Lower Don Valley flood defence scheme, Boeing's first European manufacturing facility, the University of Sheffield's state of the art Faculty of Social Sciences hub and the award-winning Great Yorkshire Way, a 5.5 km link road between the M18 motorway and the A638 Great North Road in Doncaster.

The firm is contributing to the development of new services and skills, needed by the engineering profession to meet pressing new challenges – for example, new models of project finance, carbon management and climate resilience, social inclusion, sustainability, digital delivery, design for manufacture, and smart infrastructure.

Mott MacDonald has received widespread recognition for leadership shown on workplace equality, diversity and inclusion.

Mott MacDonald, 4th Floor, Derwent House, 150 Arundel Gate, Sheffield, United Kingdom, S1 2JY

0114 276 1242   sheffield@mottmac.com   www.mottmac.com

Ancon Ltd

Ancon Ltd can trace the company's origins back to George Clark of Sheffield founded in 1882. George Clark merged with Ancon Stainless Steel Fixings in 1992. Today Ancon's headquarters are in Sheffield with businesses located in Mainland Europe, the Middle East, Australia and New Zealand. They are part of CRH, a leading global diversified building materials group.

Ancon designs and manufactures a wide range of specialist fixings for the construction industry. These range from support and restraint systems for masonry cladding to specialist high strength connectors for concrete construction. They have an international customer base with major projects including the Queensferry Crossing in Scotland, The Palm in Dubai and The Shard in London.

In 2018 and 2012 the company received the Queen's Award for Enterprise in Innovation for the successful introduction and ongoing development of an advanced composite, low thermal conductivity wall tie range and a unique lockable dowel system for post-tensioned concrete construction respectively. In 2015, they received a Queen's Award for International Trade, in recognition of the company's export growth in existing and new markets.

Ancon Ltd, President Way, President Park, Sheffield, S4 7UR, UK

0114 275 5224

info@ancon.co.uk
www.ancon.co.uk

DavyMarkham Ltd.

David and Dennis Davy started on a modest scale from 1831 until 1851 in the Lady's Bridge area of the city. The company then acquired the Park Iron Works at Norfolk Bridge. Davy's initially built locomotives but quickly became established as the machine builder of choice for the local steelworks, producing forging presses. They moved to the Darnall site in 1921 and continued to build machines for the most advanced factories around the world. Projects they have worked on include Jodrell Bank radio telescope and the Thames barrier. Davy merged with Markham & Co., the mining and tunnelling engineers of Chesterfield in 1997, taking the name DavyMarkham Ltd in 2006 before a management buy out the following year. DavyMarkham became part of Hindustan Dorr-Oliver Ltd before taken over by Hughes-Armstrong Industries in 2014.

DavyMarkham was a Tier 2 member of the Nuclear Advanced Manufacturing Research Centre. They made key components for bridges and tunnels, transportation systems and flood control systems, metal industries, mining and power generation.

Typical projects would include The Gateshead Millennium Bridge, Selby Bypass Swing Bridge and the Tsing Ma - Lantau Bridge, Hong Kong, Stainless Steel Knife Gates Valves for Changi WTW, Singapore and Drum Gates for various Scottish Reservoirs. DavyMarkham have manufactured Cutter Heads and Shields for a number of TBMs in use world-wide, including the Channel Tunnel Rail link and the Jinping Hydro Power Project in China.

Sadly, DavyMarkham Ltd went into administration due to cash flow difficulties in February 2018.

Outokumpu

Outokumpu is a world leading manufacturer of stainless steel. It produces approximately 2.6 M tonnes of steel each year from its plants around the world employing around 12,000 people. This Finnish company merged with Avesta Sheffield in 2001. Outokumpu started in 1910 as a copper mining and production company. It diversified its mineral portfolio but only started steel production in 1976. Avesta Sheffield itself having been formed through the merger of British Steel Stainless with the Swedish company Avesta in 1991. British Steel Stainless can trace its origins back to Firth Brown Ltd and the discovery of stainless steel by Harry Brearley in 1913. The company continues to invest in research and development producing specialist high quality stainless steel alloys having sold most of its other interests.

The Sheffield facility includes a long melt shop, continuous casting, a bar finishing facility, rod mill and major distribution centre.

Outokumpu, PO Box 161, Europa Link, Sheffield S9 1TZ

0114 261 6144   sales.bar@outokumpu.com
                                                                www.outokumpu.com

Sheffield Forgemasters International Ltd

The company can trace its origins back to the mid 18th century. However, it around 1805 when Edward Vickers and George Naylor established iron and steel interests near Millsands. By 1851, Vickers was able to show at the great exhibition the largest ever casting of 24 cwt (1219 kg) requiring the co-operation of several local works to simultaneously produce over 40 crucibles of steel. They built the River Don works in 1864 taking advantage of the latest technologies. This continued to expand and by 1870 it had become on of the two largest steel works in the world. The company specialised in railway, marine and armament works. In the 1920s and 30s various Sheffield steel companies merged to form English steel. Nationalisation in 1967 and then amalgamation with Firth Brown as a private sector company in 1983 formed Sheffield Forgemasters. This was subject to a management buyout in 1988, and after being sold, again in 2005. The resilience of the management and work force have kept the company going through times of adversity to create the successful business of today.

SFIL still produces the largest castings in the western world at 350 tonnes and up to 16.5 x 7.5 x 4.6 m in size. It has a 10,000 tonne forging press, the largest in Europe. However, subject to obtaining the necessary finance, it is planning, to install a 15,000 tonne forging press. This will be able to make the ultra-large components needed for the next generation of nuclear generating plants. There is only one other forge of this size in existence in the world today. The company remains at the forefront of technology, being a world leader in the manufacture of offshore castings and rolling mill rolls. The company continues to supply an increasing global demand for high quality engineered products to key industries such as defence, nuclear, oil and gas exploration, power generation, marine and construction.

Sheffield Forgemasters' specialist services ranging from design consultancy to engineering production solutions. SFIL's offshore engineering expertise is extensive and applied to buildings and bridges, and is relevant to all heavy steel manufacture requiring design or contract management. SFIL is also the world's leading supplier of large, safety-critical steel castings to the offshore industry.

Sheffield Forgemasters is a Tier 1 member of the Nuclear Advanced Manufacturing Research Centre.

The individual buildings are comparable in size to the EIS at over 2 hectares in area but taller, stronger and less prepossessing. The total building area is of the order of 14 ha. These house massive machines with complex foundations of 1,000s of tonnes to provide the stability needed. These are capable of machining items up to 22 m long or 6.2 m diameter to very fine tolerances.

Sheffield Forgemasters International Ltd, P.O. Box 286 Brightside Lane, Sheffield S9 2RW

0114 2449071

sales@sfel.com
www.sheffieldforgemasters.com

Ancon

Daisy Spring Works, Sheffield is an example of the use of their balcony fixing systems. The systems efficiently do their job but remain invisible.

Over 100,000 Ancon Rebar Couplers were used in the concrete support towers, end piers and road deck of one of the longest cable-stayed bridges in the world. The Queensferry Crossing was officially opened on 4th September 2017 by Her Majesty The Queen.

Sydney Olympic Stadium utilised Ancon components to connect and transfer load between elements of the structure in entirely controlled and predictable ways such as allowing movement when needed.

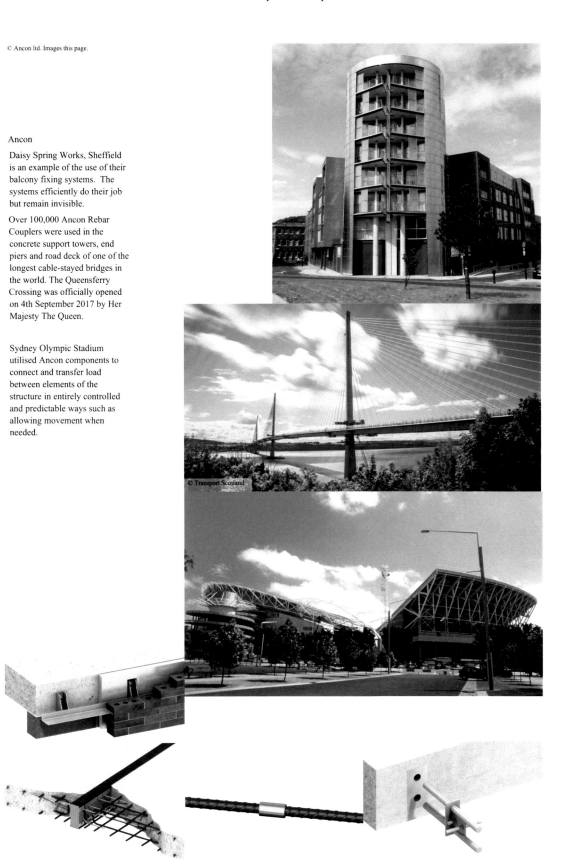

© Transport Scotland

DavyMarkham

This 10 m diameter Tunnel boring machine cutter head is typical of the components created to allow tunnels to be safely and economically cut through a wide range of ground conditions.

Tsing Ma bridge in Hong Kong at 2160 m long was the second longest span in the world when completed in 1997. The cables,their connections supports and anchorages carry high loads and must not fail. DavyMarkham (with Sheffield Forgemasters) provided key components for this, such as the bridge saddles that transfer the weight of the bridge from the cables to the towers.

Sheffield Forgemasters are specialist in high quality large scale precision engineering often in partnership with other local engineering companies.

Top: 200 t mill assembly.

Bottom: Hydro turbine shaft

Outokumpu

Sheffield Stainless melting and continuous casting (SMACC) melt shop.

Discharge from electric arc furnace.

SMACC produces semi-finished products: slabs, blooms, billets and ingots in an extremely wide selection of grades and an industry-leading range of shapes and sizes. The exceptional flexibility of these melt shops means production schedules can be quickly adjusted to provide short lead times.

Newly drawn Wire Rod Coil at Sheffield Alloy Steel Rods (ASR)

Bar and wire producers, as well as welding companies, rely on Sheffield's ASR wire rod mill for uniquely specialized products in a wide range of grades. ASR uses SMACC feedstock billets to produce wire rod in round, hexagon, and square shapes, as well as rebar coil. Sheffield delivers premium quality, industry leading technical service, and tailored solutions set Sheffield in a class of its own.

Gazetteer

Items 1 – 32	**Map 1 - City Centre**
Items 33-39	**Map 2 - Mid Don Valley area**
Items 40-59	**Map 3 - Lower Don Valley area**
Items 60-67	**Map 4 - East Sheffield**
Items 68-77	**Map 5 - Sheaf Valley area**
Items 78-86	**Map 6 - Inner West area**
Items 87-106	**Map 7 - North West**

The following items lie on or close to the relevant walking trail at time of compilation.

Sheffield : A Civilised Place	Items 1 - 32
Norfolk Heritage Trail	Items 8, 14 - 21
Upper Don Walk	Items 28,29, 33, 36 - 39, 95, 97
Five Weirs Walk	Items 28, 29, 40 - 49, 52, 55 - 58
Iron Age to Steel Age Walk	Items 35, 36, 51
Sheffield Country Walk.	Items 52 - 57, 60 - 62, 64 - 67, 74, 93, 106
Cuckoo Way	Item 67
Sheaf Valley Trail	Items 68 - 77
Sheffield Round Walk	Items 68, 69, 74, 77 - 79
Inner City Round Walk	Items 36, 69, 80 - 84
Trans-Pennine Trail	Items 23 - 25, 41 - 43, 40b, 53 - 59, 63 - 67, 99 - 102, 104 - 106
Yorkshire Water Walks	Items 89, 90, 93, 96, 98, 99
Severn Trent Water Walks	Items 87, 88

Please note: the inclusion in a project in this listing does not imply that it is open to the public.

Note: W-ICEY&H2009:

W- winner; HC- highly commended; C- Commended; F- finalist

ICE(Y&H)A is the Institution of Civil Engineers Yorkshire & Humber Awards.

IStructE is the Institution of Structural Engineers Award

BCSAA is the British Constructional Steelwork Association Awards.

BCIA is the British Construction Industry Awards.

SCTA is the Sheffield Civic Trust Awards.

2009 - year of award.

HEW - Historical Engineering Work. - See Labrum or Rennison.

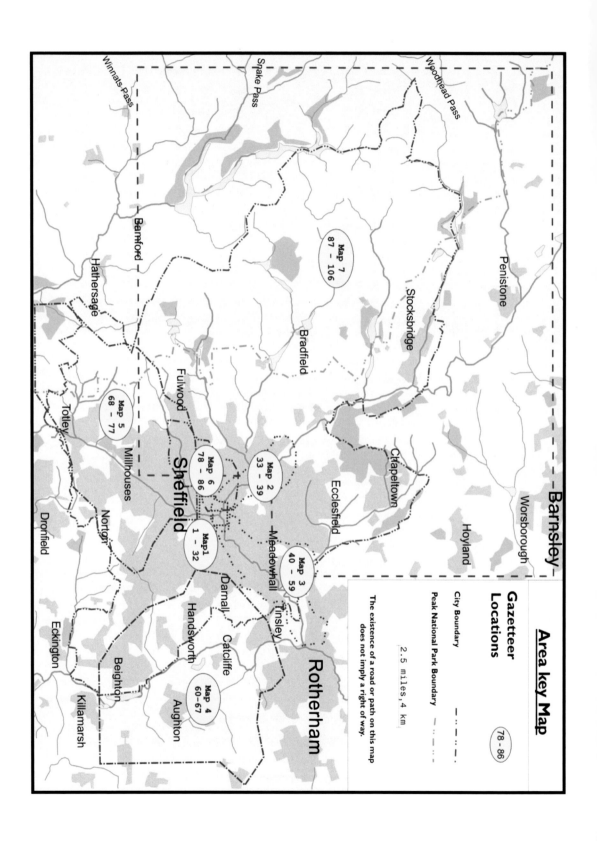

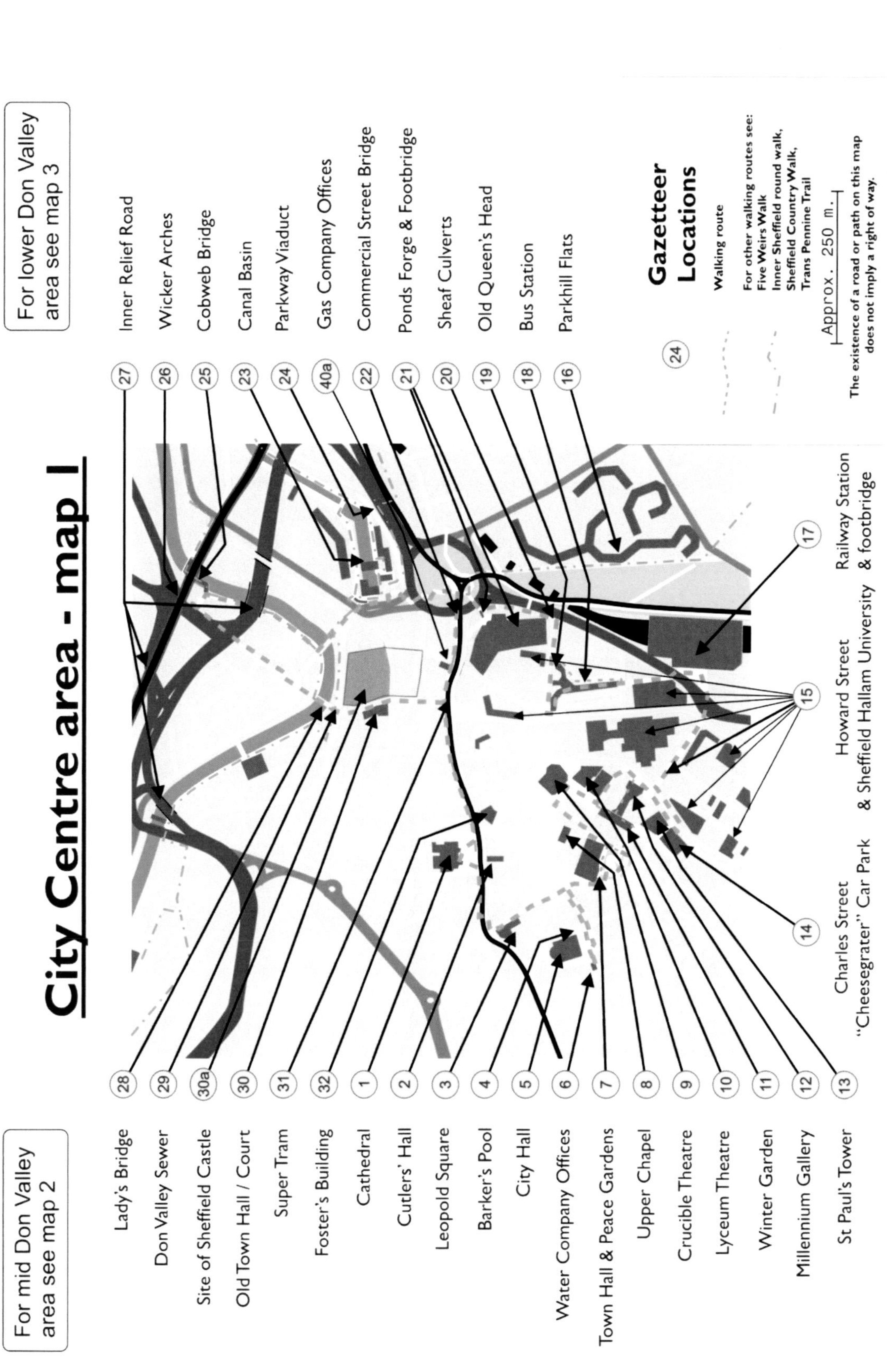

City Centre area - map 1

For mid Don Valley area see map 2

For lower Don Valley area see map 3

27 Inner Relief Road
26 Wicker Arches
25 Cobweb Bridge
23 Canal Basin
24 Parkway Viaduct
40a Gas Company Offices
22 Commercial Street Bridge
21 Ponds Forge & Footbridge
20 Sheaf Culverts
19 Old Queen's Head
18 Bus Station
16 Parkhill Flats

28 Lady's Bridge
29 Don Valley Sewer
30a Site of Sheffield Castle
30 Old Town Hall / Court
31 Super Tram
32 Foster's Building
1 Cathedral
2 Cutlers' Hall
3 Leopold Square
4 Barker's Pool
5 City Hall
6 Water Company Offices
7 Town Hall & Peace Gardens
8 Upper Chapel
9 Crucible Theatre
10 Lyceum Theatre
11 Winter Garden
12 Millennium Gallery
13 St Paul's Tower

17 Railway Station & footbridge
15 Howard Street & Sheffield Hallam University
14 Charles Street "Cheesegrater" Car Park

Gazetteer Locations

24 Walking route

For other walking routes see:
Five Weirs Walk
Inner Sheffield round walk,
Sheffield Country Walk,
Trans Pennine Trail

Approx. 250 m.

The existence of a road or path on this map does not imply a right of way.

139

Map 1 - City Centre - Sheffield - a civilised place discovery trail.

1. Cathedral

The cathedral was formed from the former parish church when the diocese of Sheffield was created in 1914. The church has a claim to be the oldest surviving building in use in Sheffield, but see also Ecclesfield Church. The church of St Peter and St Paul is recorded as being built in 1101 and rebuilt in 1280. Only fragments survive in the chancel of these early buildings. Sources differ as to whether these fragments of Norman masonry relate to the 1101 construction or to the rebuild of the 1280. The existing church was replaced in 1430 to the latest style to accommodate the growing population of the parish. The Chancel was largely rebuilt in the late 18th century. This was when John Carr, the bridge engineer turned architect, was responsible for some alterations in the 1770s. The nave was completely rebuilt in 1805 having, fallen into disrepair, and again remodelled in 1878-80. When the parish church became a cathedral in 1914 further substantial alterations were planned. Some work took place in the late 1930s, revised again and completed in 1966. The cathedral has just completed further alterations to improve access and facilities for all users.

Another claim to fame for the cathedral is that it was the first building in Sheffield to use electricity for use other than lighting when it installed a 3kW fan to power the organ in June 1894.

Www.sheffieldcathedral.org.uk

OS ref: SK 354 875

2. Cutlers' Hall

The Cutlers' Hall has been on this site since 1638, 14 years after the foundation of the company. The present building dates from 1832 with additions of 1867 & 1888. The Cutlers' Hall serves as the focus for the company activities and also as a social venue for the town and city.

Cutlery is documented as having been made in the area for over 700 years. By the sixteenth century the quality was improving and steel, as opposed to iron, being made locally albeit with imported ore. By the 1580s they were being exported widely with a growing reputation for their quality. Until 1614 the trade was regulated by the court of the manor of Hallamshire. At that time Gilbert, seventh Earl Shrewsbury, set up a company based upon the manor court system to oversee the trade in his manor. After his death, two years later, the manor passed to the Howards, Dukes of Norfolk who did not live in Sheffield and the protection and patronage of a powerful local lord was reduced. Ten years later an Act of Parliament established The Company of Cutlers in Hallamshire to have jurisdiction over "all persons using to make Knives, Blades, Scissors, Sheeres, Sickles, Cutlery wares and all other wares and manufacture made or wrought of iron and steele, dwelling or inhabiting within the said Lordship and Liberty of Hallamshire, or within six miles compasse of the same..." Edge tool trades were later included and the steel manufacturers were admitted to the company in 1860.

The company had the responsibility for regulating the quality of workmanship, registering marks and overseeing the apprenticeship system and admitting Freemen to the company. It is from the Commonalty of Freemen that the Master, Wardens, Searchers and Assistants are appointed to carry out the company's duties. The company has remained an influence and benefactor on the local community throughout. It has promoted schemes to improve transport links to and from the area such as the Sheffield Canal and various Turnpikes. However, it has also aided the poor and given donations to local schools and the General Infirmary amongst others. The company never had the riches of the London Livery companies, but never the less sought to support good causes where it could and helped in the development of the universities.

The Company of Cutler's in Hallamshire now promotes and supports all manufacturing industry in South Yorkshire as well as Sheffield Cutler's, Silversmiths and steel manufacturers.

Www.cutlers-hall-sheffield.co.uk

www.cutlers-hallamshire.org.uk

OS ref: SK 354 874

3.   <u>**Leopold Square**</u>

The Elementary Education Act of 1870 was the first of a number of acts of parliament passed between 1870 and 1893 to create compulsory education in England and Wales for children aged between five and 13. The act required that local education boards should be established to ensure there were sufficient places to provide elementary education for all children aged between five and 13. The schools should be publicly funded, but that parents had to pay (modest fees) for their children's education, unless they could not afford to. Attendance would be compulsory, that religious teaching should be non-denominational, and that parents could withdraw their children from religious education. The schools should be regularly inspected to maintain the standard of education. Prior to this, education was provided by churches and individuals. School Boards were abolished under the 1902 Education Act when local councils took over responsibility for education of children including those with special educational needs. However, the building programme continued for another decade. The school leaving age rose to 14 in 1921 (most pupils already stayed on to this age), 15 in 1936 and 16 in 1973. Further schools were built across the city as it grew and new housing estates created.

Sheffield was one of the first areas to set up a board and start building schools to accommodate the children. In what is now the city of Sheffield 64 board schools were built in the period up to 1914 with the first opening in January 1873 and 14 opened by the end of 1875. The school building programme was a matter of civic pride in Sheffield and this was often reflected in the architectural style of the buildings.

These listed buildings were the original Firth College, Central School and the local School Board offices. From the outset they were designed as a unified scheme. Firth college was opened by Prince Leopold in 1879. The Central schools were to provide higher level education to deserving and clever pupils irrespective of class or means. Central schools often had a more technical bias than grammar schools. This building together with the offices opened the following year. Further buildings were added through to 1899 providing education from infants to university level as well as administration. The Board offices have become a hotel, the college offices, the schools residential space over restaurants.

This is a good example, amongst many across the city of the refurbishment of buildings rather than replacing them. This has been widely done in the city centre and riverside areas. This not only maintains the character of an area it also is an efficient use of resources. It does, however, require considerable skill to understand how the existing structure behaves; will respond to changes and how to make alterations safely and efficiently.

One building had all its floors removed to replace four storeys with seven. Another building was demolished in its entirety except for the facade which has been carefully tied to the new structure.

The need for extensive temporary works was removed for the building in Orchard Lane by undertaking a detailed installation sequence, allowing a three-storey steel frame and new foundations to be erected within the building, providing support to the facade and listed attic roof structure before removal of the internal load-bearing walls and floors.

For the building on Leopold Street, an internal facade retention system was used. This allowed the sequential removal and replacement of each existing timber floor. Due to large floor to ceiling heights additional mezzanine levels were inserted. To the rear of this building, the existing gym hall was partially demolished and a new seven-storey steel frame inserted and tied into the front half of the building. Existing timber floors, cast iron columns and concrete filler joist floors had to be inspected and checked for their new loading conditions.

The internal courtyard was re-profiled with concrete retaining walls to allow access into the areas at basement level.

The designers were BSP Consulting with Axis Architecture, contractor Gleesons. This scheme was the winner of Citizen's Award for the Best Building in the Sheffield Civic Trust Awards 2010.

OS ref: SK 352 873

4.   Barker's Pool

This area on the western edge of the mediaeval town derives its name from a large cistern holding rain and spring water. The present water features can be considered as a reminder of the origins of this district. Although first recorded in 1567, the cistern probably dates from around 1434 when a Barker family is recorded in the area. This supplemented the supply to individual wells throughout the town. Most people had to collect their water but some larger houses had a piped supply to their individual cistern. The cistern was enlarged and its supplies enhanced in the late 17th and early 18th centuries. In the mid 18th century it would appear to be approximately 20m x 37m in area. (Roughly a sixth the size of a football pitch.) It was demolished around 1793. Remnants of what is thought to be the cistern were discovered recently during ground investigation work in the area. Although the pool was demolished in the late 18th century a public water pump was located here for most of the following century.

A notable feature of Barker's Pool today is the city War Memorial. Completed in 1925, following a design competition, its design complements the City Hall which was still awaiting funding and construction at the time. It was designed by C. D. Carus

Wilson the head of the University School of Architecture at the time with structural design by his colleague Joseph Husband, the head of the Civil Engineering department. It consists of a slender 29m tall steel mast rising above an 5.5m tall bronze sculptural base. The mast was fabricated by Earle's Shipbuilding and Engineering Co of Hull. (Which was notable for building a "flat pack" steamer for shipping to Peru - it served customers on Lake Titicaca for over 50 years.)

Another memorial of note is the new statue of the Women of Steel which celebrates the women of the city that worked in the heavy steel industries during the world wars.

OS ref: SK 352 872

5.   <u>City Hall</u>

The City Hall was built from 1929 to 1932 by George Longden Ltd of Chapeltown to designs E. Vincent Harris, architect. The roof to the Oval Hall is supported off massive reinforced concrete beams 10 feet deep spanning a clear distance between the support towers of 105 feet - the largest in Europe at the time. The hall has a reinforced concrete construction to all the floors, main walls and roof. This work was designed by The Considère Construction Company Ltd of Westminster. It is likely that they were acting as a specialist design consultant under the architect. However, it is also possible that they had acted as specialist subcontractors to the main contractor. Approximately 1000 tons of "Stribar" reinforcing steel was used together with 25 tons in each of the two main roof beams. Stribar was manufactured by United Steel Strap and Bar Mills of Sheffield. Mr A Howell was the Clerk of works supervising the construction with Mr Harditt Singh, a Civil Engineer, visiting to inspect the structural works. George Longden Ltd was at the time run by Ann Longden who had taken over as managing director on the death of her husband in 1922. She became the city's first woman Lord Mayor in 1936 and was granted the Freedom of the City in 1949.

Conceived immediately after WWI a design competition was opened in February 1920. Of over 40 entries received by August 1920 that of E. Vincent Harris was chosen. There was much discussion on the details of the design and scope of the works. Shortage of funds for the scheme caused delays, but by March 1926 a decision to proceed was taken. Eight local firms were invited to tender. The council being eager that the scheme create employment for local people, especially ex-servicemen. George Longden's bid was lowest and they were provisionally awarded the contract. There were further delays as a major water main had to be moved and, significantly, the council did not have vacant possession of all of the site. It was not until autumn 1928 that the last premise in Holly Street was vacated and the contract could be finally signed and sealed. The building opened to a gala concert in September 1932. Originally intended to house 3500 people the number was reduced to 3000 during the construction to allow larger seats and aisles. The number has since been reduced further to enhance both comfort and safety. It now is licensed to hold up to 2271 people. The building also houses the 550 seat Memorial Hall and large basement Ballroom. The air-conditioning system was also state of the art. This grade 2* listed building was extensively refurbished in 2003. This opened up areas of the building to improve public access and back stage facilities. As with the Crucible Theatre, much of the work undertaken was to introduce efficient heating and ventilation while at all times preserving and enhancing the character of the building. Arup, the engineers for the refurbishment used advanced computing techniques to model the work.

While advanced for its time, the engineering of auditoria and stadia has developed significantly over the intervening years.

Www.sheffieldcityhall.co.uk

OS ref: SK 352 872

6.   **Sheffield Waterworks Company Offices**

The Palazzo style building to the west of the City Hall was built in 1867 as offices for the Sheffield Waterworks Company and is grade 2 listed. The Waterworks Company was set up in 1830 and built most of the water supply reservoirs to the north west of the city. The company was bought out by the town corporation in 1888. This building was built on the plot of land occupied by the stone cistern built in the early 1800s to receive water from the new reservoirs to the west of the town. It represents the continuation of this area as the focus of water supply for the city through to the end of the 19th century. Many people will recall its later use as the headquarters of the National Union of Mineworkers.

OS ref: SK 352 872

7.   **Sheffield Town Hall & Peace Gardens**

Through the nineteenth century, the city had grown considerably from 60,000 to well over 300,000 people. Changes in legislation brought increasing responsibility upon the council to provide for its citizens. By the 1880s the old town hall was too small to house everyone and offices were located across numerous locations and public meetings were held in places such as the Cutlers' Hall, Assembly Rooms or library. The council took over responsibility for the roads in 1884 and water in 1888. The following year a competition was set up to design a new town hall on land next to St Paul's Church. The competition was won by E. W. Mountford, Architect and the construction contract subsequently awarded to Edmund Gabbutt of Liverpool. The building was opened in 1897 by Queen Victoria. It was later extended in 1914-23 and further extensions planned in 1938 which were never carried out. The building was designed from the start to use electricity for lighting. One notable feature of the main facade is the frieze of figures representing local arts and industries. The building is faced in a sandstone from the Stoke Hall quarry near Grindleford, Derbyshire. This rock has a better composition and form than the local sandstone used on the old town hall. This has allowed the carving of the friezes and ensured that the weather and air pollution have been kinder to the building's appearance.

Another extension was eventually built from 1973-77 to the East of Norfolk Street, in a modernist style with reinforced concrete panels to once again house disparate council functions that had become scattered across the city. This was demolished in the 1990s to make way for the Millennium Galleries complex and St Paul's Tower. Many functions housed in the extension were transferred to the newly completed Howden House to the South. Much of the engineering department went to new offices in the lower Don Valley regeneration area.

St Paul's Church, an early 18th century baroque style church, had been demolished in 1938 to make way for the proposed extension. The expectation of war caused the postponement of the extension and a temporary garden was laid out. However, it acquired the nick name Peace Garden in reference to the September 1938 summit in Munich after which the Prime Minister signalled "*peace in out time*". Its official name only changed from St Paul's Garden to The Peace Gardens in 1985 in memory of 40 years since the dropping of the atomic bombs bringing to an end WWII. The garden was completely rebuilt in 1998 as part of the Heart of the City regeneration project and as a millennium project. Notable features are the Goodwin Fountain and Holberry Cascades, named after a noted 20th century benefactor of the city and the 19th century Chartist Leader, respectively.

Cheney Row, running along the side of the Town Hall, includes the "City of Sheffield Standard Measures of Length", originally presented to the people of Sheffield in 1910 by The Earl Fitzwilliam to allow citizens to make their own checks on their legal requirements. We now have the Council Trading Standards department to enforce the correct measurement of goods.

The walls and balustrades have been carved from the same sandstone as the adjoining town hall. However, the stone used in the paving and seating are from a wide range of sources to achieve the required colour texture and durability.

The landscaping of the Peace Gardens has won several awards from amongst others the Royal Institute of British Architects, Royal Town Planning Institute and the Civic Trust.

The redevelopment of the Peace Gardens and "Gold Route" was a project known as Heart of the City. Now Heart of the City 2 is underway. Formerly known as Sheffield Retail Quarter this £480M redevelopment will provide much needed new retail and mixed use space to the highest standards while respecting the historic aspects of the area from Barker's Pool to Charter Square and Pinstone Street.

Phase 1, situated on the former Grosvenor Hotel site, is a multi-level, mixed-use commercial development which will house major international company HSBC as anchor tenant – providing a real boost to the city's core business and retail cluster. Due to be completed in spring 2019, its lower levels will comprise of state-of-the-art retail and leisure space, with four levels of commercial office space and a rooftop terrace situated above.

Arup is also delivering the later phases of the development which comprise of a major new mixed-use facility of office, residential, retail, leisure and food units. In addition to providing full multidisciplinary engineering services, during the design process Arup took into account the wide variety of space types across the masterplan, developing a coordinated, site-wide energy strategy that can be supported by the utility infrastructure across the development.

OS ref: SK 353 872

8.   Upper Chapel

This Unitarian Chapel was originally built in 1700 and is the earliest surviving building in Sheffield to be built substantially of brick and so marks the start of the building of modern Sheffield. However, brick had been used for sections of buildings before this. The first house to be built in the town had been built four years previously. By 1725, brick was being widely used to replace timber houses. The earliest known surviving house is from 1728 in Hartshead at the corners with Fig Tree Lane and St Peter's Close. The Paradise Square housing development being started eight years later.

This chapel, the first nonconformist chapel in the town served a congregation of approximately 1,000 people, that is around a sixth of the town's population. The chapel was visible from and faced onto Fargate accessed down Pepper Alley, having been built in a burgage plot. Many of the other plots behind the Fargate properties remained gardens through most of the 18th century. Through the century, building encroached on the frontage and Norfolk Street was developed, expanding the town area. In 1847 the chapel was rearranged, the roof raised by several feet to allow the insertion of the balcony, and the present stone Palladian style frontage to Norfolk Street created.

Www.ukunitarians.org.uk/upper

OS ref: SK 354 873

9.   Crucible Theatre

The Crucible Theatre was built in 1971 to a modernist design by Renton Howard Wood Associates, architects with Ove Arup Associates consulting engineers. It is considered of national importance in the history of theatre design. The building is principally built of reinforced concrete. Architecturally, it is noted for the thrust stage, concrete block work and fair-faced in-situ concrete. The main auditorium has a thrust stage allowing all of the 1000 audience to be within 18 metres of the stage. The seating is on a single steeply raked tier of reinforced concrete which originally housed ventilation ducting for each seat. The 400 seat studio theatre is an intimate fully flexible location for small theatre and musical performance. The theatre building gained a grade 2 listing in November 2007 just prior to undergoing an extensive refurbishment.

The refurbishment involved, a new roof, subtle extensions to improve internal access, a new first floor extension to the front and a new plant room on the roof. They also completely replaced the electrical and heating and ventilation systems - the major component of the scheme comprising over 160km of cabling. This improved facilities for both performers and audiences while again maintaining the unique ambience of the venue to the extent that the casual visitor will see little other than cosmetic changes. This two and a half year project was complicated by the need to restore the building to full public operation each May for the World Snooker Championships. Thus the main auditorium was completely refurbished in an early phase and then sealed as the rest of the building underwent its make over. Sections of the reinforced concrete structure had to be precisely demolished to make way for new space without damaging the rest of the building and permitting new elements to be connected to the old. In many cases the new steel work required on site adjustment to achieve a perfect fit as until work was underway the exact position of key sections of the existing structure were unknown with sufficient accuracy. The new plant room is constructed from a floating steel work grid and frame weighing 60 tonnes above a section of the existing roof with stub columns transferring the load to precisely located points above existing columns. The existing roof was not strong enough to carry the new loads. The former plant room is now an open plan office suit. The theatre now claims to be the greenest in the country, with very high efficiency lighting heating from the district energy scheme and recycled materials used in the refurbishment.

The Adelphi Room extension is named after the Adelphi Hotel that occupied part of the site prior to the construction of the theatre. The Adelphi was famous as the location where Bramall Lane Cricket Club (later Sheffield United), Yorkshire Cricket Club and Sheffield Wednesday FC were all founded. Some of the foundations to the hotel were reused to support part of this extension and the old cellars found during construction back-filled with crushed waste material from the excavation.

Designers for the restoration were Burrel Foley Fischer LLP architects with Price Myers consulting engineers. Theatre specialist was Theatre Plan and Michael Popper Associates LLP the building services consultant. The contractor was Banner Holdings Ltd, with their steel work subcontractor undertaking some design elements.

Www.sheffieldtheatres.co.uk

OS ref: SK 356 872

10.   Lyceum Theatre

The Lyceum Theatre was originally built in 1893 but altered only four years later to create one of the most beautiful theatre in the country, now being grade 2* listed. Through the 19th century cast iron columns were used in theatres to support balconies and this was the case with the original design with six columns being used. From the 1850 a few examples were built with a partial cantilever formed of cast iron posts and beams. However, the introduction of steel girders from 1890 allowed for more complex designs and the following two decades were the heyday of British theatre construction. W. G. R. Sprague remodelling of the earlier work here designed by W Emden and Holmes and Watson used these latest techniques with steel cantilever balconies. He also improved the corridors and stairways to create "one of the most perfect and safe [theatres] in the kingdom" which could be evacuated in 60 seconds.

The complexities involved meant that a team of designers was required. An architect could not alone use traditional rules to proportion the building elements and relied upon the services of a structural engineer to new levels as well as specialist theatre consultants and lighting engineers. The most successful projects were, as now, those where the design team worked closely together respecting each other's knowledge and worked in collaboration with the contractor.

Having been closed and neglected for many years it was restored in 1989-90 creating a modern operational theatre within the historic fabric and maintaining the grandeur of the old auditorium. This work was undertaken as part of the cultural element of the World Student Games of 1991 and designed by Arup with Renton Howard Wood Levin architects. This involved numerous delicate structural alterations and sympathetic additions. The south side of the building was removed and an extension added to vastly improve the public circulation area and accessibility. Extensions to the east considerably enlarged the back stage area. The basement below the stage was also enlarged requiring underpinning of the proscenium arch and other key parts of the Victorian structure. All this work had to be done while conserving the ornate auditorium and stucco facade. Recently, areas of the stucco have been invisibly repaired. Water damage had caused the stucco to become detached from the brick structure behind. The stucco was stuck back to the wall by a system of injecting adhesive into the gap through small drill holes. Where more substantial repairs had to be made to the wall structure, this was carefully done and new plain stucco applied to match the original and cast mouldings inserted as necessary for the ornamentation.

Www.sheffieldtheatres.co.uk

OS ref: SK 356 872

11.   **Winter Garden**

The building, opened by the Queen on 22 May 2003, houses collections of over 2000 plants from around the world. The displays tell of the importance of plants. It is a popular meeting spot. The Winter Garden is designed with and linked to the Millennium Gallery and the Mercure St Paul Hotel. They were built in 2002 to designs by Buro Happold with Pringle Richards Sharratt as architect. The principal form of the Winter Garden is of inverted catenary arches. A catenary is the shape taken up by a chain hanging by its ends. This is very efficient when supporting a load evenly along the curved length of the arch and lent itself to the use of glulam timber with stainless steel joints. Glulam (Glue-laminated) timber is formed by gluing together strips of wood. This allows the removal of imperfections and the process allows the engineers to specify larger size components than traditional sawn timber. It also facilitates the creation of curved members with very little waste. Furthermore the sections can be modified to be strongest at those areas where they carry most load. Provided the timber and steel are recycled or the energy recovered when the structure is eventually demolished this is a very efficient low carbon form of construction. The timber is a naturally resistant species and so untreated and will weather to a silver grey. Careful detailing of the construction should also mitigate against the risks of rot. The arches are up to 21m high and 22m wide creating a building 70m long. The rainwater falling on the roof is collected into underground tanks for use in the irrigation of the plants.

The overall form of the building is very economical in its use of resources. It is heated, as are many of the city centre buildings, by the District heating scheme. The heat comes from the city energy recovery facility on Bernard Road.

Www.museums-sheffield.org.uk

OS ref: SK 355 871

12.   **Millennium Galleries**

The Millennium Galleries are integrated with the Winter Garden - designed by the same team at the same time. There are four galleries which house diverse temporary art displays from around the world and permanent collections of craft silverware and cutlery items associated with the city together with the Ruskin Art Collection. The building was designed to conform to international standards for environmental control of display spaces. These specify limits on temperature, humidity and light levels to protect fragile works of art.

The building makes extensive use of high quality reinforced concrete. Exposed concrete is increasingly being used in buildings for both its architectural qualities and as an engineering solution to temperature control. The massive material acts as a heat sink and stores heat evening out temperatures and so reducing the need for extra heating or cooling. This technique is becoming less uncommon now, but was considered pioneering a decade ago. The main elements of the structure, including

148

long span roof arches, were precisely made in a factory as precast units and fitted together quickly on site. The concrete columns are also used to circulate the conditioned air to the main galleries. Accordingly, it was the winner in 2002 of the Concrete Society Award - Building category.

www.museums-sheffield.org.uk   OS ref: SK 355 870

13.   St Paul's Tower

St Paul's Tower is now the tallest building in Sheffield at 32 storeys, 101m high. This and the shorter linked 12 storey tower provide 316 apartments and 22,000 sq. ft. of retail and leisure space and 88 basement car parking spaces. This building is approximately 1/3 of the height of the newly built Shard in London which is now the tallest building in the Europe Union. The Mercury City Tower in Moscow has just become Europe's tallest building and is approximately ten percent taller than the Shard. In comparison the Burj Khalifa in Dubai, United Arab Emirates is the tallest building in the world at 829.8m tall - over eight times the height of St Paul's Tower!

St Paul's Tower has been built by Shepherd Construction to designs by WSP consulting engineers with Conran+Partners as architects. An in-situ reinforced concrete frame provides a robust core connected to the basement box construction creating a stiff raft base cut into the rock of the hillside. The tower floors are post-tension reinforced concrete. This is where the slab is compressed by cables running through it. This allows a thinner slab to be used than a conventional design. In tall building this gives the advantage that the repeated slight saving in storey height add up to an additional one or two storeys within the building. This gives more usable, and lettable, space for the same volume of building. Off-site prefabricated units have been used elsewhere to provide a high quality safe and rapid construction - notably with the glass facade and some internal fittings. The facade was erected by Wicona Projects using the site cranage and working from inside and so avoided the need to erect scaffolding. The UK has some of the most advanced design standards in the world for tall buildings and our engineering expertise is used world wide in their construction.

OS ref: SK 354 871

14.   "Cheese-grater" car park

The adjoining Charles Street 530 space car park was built by J F Finnegan and Tarmac Precast Solutions with engineering design by Capita Symonds Structures for Q-Park. The compact city centre site and neighbouring construction activities potentially complicated the construction process. However, extensive use of precast concrete facilitated fast construction and excellent quality of finish. Piled foundations support the structure. The basement and ground floor are of in-situ reinforced concrete with the 9 storeys of precast floors and columns above. This allowed completion of the superstructure frame within just 14 weeks.

It won the peoples award for best building in the 2008 Sheffield Civic Trust Awards.

Www.q-park.co.uk   OS ref: SK 354 870

15.   **Howard Street and Sheffield Hallam University**

This area of the city was laid out in grids, in the late 18th Century, as the first planned expansion of the town. Initially it was intended, by the Duke of Norfolk, primarily as a housing district for up and coming manufacturers. It instead developed as a centre for cutlery and light steel trades. This group of buildings predominantly uses brick as a construction material. The first building recorded as utilising brick was the Upper Chapel on Norfolk Street (near the Crucible Theatre) in 1700. Over the intervening decades there had been a progressive move towards brick as properties in the town were rebuilt as its relative cost decreased and availability increased. Brick also provided a significant benefit in its fire resistance in a town with so many hearths.

Numerous buildings from the early development of the area remain, Butcher's Works on Arundel Street being a notable example and largely intact. This area, and Butcher's in particular, produced many of the hand tools needed in the development of America, such as the Bowie knife. It remains a centre for Sheffield famous cutlery and silver trades.

The area is also the home of Sheffield Hallam University. Sheffield Hallam University (SHU) can trace its roots back to the Sheffield School of Design that was founded in 1843. The School of Design merged with Sheffield Training College in 1969 to form Sheffield Polytechnic. Further mergers with the other city teacher training colleges in 1979 created the Sheffield City polytechnic that then became Sheffield Hallam University in 1992.

The university has long had a strong reputation in the teaching of technical subjects. In 2017 the STEM centre became a regional centre of excellence in the teaching of this group of subjects (Science, Technology, Engineering and Mathematics). It provides staff and students with cutting edge robotics, automotive and electrical laboratories, and teaching space and a stunning new atrium with exhibition space. It is located in a prominent position directly opposite Sheffield Station and is named after nineteenth century award-winning British engineer, mathematician and physicist, Hertha Ayrton.

SHU is ranked 69th in the 2018 complete university guide with two subjects in the top 10. There are more than 31,000 students studying here. It has ambitions to be the world's leading applied university in a master plan for the next 15 years. An applied university being one that offers teaching with a practical purpose for specific careers and jobs. SHU is a key partner in the Advanced Well-being Research Centre at the Olympic Legacy Park.

Most of the buildings of Sheffield Hallam University City Campus required special foundations as much of the area was riddled with abandoned mine workings.

Howard Street forms part of the "Gold Route" from the railway Station through to Devonshire Green. This overall scheme won the Landscape Institute President's Award and Neighbourhood Award and this element, with the Sheaf Square in front of the Station, the 1-5 ha category, in 2007.

The "Gold Route" aims to provide an inviting pedestrian route through the city centre. Note the mural of Harry Brearley, the inventor of Stainless Steel, on the back wall of The Hallam Hotel pub.

OS ref: SK 356 870

Sheffield Hallam University The Heart of the Campus building at the Collegiate Crescent campus won the Institution of Structural Engineers Yorkshire Region Building of the Year award in 2014.

Www.shu.ac.uk

OS ref: SK 339 863

16. Park Hill Flats

From Howard Street there is a good view across to the internationally famous Park Hill Flats. Completed in 1961, after four years of design and three of construction, these now grade 2* listed buildings (the largest in Europe) provided street in the sky for the people of Sheffield. It was designed in house by Sheffield City Council. The "Brutalist style" project made the names of up and coming architects Jack Lynn and Ivor Smith. Part of the post war slum clearance programme, they were initially very popular and provided every modern convenience at the time. Over the intervening years they had become neglected and aspects no-longer suited contemporary modes of living. They are now undergoing a major facelift by developer Urban Splash. This will create homes suited to modern living while retaining much of the good character of the original scheme. The structural frame remains in good order is being retained with only minor repairs and alterations. All architectural and internal features are being replaced. The coloured brick infill panels to the external walls are being replaced with colourful insulated aluminium panels. Parts of the near contemporary and similar Hyde Park Flats scheme, a little higher up the hill, were likewise refurbished - in 1991 initially as accommodation for the World Student Games and subsequent as public housing. The remainder of Hyde Park were demolished as were the smaller Kelvin Flats complex elsewhere in the city.

Phase 1 under architects Hawkins-Brown working with Studio Egret West has created 260 new flats and commercial and public art spaces. Phase 2, under architects Mikhail Riches will create a further 200 flats out of a projected total of 874 together with more shops. In 2013 Phase 1 received a RIBA Yorkshire Award, a RIBA Yorkshire Conservation Award and a RIBA National Award and was short-listed for the coveted RIBA Stirling Prize for the best building of the year.

Led by S1 Artspace, Arup is providing civil and structural engineering for the project, which will include a gallery, artists' studios, learning spaces, production workshop, live/work flats, café and shop.

www.urbansplash.co.uk/residential/park-hill

OS ref: SK 361 872

17.   Sheffield Railway Station & Station footbridge.

The Midland Railway was constructed in Sheffield in 1868-70 by Benton & Woodiwiss to designs by John Crossley of Derby. This railway provided the first direct line service to London. Previously, services had to change on to the earlier Midland Line at Rotherham. The 1.85km Bradway Tunnel of 1870 gave access to Chesterfield and the line south via the Drone Valley. The construction of this railway was the catalyst for the development of the Sheaf and Drone valleys for both industry and housing. The small stations built along the line quickly became popular for people to commute into the town. Of these only Dore (and Dronfield) remain.

It was not until 1893 that the 5.7km Totley Tunnel was completed to give a fast route through to Manchester avoiding the steep climb to the Woodhead Tunnel or long diversion via Ambergate.

Much of the station front you see today is the 1905 extension, a grade 2 listed building. The station forecourt was glazed to create a lobby in 1991. Some of the original buildings are to be found on platform 2.

The line from Dore through to Meadowhall was increased from two to four tracks at the time of the 1905 extension. This was reduced again in the 1960s. It is now proposed to improve the Dore to Chinley Line and possibly redouble the main line track through the city to remove capacity bottlenecks.

The station has won the IHT/Mouchel Parkman Accessibility award and National Rail Heritage Award for the recent improvements. The improvement to the space in front of the station was a finalist in the National Transport Awards and winner of a category of the Landscape Institute Awards in 2007.

The main footbridge across the station was completely replaced in 2003 to improve the quality of access to the platforms and to provide a new link to the re-sited Supertram stop just beyond the station. The final section of the bridge from platform 6/8 to Granville Street was funded by the South Yorkshire Passenger Transport Executive, the remainder by Network Rail.

The new main section of the new bridge could not be installed by crane due to the crowded environment of an active railway station and the distance to clear space beyond. Only the link from platform 6 to the Supertram could be craned in after being prefabricated off-site. The existing bridge formed a temporary works platform to allow the construction of the new bridge. At this stage the new bridge was jacked up, the old bridge was then cut out and lowered onto a railway engineering wagon for removal. The new bridge was then lowered onto its support bearings. This happened one span at a time, during a temporary closure of that section of line only. During the works public access to the platforms was maintained by temporary access routes. Thus a fully disabled accessible link, was created with minimal disruption to the station users and rail traffic. The designer was Ferguson McLiveen of Middlesborough and the contractor C Spencer Ltd of Barrow on Humber.

The station is now managed by East Midland Trains.

HC - ICEY&H 2004.

www.eastmidlandstrains.co.uk/stations/sheffield-station

OS ref: SK 358 869

18.   Sheffield Passenger Transport Interchange

Sheffield Bus Station was renewed as the Passenger Interchange in 1990 to provide a safe and efficient centre for public bus and coach services. The location is the nearest area of flat ground to the city centre and is relatively close to the railway station and ring road junction 2. The layout was carefully designed to provide a free flow of both bus and pedestrian traffic. In addition to secure fully sheltered, accessible waiting areas it provides passenger facilities, information and kiosks.

The interchange mainly serves long distance routes.

www.travelsouthyorkshire.com   OS ref: SK 358 872

19.   Old Queen's Head

One of the oldest buildings in the city, grade 2 listed, the Old Queen's Head is part of a 15th century timber framed hall - "The Hall in the Ponds". This was part of the estate of the lord of the manor. The surviving remains represent only one wing of what was an extensive building up to at least the 18th Century. The public house was originally in the building next door, long since demolished. The building was refurbished in the 1950s and sensitively renovated in 1992-3 by Eastwood and Partners as part of the development of the Passenger Transport interchange.

It is now considered that the repair of heritage structure like this is best dealt with by a registered Conservation Engineer (the register came into existence in 2005) who has shown through practice and training detailed knowledge of historical building techniques, the interaction of new and old materials, conservation principles and best practice. As this is a relatively new scheme, clearly there will be many competent engineers who are not registered.

OS ref: SK 358 872

There are around a dozen timber post and frame constructed building known to be remaining around Sheffield, although in most cases all the timber framing is hidden behind later stone or brick facades and in private ownership.

These post and truss framed houses would have been typical of those of wealthy farmers or of a lesser manor house in the region in the late mediæval and early post mediæval period.

Another good example, only slightly further afield, that can be seen from a public highway is to be found at Gunthwaite 3 km North of Penistone. Here is a 165 ft long king post framed barn believed to date from 1580.

20.   River Sheaf Culverts

The River Sheaf was culverted in sections through the 1860s from a point near what is now Granville Square down to its confluence with the River Don near Blonk Street. The first section to be enclosed was between Commercial Street and Broad Street where the Sheaf Market was created over the river course. Subsequently, Castlefolds Market was built adjoining the newly rebuilt Norfolk Market on land reclaimed over the river. Under the Castlefolds market the ground level was raised to match that of the adjoining Norfolk Market Hall. The Midland Railway was granted permission to construct their line along the Sheaf Valley in 1864, but were delayed building in the lower part of the valley until 1868. In order to create space for the line, station and Sheaf Street approach road, the river was culverted on a new alignment.

The form of these culverts vary in the different sections. The section furthest upstream at Granville Square is the most recent. Constructed in 1991, in response to road alteration, it is a reinforced concrete box section made by shot-crete. A technique where concrete is sprayed at high pressure into place. The main section through by the station and under Sheaf Street is of linked twin brick channel with a shallow brick arch over them. Each channel is approximately 7m wide and 3.6m high to the crown of the arch. The Porter Brook enters from the side part way along this 750 m long section. Along one section of approximately 100 m there was sufficient height to create a single span vault. A brick parabolic arch approximately 11m wide by 6m high was employed. [A parabola is the shape taken up by a chain where the weights attached to it give a uniform load along the straight length of the span, as opposed to the length of the curve in the catenary. This produced an efficient shape for carrying a general pressure from above.]

There is a short section of open channel near the bottom of Pond Hill, before it re-enters twin culverts roughly parallel to Sheaf Street before crossing the Sheaf Market car park, under the present Sheaf Market buildings to the outfall at the confluence of the Sheaf and Don upstream of Blonk Street Bridge.

There are large steel grill screens across the rivers just upstream of their entry to the culverts. These prevent debris - from general weeds to trees, shopping trolleys, bags and general litter - entering the culvert and causing a blockage. These screens have to be frequently scarped clean of debris, partly by hand and partly by mechanical rake or grab.

OS ref: SK 358 872

21.   Ponds Forge International Leisure Centre & footbridge.

Ponds Forge provides Olympic size swimming and diving facilities - arguably the best in the country. It was designed by Arup with Faulkner Browns architects in 1989 and built along with numerous other facilities for the World Student Games of 1991. The scheme was designed to meet the needs of the community users as well as national and international athletes. The pools incorporate the latest designs in floating floors, mobile bulkheads and water treatment to achieve this. The main pool area, sports hall and central core area are designed as three structures with movement joints between them. This allowed the separate areas to be built independently at the same time. The main roof construction is of exposed tubular steel trusses forming a diagonal grid across the entire width of the building, described as most impressive by the BCSA judges.

The building is situated on the site of former industrial works and near to the course of the River Sheaf. This required careful design of the foundations. Some of the foundations of the forge were so large that they have been left in place and the new building constructed around them.

The main contractor was Mowlem Management while the Steelwork contractors were Robert Watson & Co (Constructional Engineers) Ltd, Steelcon Ltd and RJD Fabrications Ltd for the three sections of the building respectively.

On the site of the Ponds Forge International Leisure Centre the Sheffield Electric Light and Power Company had grand offices built in 1896. The offices were demolished in the mid 20th century. In 1898, the city corporation bought out the electricity company and provided electricity for Sheffield through to the nationalisation of power generation in 1948.

C - BCSAA1991

www.ponds-forge.co.uk

OS ref: SK 359 874

The footbridge into Ponds Forge Swimming Pool building was required by the client, Sheffield for Health Ltd, to be "interesting and imaginative" and the engineer (SCC Design and Building Services) worked closely with architects to produce this dramatic design. Tensioned cabling is used to stiffen the slender structure to eliminate effectively dynamic responses. The intricacy of the design pushed the boundaries of analytical method at the time and required very high quality workmanship from the fabricator, RJD Fabrications Ltd of Rotherham.

C-ICEYA1995

OS ref: SK 359 875

22.   **Commercial Street Bridge**

Commercial Street Bridge spans one of the busiest traffic roundabouts in Sheffield and the culverted River Sheaf. It carries two tracks of the Supertram and a pedestrian walkway. The bridge consists of a tied arch span of 74 m and two simple side spans of 12.5 m and 18 m. The design objectives of the bridge were to create an imposing structure that enhances its surroundings and unifies the locality. Great care was taken in the detailing to create a structure that would be easy to build and maintain as well as efficient in the use of materials and aesthetically pleasing for this key site in the city. The main longitudinal beams of the deck, which are hung from the arch, tie together the ends of the arch. This mutual support mechanism avoids the need for complex foundations. The hanger rods are connected to the structure with specially shaped castings which gave full adjustability for construction and contribute to the aesthetics of the bridge.

The concrete decking is continuous across all three simply supported spans to eliminate potential maintenance problems of movement joints. It acts compositely with the deck beams to efficiently utilise the materials. The slab was carefully designed to accommodate the flexing that inevitably will occur at the intermediate piers. The designer was Sheffield City Council Design and Building Services and main contractor Balfour Beatty Power Construction Ltd.

The centre of the traffic island of Park Square Roundabout is now a delightful modern meadow in summer months. Professors Nigel Dunnett and Stephen Hitchmough of the University of Sheffield have been pioneering contemporary meadow design as a landscaping method for several year starting in some of the city estates. These were famously deployed at the Olympic, now Queen Elizabeth, Park in London for the 2012 Olympic games. They use a selection of annual and perennial native and foreign wild flowers to create a low maintenance sustainable tapestry of colour. This improves the bio-diversity of the area. Also by being a more engaging landscaping formerly unloved grey areas can become green. This has additional benefits in terms of flood control and public well being. They are now being widely adopted elsewhere.

W-ICEYA1995 C - BCSAA1994

OS ref: SK 359 875

23.   Victoria Quays - Sheffield Canal Basin.

The Sheffield Canal, by William Chapman, was not begun until 1815 and was completed in 1819, although the River Don had been made navigable to Tinsley by 1751. The many water wheels on the river between here and Tinsley precluded improving the river and also barred the use of river water to supply a canal. The canal obtained its water supply from the drainage waters from the local collieries. The canal was built to accommodate the Yorkshire Keel boat which plied the regions river system. Consequently, it is wider than the canal system in the Midlands and elsewhere, such as the Chesterfield Canal, that was developed by James Brindley.

The original terminal warehouse remains and has been sympathetically restored. The central archway originally gave access for boats to be unloaded under cover. The other buildings around the canal basin are mid to late 19th century, such as the 1860 grain warehouse which projects over the side of the basin

The Straddle Warehouse of c. 1900 being notable. This building has a steel and iron frame, with masonry and concrete in-fill. Its design allowed the unloading/loading of several barges under cover at the same time using overhead cranes within the building.

The adjoining arches and coal staithes were built in 1855 by which time the canal was owned by the railway company. They allowed coal to drop into the stores directly from the wagons on the tracks above through holes on the roof. Several of these now house cafes.

Www.fiveweirs.co.uk

www.canalrivertrust.org.uk

OS ref: SK 360 877

24.   Parkway Viaduct

Parkway Viaduct carries the Supertram beyond the roundabout east alongside the Sheffield Parkway link road to the M1. It is a post-tensioned glued segmental reinforced concrete structure 295 m long with spans of 55 m. Each of the 115 concrete sections was a different shape and size and was cast in a production yard against its neighbour to ensure a perfect fit before being moved to site for erection. Each span was built out from the piers working in both directions at once to balance each other until the span was closed. The successive sections were glued and fastened to the preceding sections by high strength steel cables threaded through the sections at carefully selected locations. This form of construction could accommodate the sweeping geometry of the line while minimising disruption to the traffic on the nearby roads. Attention was paid in the design process to facilitate both the construction and future maintenance. The designer was Sheffield City Council Design and Building Services and main contractor Balfour Beatty Power Construction Ltd.

C-ICEYA1995

OS ref: SK 360 876

25.   Cobweb Bridge

The Cobweb Bridge is a 100m long, 3m wide cycle and pedestrian route over the River Don and under the Wicker Arches Viaduct. It is a key section of the Five weirs walk. It was not allowed to obstruct the river flow and so was suspended from the viaduct arch using a complex network of high strength stainless steel cables. Although the weight of this walkway is not excessive in comparison with the weight of the many trains which used to pass over the viaduct it was necessary to carefully assess how it could be safely attached to the 150 year old structure. This involved careful assessment of how the arches were actually built. All works had to be approved by English Heritage who safeguard the country's built heritage. The design was by Sheffield City Council Design and Building Services with Paul Mallander and Richard Coe Architects. It was built by Thyssen with JHM Drilling and Grouting of Doncaster as specialist subcontractor fixing the anchors.

HC-ICEY&HA2004

Www.fiveweirs.co.uk

OS ref: SK 360 880

26.   Wicker Arches.

This grade 2* listed building (Hew ref: 0498) remains an important landmark today although much of it is obscured by nearby development. The Wicker arches are part of the 40 span viaduct carrying the Manchester Sheffield and Lincolnshire Railway across the Don Valley. Originally the viaduct had 42 arches, the three here, 12 to the west and 27 to the east across the river valley. However, two were removed at the west end for highway improvements and replaced with a steel bridge. The viaduct took four years to construct and was completed in 1848. It was designed by (Sir) John Fowler with assistance from Weightman, Hadfield and Goldie, architects in recognition of its prominent position spanning one of the town's principal routes. It was built by Miller, Blackie and Shortridge, contractors. Many of the arches not spanning the river, canal or roads have brick in fill frontages enclosing two or three storey workshops. The Victoria railway station, now largely demolished, was built along a section of the viaduct.

The principal section across the Wicker highway is described by Rennison as: "A 21.9m span four-centred arch giving 9.1m headroom. The voussoirs continue upwards across the spandrels to the horizontal moulded course. The 3.66m span side arches are semicircular, much lower and surmounted by heraldic decoration. The whole is framed in a rectangular portal and built in good quality ashlar." This once busy railway is now a single track freight line to Stockbridge steelworks.

OS ref: SK 359 881

27.   Sheffield Inner Relief Road

The latest Sheffield Inner Relief Road extension, between Shalesmoor and Sheffield Parkway, creates new links and directs traffic away from the city centre. It includes a 40m span railway bridge, replacing the end two arches of the Wicker Viaduct, a 35m span bridge over the River Don, 15m high retaining walls and high quality public landscaping. The previous phase also included similar sized bridges

157

over the Don, under the station approach to the Victoria Hotel and over the canal and a major interchange with the A610 Parkway road to the motorway.

The inner ring road now links all the major routes radiating from the city relieving congestion in the city centre and improving access for businesses. It forms a missing link in the ring road planned since the 1970s.

The project team worked hard to engage with local residents and businesses to minimise any adverse impact both in construction and the final scheme. A co-located team ensured a totally collaborative and innovative approach. Designers: Sheffield City Council Design and Project Management Services with Arup, Contractor: Birse.

W-ICEY&HA2009 C-ICEY&HA2005

OS ref: SK 349 881 to SK 364 877

OS ref: SK 357 878

28.   Lady's Bridge.

This is a grade 2 listed building and Historical Engineering Work (ref: 0915). A ribbed arch bridge of five spans of 20 to 23 feet between 6 feet thick piers was built in 1486 by William Hyll for the sum of £66/13/4 with the materials being supplied by the town parish. The contract for this work is a rare survival from the time. Record of repairs in 1573 also exist. This bridge replaced an earlier one constructed in 1150 for the lord of the manor. During the mediaeval period it was common for chapels to be associated with major bridges. Travellers would make a donation to the chapel in thanks for a safe journey and this helped fund the upkeep of the bridges. The chapel to "Our Blessed Lady" was situated a little to the east of the south end of the bridge at the foot of Waingate. The Chantries Act of 1547 suppressed religious guilds and their bridge chapels, such as here. The chapel became an almshouse before being demolished in the mid 18th century. As a result the bridge lacked a clear income for repairs. Thus, as a result of the Statute of Bridges of 16 years before, the county magistrates determined that as the bridge was of more than local significance it should be maintained at the expense of the county rate payers. Only four bridge chapels are known to remain in the country. The nearest one is to be found at Rotherham.

This bridge still forms the heart of the present structure. The 4.42m wide structure was widened by 2.97m on the west side and re-profiled to reduce the slope of the road in 1761 by John Carr of Horbury, Leeds working with John Watson jr. This work was also of stone arches on piers. In 1909 the earlier bridge elements were examined and found to be in good repair. At the time the masonry was described as being a gritstone similar to that found on Wadsley common or in the Rivelin district. This would suggest the Loxley Edge Sandstone. The original section was a ribbed arch structure with five ribs to the shallow pointed arches. The outer ribs were chamfered to improve their appearance but the inner ribs which could not be seen were left square cut.

On the north bank the Wicker tilt mills were built over the far channel, which acted as its goyt from the 1750s. To the south, slaughter houses were built just down stream over the river bank in 1786 at about the time the bridge was widened by a 4.47m on the eastern, downstream face. These closed in 1930 and Castlegate constructed over their line. Blonk Street and its bridge over the river were built in 1830 when the markets were further redeveloped to improve access between the canal basin and the Wicker.

A further widening by 4.32m took place, this time to the west in 1864, after flood damage. This was again in stone and matched the 18th century work. The local authorities had been lobbying the West Riding magistrates for some time to improve the bridge to accommodate the increasing traffic passing the area. After the flood the county magistrates paid £700 for the bridge repairs and improvements on the proviso that the town took over responsibility for future maintenance. It should be noted that this was the first bridge downstream not to have suffered serious damage in the flood. New cast iron balustrades were installed as part of these works.

In 1909, a further 3.05m of width was added on the east side using cast iron beams and lattice girders on cast iron columns and the existing cast iron balustrade on that side moved to the new downstream face of the bridge.

Encroaching development has obscured some of the structure.

OS ref: SK 357 878

29.   Don Valley Interceptor Sewer

From Shalesmoor to the Sewage Treatment works at Blackburn Meadows 8km of sewers along the Don Valley and 2km along the Sheaf Valley were tunnelled with work beginning in January 1979 and being completed in 7 phases by 1998. These intercept flows that would otherwise have entered the river.

The initial late 19th century and early 20th century sewers were generously built to carry the sewage flows but carried both foul and storm water and so were designed to overflow into the river at times of heavy rain. Since the original sewers were built the city had, of course, expanded so that a 40 % larger area drained to the system serving a 60% larger population, each of which was using 8 times as much water. Over time the over flow weirs had been raised to contain the increasing dry weather flow of sewage. However, this meant that there was a decreasing amount of space in the sewer network to accommodate the run-off from storms. This increased the frequency that the sewers overflowed into the city's river. By the late 1960s it was recognised that such practices are no longer acceptable and a new bypass system was needed. It took a further decade to find the finance and get a scheme approved.

The new work had to be tunnelled at low level to intercept all the flows and avoid the disruption to the streets which would have occurred if local replacement had been adopted. Parts of the tunnel are up to 5.5m diameter (large enough to take a double decker bus). In order to construct the tunnels 13 shafts 20-23m deep were constructed. Tunnel boring machines were used to cut through the rock and help install the concrete lining sections for the main tunnel. These were DOSCO road headers with a Lamice face shield in phase 1 and a Stelmo face shield in phase 2. The traditional drill and blast technique was used for the smaller branch tunnels and subsequent phases. Particular attention had to be paid to the design and execution of the blasting in some areas, particularly near the city centre. The line of the tunnel passed very close to several buildings housing vibration sensitive computer equipment operating 24 hours/day. This placed strict limits on the ground accelerations that could be allowed. Excavated material was transferred by conveyor and an underground railway to the nearest shaft to be craned out. The scheme included an extensive programme of test boring to identify the changing ground conditions, abandoned mine-workings and also check for the possibility of unexploded bombs remaining from the Sheffield Blitz. Phase 1 experienced difficult ground conditions and problems with the boring machine, causing delays and cost overruns. In contrast phase 2 was completed early and under budget.

Once a phase of tunnel was complete and flows transferred the existing brick sewers were drained, inspected thoroughly and cleaned, repaired and relined with concrete. Although then slightly narrower than before the smooth surface of the walls free of obstruction allowed the refurbished drains to carry a greater flow than previously was the case.

The project included a 29.5m diameter shaft 28m deep at Blackburn Meadows. The segmental outer wall of the shaft was lined with reinforced concrete cast by slip forming to eliminate joints. The shaft houses pumps capable of handling over 660,000 m³/day and lifts the water up to the treatment works. Facilities were included to allow easy maintenance and up grading of equipment. The control building is heated with waste heat recovered from the pumps.

The scheme also incorporated telemetric equipment in the tunnels to monitor the flows continuously. This together with improving computer equipment and techniques allows the water to be carefully controlled at all times, within the bounds that nature allows. The Don Valley Sewer is part of a larger strategy to improve flood control in the Sheffield area. Elsewhere, such as at Abbeydale Millhouses park, large storage tanks have been constructed to store sewerage flows at times of flood with improved screening on the emergency overflows.

The designer was Yorkshire Water Authority.

(Phase1) W-ICEYA1984

OS ref: SK 348 882 to SK 396 917

OS ref: SK 357 878

30. Old Town Hall

This Town Hall was built in 1807-8 to house the offices of the Town Trustees and the manorial Court. This was the town's first purpose built court. It replaced an early 18th century building, since demolished next to the parish church. In Sheffield it was the Town Trustees that were responsible for the town roads and sanitation. Sheffield long had an unusual governance structure after most towns had become fully independent boroughs, retaining many aspects of the old manorial system. The trustees remained in charge of the roads for around 40 years after the formation of the town council. Sheffield became incorporated as a borough in 1843 and Petty Sessions and Quarter sessions courts were held here from 1847. The police station, built in 1866, was next door and linked to the court by tunnels. Sheffield had had its own police force since 1818. The striking clock tower was also part of the 1866 works.

Upon completion of the New Town Hall in 1896, the entire Old Town Hall was remodelled and extended to act as courts. New Magistrates courts were opened next door in 1979. New county and family courts opening at West Bar in 1996 and 2003, replacing these court facilities. The (grade 2 listed) building currently awaits a new use.

www.sheffieldoldtownhall.co.uk

OS ref: SK 357 877

30a Sheffield Castle inner bailey is thought to lie to the east of Waingate towards the river with the outer bailey then extending south up towards Fitzalan Square. An Anglo-Saxon royal hall fortified with a ditch is believed to be the origin of the castle. After the harrying of the north, this was replaced with a Norman timber motte and bailey castle in around 1100. This was destroyed by a fire in 1266 and four years later the replacement stone castle was completed. At a reported 1.66ha it was one of the largest castles in England. Further work was carried out in the 1440s building a great tower and great hall amongst other buildings. Part of this involved bring 60 waggon loads of stone from Roche Abbey. By the 16th century the castle was considered cramped by the Talbots who developed Sheffield Manor Lodge as a principal residence. In 1570, Elizabeth I committed Mary, Queen of Scots, to the custody of George Talbot. Mary was held prisoner in Sheffield Castle until 1584. The castle was demolished in 1649-50 after the civil war.

The area was developed over the coming centuries. Much of the earlier town was subsequently altered in the town's 19th century development. This included new market buildings taking much of the trade off the local streets. The area was extensively damaged in the blitz. The 1960s castle market building was a good modern version of the function of the old traditional market hall with both stalls and shops on several levels. By making use of the sloping site it was possible for people to access the markets on three levels, thus encouraging use on all levels although the first floor walkways later proved unpopular.

The site has now been cleared of the 20th century buildings and excavations are taking place to re-discover the castle. It is then planned that parts of the castle remains will be on display in a new park area amongst a mixed use development. Previous excavation have found Roman, Saxon and mediaeval pottery as well as bronze age flints attesting to the deep history of the site.

Www.friendsofsheffieldcastle.org.uk   OS ref: SK 358 877

Sheffield Castle had a large park associated with it since Saxon times. This extended to an area of up to 1,000 ha. **Sheffield Manor Lodge**, was built with-in the park with extensive views across the lords estates. In the 16th century this was extended to a comfortable residence. However, in the 17th century the house fell into disrepair. In the 1870s the Duke of Norfolk began the restoration of the Turret House. Sheffield Museums took over the site in the 1970s. In 2002 it passed to Green Estate who have developed it into a visitor attraction.

Www.sheffieldmanorlodge.org   OS ref: SK 376 865

31.   Sheffield Tramways

Sheffield first tram network began in 1872 growing over the following 40 years and finally closing in 1960. Work began on the Supertram in 1991 after years in design with the first section being opened in March 1994 and the last part of the 3 line network opening in October 1995. Of the 29 km long network, requiring 60 km of track, 50% is on street and 30 new structures were required. This was the first modern

UK tramway to have low level cars which makes on street stations less intrusive. On street the track is laid in a reinforced concrete bed with the rails secured in channels using an elastomer to provide electrical insulation and vibration damping. Off street conventional ballast and sleepers are used. The on street sections were carefully designed and stations located to provide a coherent and easily understood layout to facilitate access for people with a range of disabilities while not adversely affecting local property.

Tram-trains came into operation in October 2018. These hybrid vehicles are the first in the UK to be able to run on both tram and main line railways. The University of Huddersfield helped design wheels that can safely operate on the differing profile rails. The tram-trains also have to work on the differing power and signalling systems without interruption and accommodate the platform designs of the two systems.

Www.sheffieldsupertram.co.uk

OS ref: SK 326912 to SK 438 817

OS ref: SK 357 875

32. Foster's Building

The four storey Foster's Building at the corner of High Street & Fargate was the first Sheffield building, in 1894, to have a lift. The top of the lift shaft is clearly visible, although sympathetically cloaked by the architect, in the roof line at the east end of the building.

Now divided into five shops it was originally a single shop for William Foster and sons Ltd, Gentleman's outfitters. In other respects, the building is similar to numerous late Victorian buildings of the town centre being of solid masonry walls and heavy timber floors on massive timber or steel beams.

Elisha Otis invented the safety lift in 1852. Building started to grow taller in the 1880s with the adoption of steel framing after basic steel production had been discovered in 1879 allowing mass steel production. The first "skyscrapers" started to appear in places like Chicago from around 1883, but it wasn't until the cost of steel production fell and the development of reliable electric motors c.1888, that passenger lifts became a reality and tall building became more common. The first "skyscraper" in the UK is now thought to be a furniture warehouse in Stockton on Tees constructed in 1896. It wasn't until after 1906 that the economies available from steel framing became accepted.

OS ref: SK 355 874

G1.1   Most of what you can see of Sheffield cathedral dates from 1430 with more recent additions and alteration. However, at 1101 as a recorded date of construction, it may the oldest surviving building, although it has been completely rebuilt in the intervening years.

© Sheffield Cathedral Chapter

G1.2   Cutlers Hall is the headquarters of the Company of Cutlers in Hallamshire.

G1.3   Leopold Square. Education board offices of 1870 and school creatively converted to shops, offices and an hotel.

G1.4   The City Hall concert hall was completed in 1932 with world leading engineering.

G1.5   Barker's Pool was the site of the town's water supply from the mediaeval period to the end of the 18th century.

G1.6   The city's war memorial was erected in 1925. The 95 feet (29.0 m) high steel mast was at the time the tallest free standing pylon.

G1.7   A recent addition to our commemoration of people's effort during war time is the statue of women who worked in the steel trades in Sheffield.

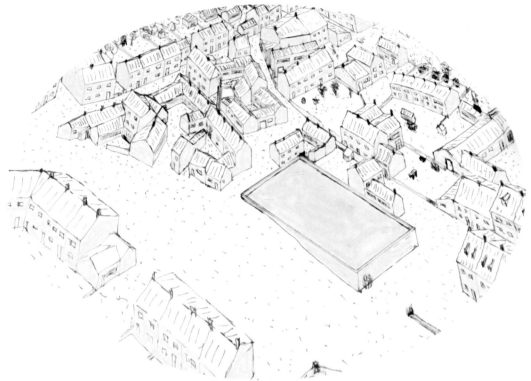

G1.8   A Sketch of Barker's Pool looking North West showing a reconstruction of how it may have looked in the late 18th century.

G1.9   Sheffield Water Works Company offices on Division Street.

G1.10 & G1.11   Sheffield Town Hall was opened by Queen Victoria in 1897. Sandstone was brought by rail from Derbyshire for this building.
The Stoke Hall quarry's stone being easier to carve. This allowed the creation of the frieze depicting the arts and industries of Sheffield.

G1.12 The Peace Gardens were originally created in 1938/9 when the sight had been cleared for an extension of the Town Hall. It only officially received the name in 1985. The gardens were redesigned in 1998, winning awards as a result.

G1.13   Cheney Row has linear measure scales set in the paving and wall.

G1.14 Winter Garden from Tudor Square.

G1.15 Internal view showing glulaminate timber arches and steel bearings.

G1.16 Upper Chapel front.

G1.17 A side view showing change in brickwork. The Victorian brick is lighter coloured, the original late 17th century bricks darker.

G1.18 Crucible Theatre, noted for its concrete construction with the new steel framed Adelphi room extension to the fore.

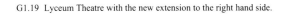

G1.19 Lyceum Theatre with the new extension to the right hand side.

G1.20 Millennium Galleries. When you walk along inside notice the excellent finish on the exposed concrete construction. This is something much more readily achieved when made in a factory.

G1.21 Q-park Charles Street car park is nicknamed the "Cheese-grater" due to the appearance of the cladding panels.

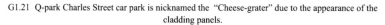

G1.22 The St Paul's Tower
is 101 metre high.

G1.23 Howard Street part of the Sheffield "Gold
Route" through the town towards the University.

G1.24 Sheffield Hallam University Sheaf and Hertha Ayton buildings with Park Hill Flats beyond.

G1.25 Park Hill Flats - the completed Phase 1 of the redevelopment.

G1.26 Midland Station forecourt - Sheaf Square showing modernised 1905 frontage.

G1.27 The photograph below shows the earlier frontage from 1897.

Picturesheffield.com s14726

G1.28 The 2003 Footbridge providing step free access to all platforms and the Supertram stop. (Courtesy of Network Rail.)

G1.29 Sheaf Square - Cutting edge sculpture.

G1.30 Sheffield Passenger Interchange - Bus station.

G1.31 Old Queen's Head - the "Hall in the Ponds" dates back to the 15th century.

THE HALL IN THE PONDS, AT SHEFFIELD.

G1.32 Old Queen's Head as recorded in the late 19th century.

G1.33 The construction of the railway in the late 1860s and consequent building of Sheaf Street required the River Sheaf to be culverted. This point is currently the only open section of the river within the city centre. These culverts are generally shallow arches, as seen here, but beneath the station area a taller arch was built.

G1.34 The Ponds Forge swimming and leisure centre provides world class aquatic facilities.

G1.35 Ponds Forge swimming and leisure centre -Main roof trusses. (Courtesy of SIV)

Picturesheffield.com s12676

G1.36   Sheffield Electric Light and Power Company Sheaf Street power station. c 1905.

G1.37   Sheaf markets with SELP offices beyond.

Picturesheffield.com s01964

G1.38 Ponds Forge footbridge is architecturally interesting.

G1.39 Commercial Street bridge carries the Supertram line across Park Square.

G1.40 Canal Terminal warehouse and adjoining grain store.

G1.41   Dorothy Pax, the last surviving Yorkshire Keel Boat on the canal. She has since been broken up. A bar in Victoria Quays is named in her honour.

G1.42 The design of the Straddle warehouse - allowed goods to be lifted directly upwards under cover by hoist into the warehouses.

G1.43 When the railway company bought he canal they built there goods yard to the north of the basin. This was raised and one line built over a series of arches. These formed coal staithes where coal could drop directly from the wagon to the bays below to facilitate the loading of the merchants carts for distribution to customers.

G1.44 Coal Merchants offices.

G1.45   Swing bridge over canal.

G1.46 Sheaf Quay is built in the 1820s in the form of a country house but was the office of Sheaf Works an early integrated steelworks producing cutlery and edge tools for William Greaves. It was converted to offices in 1989.

G1.47 Parkway viaduct .

G1.48 The Smithfield Butterfly Footbridge over Don was built in 2011 to provide pedestrian access across the river to the new Riverside office development. It has a 40 m span carried by 6 m high arches of tubular steel canted outwards. It also forms part of the river flood defences. The bridge has de-mountable barriers that can be deployed to seal the area to the level of the adjoining retaining wall parapet. The wall incorporates large flap valves to allow drainage into the river but prevent river water escaping.

G1.49 & G1.50   The Cobweb Bridge is so called because of the way it is suspended from the Wicker viaduct masonry by a web of stainless steel wires. This was to prevent any impediment to the flow of the river.

G1.51 The Wicker Arch is a monumental feature of the 660 yard long viaduct built in 1848 for the Manchester Sheffield and Lincolnshire Railway. It creates a gateway into the town.

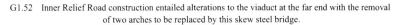

G1.52   Inner Relief Road construction entailed alterations to the viaduct at the far end with the removal of two arches to be replaced by this skew steel bridge.

G1.53 Inner Relief Road was carried over the River Don by a pair of bridges. These have steel beams supporting an integral reinforced concrete deck.

G1.54 Lady's Bridge and Wicker weir on the River Don, viewed from the west.

Sheffield Bridge over the Dun in Sheffield
This bridge is built of hewn stone, there is a quick descent from under the which is set with strong stones
and cramped with iron, maintains the head at South end from springing of arch 18 feet and at the North 3 feet.

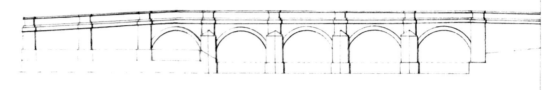

Sheffield Bridge as widened 9 feet on the West side in 1760

G1.55 Robert Carr and John Watson's Book of Bridges shows the profile of the bridge in the mid 18th century before and after the works by John Carr in 1760. Reproduced courtesy of West Yorkshire Archive Service. QD1/461

G1.56 The mediaeval arches of the core of Lady's Bridge are still clearly visible from the river as shown in this old photograph.

G1.57 The Iron columns and lattice support beams of the 1909 widening are clearly visible here.

G1.58 A short distance down stream of Lady's Bridge, Blonk Street bridge is immediately down stream of where the River Sheaf culvert outfalls.

It is hoped that this section of the River Sheaf can be opened up as part of a city park.

G1.59 & G1.60   Don Valley Interceptor sewer. Break through of tunnelling phase 1, above, construction of outfall shaft at Blackburn Meadows, right. (Reproduced courtesy of Sheffield City Council ©)

G1.61   The Old Town Hall on Waingate was the first purpose built town hall in Sheffield when constructed in 1807-8. It became entirely a court house when the present town hall was built in 1897.

G1.62   An artists impression of Sheffield Castle inner
bailey gatehouse area. This is based upon the assesment
of information prior to the 2018 evaluation excavations.
(© The University of Sheffield.)

Identified elements and Layout of Sheffield Castle

G1.63 The ARCUS (Archaeological Research and
Consultancy at the University of Sheffield) Report 669b(1)
2009, undated archive report, below, showing a conjectured
layout of castle. (Both, © The University of Sheffield.)

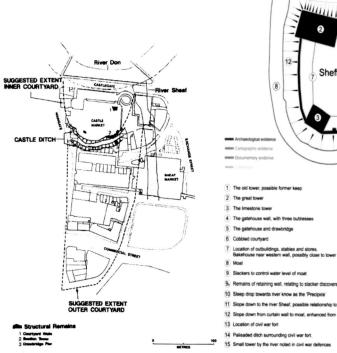

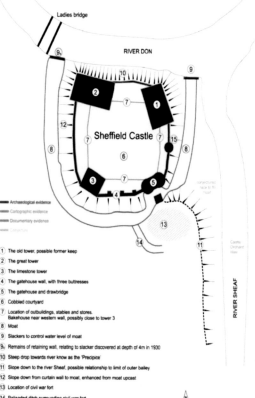

1 The old tower, possible former keep
2 The great tower
3 The limestone tower
4 The gatehouse wall, with three buttresses
5 The gatehouse and drawbridge
6 Cobbled courtyard
7 Location of outbuildings, stables and stores.
   Bakehouse near western wall, possibly close to tower 3
8 Moat
9 Slackers to control water level of moat
9a Remains of retaining wall, relating to slacker discovered at depth of 4m in 1930
10 Steep drop towards river know as the 'Precipice'
11 Slope down to the river Sheaf, possible relationship to limit of outer bailey
12 Slope down from curtain wall to moat, enhanced from moat upcast
13 Location of civil war fort
14 Palisaded ditch surrounding civil war fort.
15 Small tower by the river noted in civil war defences

G1.64   Sheffield Manor Lodge, right.

G1.65 The 1967 Castle Markets building, centre.

G1.66 Markets - Norfolk Market Hall 1851, bottom.

G1.67 Supertram operates three lines connecting Meadowhall, Middlewood and Herdings and the Mosborough townships with the city centre, plus a link through Rotherham to Parkgate.

G1.68 Foster's Building with the top of the lift shaft clearly visible on the left is a pioneering steel framed building.

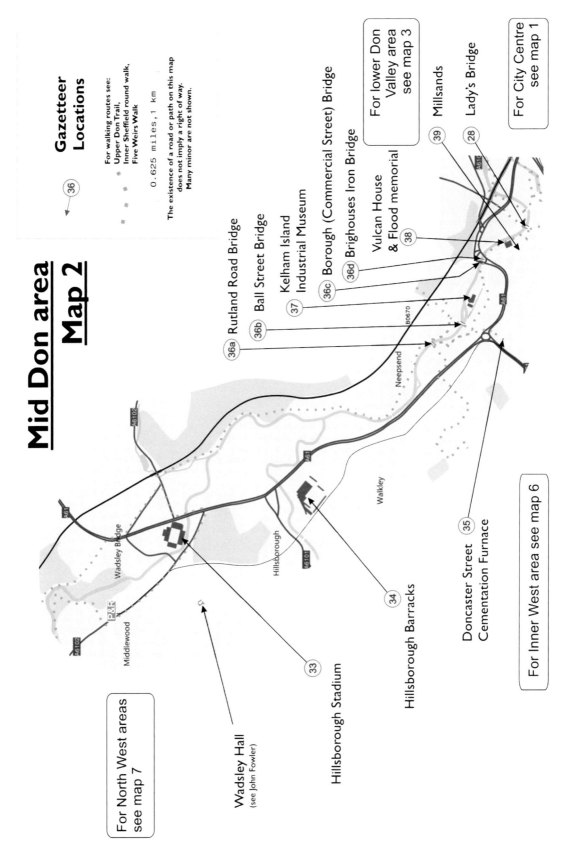

Map 2 - Mid Don Valley area.

33. Hillsborough Football Ground

Sheffield Wednesday first moved here in the summer of 1899 and was officially opened on Sep 2nd 1899 (for a Div 2 fixture between Wednesday and Chesterfield). The original South Stand had been moved to what was then Owlerton, brick-by-brick, from Wednesday's previous home at Olive Grove. At that stage the ground was still named Owlerton. In 1914, this area of the city was taken into the parliamentary constituency of Hillsborough, and hence the ground was renamed. However, until the 1950s it was commonly called "The Wednesday Ground" even by the club.

Sheffield Wednesday Football Club had been founded in 1867 as part of the Wednesday Cricket Club and adopted their current name in 1929. It is one of the oldest football clubs in the world. It should not be confused with Sheffield FC which is the oldest surviving independent football club in the world. Wednesday played their early matches at various grounds in south Sheffield moving to Sheaf House Ground for ten years from 1877. Sheaf House Ground was located off Shoreham Street south of the Bramall Lane ground, but like the others had no facilities. Olive Grove accommodated up to 20,000 spectators on occasions.

In January 1914, the new South Stand opened. Archibald Leitch designed this replacement that would seat 5,600, with further room for 11,000 standing, and boast a clock-face and finial which are still visible today. Leitch was the foremost engineer working in the field of sports stadia, designing many major stands across the country. From Glasgow, his early career was in the design of sugar processing machinery and factories. He developed a working relationship with the Clydeside Structural Iron Company who built many of the sports stands. It is not currently known if they built the stand here. Leitch's stands were typically constructed of braced structural iron, later steel, framing with timber decking. The design figures that he derived and used for crowd loading have remained in use and only slightly modified by recent research. Leitch's structure here remained almost untouched until 1965, although it is now unrecognisable from that initial design.

The most significant modernisation to the south stand took place ahead of both the 1966 World Cup, when it became an all-seater stand and, to a greater extent, Euro '96. This latter work was completed in two stages, costing a total of almost £7m, and included a new roof, and 3,000 extra seats. Recent alterations reduced the general seating capacity. The current capacity of 11,272 seats and many executive boxes. The stand also provides food concession areas, bars, concourse television, a press room, restaurant, and conference suites, and a range of office space.

The Kop has evolved to be a huge structure that houses the loudest and most partisan section of Wednesday supporters. By the time of the addition of a roof in 1986, designed by Eastwood & Partners, the Kop was the largest covered standing area in Europe, with a capacity of 22,000. It is now fully-seated, with a capacity of 11,210.

The West Stand, also known as the Leppings Lane End, has undergone several incarnations since its inception as a covered terrace for 3,000 at the turn of the century. In the 1920's a small stand was built in the north-west corner to adjoin with the North Stand. Subsequently, a 12,000 capacity, partially-covered terrace was constructed. This was demolished and rebuilt prior to the 1966 World Cup to form the basis of the current structure with seating in an upper tier above a standing enclosure.

The present North Stand with a current capacity of 9,255 was built in 1960-1 to designs by Husband & Co. It entirely replaced the earlier stand built between 1899 and 1903. At the time it was England's best new stand since the building of the East Stand at Highbury, in the 1930s, and it was the first cantilever stand in Britain to run the full length of a pitch (the second of the type after that at Scunthorpe United). This was the first stand in the country to receive a full length cantilever roof and only the second cantilever roof. It is now the oldest cantilever roof in the country. The terracing was closed for two years, and re-emerged with 2,494 seats, to add to the 4119 already in the upper tier to give a capacity of 6613.

The north-west corner underwent the same process early in 1966, to be ready for the World Cup, to complete the scheme designed by Husband & Co. It remained largely unchanged until the tragic events on the West Stand Lower at the FA Cup Semi-Final on 15 April 1989 when 96 innocent people were killed and over 700 injured. It was a two tiered, uncovered standing area, accessible through the same turnstiles as the rest of the Leppings Lane End. There were 1,382 seat installed in the north-west corner in the 1990s. However, with one exception this area has not been used for many years.

Total capacity is now 39,732. The record attendance is 72,841, for an FA Cup tie against Manchester City in 1934.

The pitch is laid with special turf comprising specially selected grasses combined with 3 % synthetic polypropylene fibres laid on a sandy bed. The fibres are stitched into the surface at a depth of 200 mm. High pressure sodium lights are shone onto the turf when it is in shadow to ensure even growth of the grass which is mown up to twice daily. With underground heating to protect it from frost, the pitch can be used several times a week throughout the year.

A new entrance to the stadium was also created in 1996 in time for the World Cup fixtures. This provides direct access to the South Stand from Parkside Road over a new bridge over the River Don. This supplements the main entrances to the ground from Penistone Road and Leppings Lane.

The Taylor report following the tragedy has led to significant improvements to the safety of all sports stadia in the country. The enquiry found that the tragedy occurred due to a failure of crowd management. This led to new research into the behaviour of crowds. All-seater stadia were introduced and the enclosing pens removed. As a result stadia since then have been able to include features in the design that aid crowd management and improve safety. Crowd management policies and training are greatly improved.

Prior to the tragedy many of the nation's stadia had seen little investment for decades and had poor visitor facilities. As a result of this tragedy all major sports stadia have had considerable investment over the last twenty five years vastly improving the facilities for all users. Some venues, such as the Sheffield football clubs have seen incremental alterations to the stadia, others such as Arsenal, Rotherham or Chesterfield have built completely new stadia. The improved facilities on offer at all stadia has markedly improved visitor comfort.

Www.swfc.co.uk

OS ref: SK 333 907

34. Hillsborough Barracks

This was built between 1850 and 1854 over 25 acres to house a regiment of cavalry and a regiment of infantry soldiers of the regular army, as opposed to the local militia. This was one of the largest barrack developments in the country and designed to the latest models of how to accommodate troops. This scheme replaced an earlier barrack built at Hillfoot at the junction of Whitehouse Lane and Penistone Road. This had been built in 1794 in response to the general government unease at the time about the risks of revolution especially in the manufacturing centres. There had been a riot in Sheffield in 1791 during the enquiry into the enclosure of Sheffield common land and at the time a troop of Dragoons had to be sent from York to restore order. In both cases they were built by a building contractor from outside the city but maintained through local contracts. The army left by the 1930s, after which parts of the site had various industrial uses. By the late 1980s it was the only surviving walled barracks in the country and was given a grade 2 listing. Geo Longden took over the site and successfully developed it as a mixed retail and business complex. The infantry parade ground is now a car park while a supermarket has been built on the cavalry parade ground. The Tudor-gothic style barrack blocks and ancillary building have been retained and converted to mixed use units.

OS ref: SK 336 896

35. Doncaster Street Cementation Furnace.

The last surviving cementation furnace is a grade 2 listed building. Built in the mid 19th century this furnace was last used in 1952. The cementation furnace was used to convert iron to steel prior to further refining in the crucibles. Bars of wrought iron were roasted in sealed sandstone "coffins" with charcoal to create blister steel. The distinctive shape of a cementation furnace was a common sight in Sheffield until the development of blast furnaces in the late 19th century.

Doncaster Street is so called because of the works that were here, of which the cementation furnace formed a part. These were the works of Daniel Doncaster and Sons Ltd. Daniel having set up a hand tool business in Sheffield in 1778. The Doncasters Group of companies is still active in precision manufacture with plants across the UK and worldwide.

There are also the remains of the lower part of a pair of cementation furnace not far away at Bower Spring. (SK 353879) These were built around 1828 and were part of the Franklin works of Thomas Turton used for just over 80 years. They are in the care of the South Yorkshire Trades Historical Society.

OS ref: SK 348 880

36. Rutland Road, Ball Street and Borough (Corporation Street) Bridges.

These three road bridges were originally built in 1854, 56 and 56 respectively. These were built in separate schemes to improve access across the river for the rapidly expanding steel industry at the time. All were badly damaged in the Great Sheffield Flood with the first two having to be rebuilt while the last required substantial repairs. All are elegant grade 2 listed structures. The area contains a collection of 19th century steel works buildings, many of which have subsequently be converted to new uses.

36a. At Rutland Road the three spans ashlar masonry arches are of elliptical form and the piers have rounded projections. The bridge initially withstood the flood waters with only the parapets washed away by the press of water and debris. However, the bridge was badly weakened by the flooding and was to be rebuilt to the same design with minor modifications.

OS ref: SK 348 886

36b. By contrast, Ball Street is of cast iron construction with three segmental arch spans of iron ribs between ashlar masonry piers. The ironwork was twisted and torn from the piers in the flood. This had been built by the Milton Ironworks of Elesecar as a footbridge, rebuilt after the flood and subsequently widened in 1900. It has recently been strengthened to remove a weight restriction on this important HGV route and ensure it has a long life.

C- ICEY&H2016

OS ref: SK 349 883

36c. Corporation Street, with the Borough Bridge, was laid out in the 1850s being completed in 1856 to provide improved access to the MSLR goods depot at Bridgehouses which opened in 1845. The bridge is formed of three segmental masonry arches with rusticated ashlar facing. There are pointed cutwaters to the piers. The robust construction on secure foundations withstood the flood waters but suffered damaged to the parapets from an increasing press of debris washed down the river.

36d. Just down stream of the Corporation Street bridge are the remains of an iron footbridge across the river. The original cast iron bridge was built in 1796. There was an earlier bridge in the vicinity presumably built of timber in 1726. It is probable that this earlier bridge gave the small settlement of Bridgehouses or Brighouse its name.

Very few iron bridges were built before the turn of the 19th century. Indeed, this may have been one of the first ten iron bridges to be built in the country. It is thought that the Walker iron foundry of Rotherham were probably involved in the construction of the original. They worked with Thomas Paine in developing iron bridge designs in the 1780s. However, as far as I know, their first completed bridge was recorded as being across the Wear at Sunderland in 1796. Thus the bridge here would have been built immediately following the Wear Bridge. Museum Sheffield have a painting of this iron bridge dated 1824.

The original bridge was destroyed in the flood of 1864 and subsequently rebuilt. Contemporary accounts state that it survived the initial flood surge but then collapsed when a mass of debris that had been temporarily held back by the Borough Bridge collided with the slender structure. The bridge although closed to the public still carries service pipes across the river and has recently been renovated.

OS ref: SK 354 882

37. <u>Kelham Island Industrial Museum.</u>

The museum houses an extensive collection of exhibits on all aspect of Sheffield's manufacturing industries from c. 1750 to the present day.

The earliest known reference to Kelham Island as a manufacturing site is from 1604 as a grinding wheel. The wheel goyt used is that of the town mill downstream near Lady's Bridge whose origins date back to at least the 12th century. The wheel was damaged but not seriously in the Sheffield flood of 1864. In 1899 the foundry building was replaced by an electricity generating power plant to supply the city tram network until the 1930s. Whereupon the buildings were used as general storage by the council. The site was earmarked for wholesale clearance in the 1970s to make way for part of the city inner ring road from Nethergreen Road to Wicker. That scheme was abandoned and the site became a museum opening in 1982.

A silk mill was built near here, just to the south of the goyt, in 1760 that was converted to cotton in 1774 and incorporating the cutler's wheel. From 1810 steam power was supplementing the water wheel. In 1815 the grinding shop was reinstated, becoming a foundry in 1829. In 1828 the cotton mill building to the south of the goyt became the town workhouse, now demolished.

The grade 2 listed weir is one of the largest and best preserved in the area and is thought to date, in its present form, from time of the development of the cotton mill at the end of the 18th century. However, a weir will have been here since the creation of the Sheffield Town Corn Mill at least six centuries earlier. It is possible that this goyt was originally a braid of the river channel and Kelham Island is a natural island.

The collection includes the last surviving blast furnace and the working 12,000 hp (9MW) River Don steam engine which drove the steel rolling mill at the Cammell's Grimesthorpe works to produce 0.38m thick armour plate from 50t ingots - a mill wider than any operating in the UK today. The rolling mill was designed and made by Davy engineering who are still building advanced steel manufacturing plant. The Bessemer converter and River Don engine together with a Bramah hydraulic press have all been awarded Heritage Hallmark Awards by the Institution of Mechanical Engineers in recognition of the milestones they represent in the development in mechanical engineering. The museum is an "anchor point" on the European Route of Industrial Heritage along with amongst others the Derbyshire Derwent Valley Mills World Heritage site. These are key sites marking industrial heritage at a world level.

Kelham Island museum and the nearby micro-brewery and associated traditional public house have led the regeneration of the area after the decline of many of the steel businesses in the latter years of the 20th century. Many former steel works have been successfully converted to housing. The museum was also affected by the flooding of 2007.

At the end of the Kelham Island Industrial Museum site is the location for the proposed New Brooklyn Bridge. This is planned to be built as part of the Upper Don Trail as a pedestrian and cycle link along the river. The bridge is to take the trail over the head goyt which creates the "Kelham Island". It will be a one tenth scale remodelling of the New York Brooklyn Bridge and celebrates the historic links between the two cities. Key components of the original bridge, completed in 1883 and many other US bridges were made in Sheffield in the works in the area. These bore names proclaiming the links to America such as Philadelphia, Toronto, Washington, Toledo and Brooklyn. The bridge will also takes advantage of the contemporary design and manufacturing skills available in Sheffield. Preliminary foundation work had started when the site was badly affected by the floods of 2007. This forced a re-appraisal of the flood risks and appropriate defences necessary along the entire river length through the city. Work on the bridge had to be suspended until this review was complete. New flood barriers were necessary at Kelham Island. These were designed by Sheffield City Council and impinged on the position of the bridge, forcing a redesign of the bridge and increasing the cost of the works. As a result of the delay and additional expense it seems unlikely that this interesting project will now be completed.

Www.upperdonwalk.org

Www.simt.co.uk

OS ref: SK 352 882

38. <u>Vulcan House & Flood Memorial</u>

Vulcan House is a state of the art office building and was procured for the Home Office from Wilson Bowden, a speculative office developer. It achieved the highest energy efficiency rating of any building in Sheffield at the time. Careful analysis by Mott MacDonald with the architect Drivers Jonas determined the optimum layout to minimise energy usage. The building is steel framed with composite flooring. Wilson Bowden organised the construction to minimise waste.

Near to Vulcan House is the memorial to the victims of the Great Sheffield Flood of 11/12 March 1864 when the original Dale Dyke Dam burst causing devastation down the river valley. The names of the 241 people who are known to have died are around the base of the memorial. This was Britain's worst engineering disaster. The entire contents of the reservoir flooded out and washed away a large part of the dam itself and much material down stream. Over 3 million cubic metres of water rushed down the valley at speeds of up to 18 mph, destroying 15 bridges and 128 buildings with many hundreds affected by the flood water.

Opposite Vulcan House, across the footbridge over the River Don, lies Nursery Street Pocket Park. This is one of a series of small green spaces being created in the city. The park replaced derelict space and is part of the river flood defences. It allows people to safely get close to the river and enjoy the wildlife while also creating a space that can safely absorb flood waters when needed. It is part of the city's grey to green strategy.

C-ICEY&H2008

OS ref: SK 356 879

39. Millsands

Millsands is the site of Sheffield Town Mill and Town Wheel. These were two of around two hundred water powered sites built on the Sheffield rivers from mediaeval times to the 19th century. On the Don between Middlewood and Brightside alone there are 36 known water power sites. Over time these provided 7 corn mills, 15 forges, 16 grinding shops, 7 rolling mills, 2 slitting mills, 2 wire mills, 1 saw mill, 1 cotton mill, 3 paper mills, 1 silk mill, 2 tanneries and 1 water pump.

The Town Corn mill probably was here from the Anglo-Saxon settlement, although not recorded in the Domesday book. A mill was recorded here in the 12th Century.

The cutler's wheel is recorded from 1740. By the 1760s the site was known as Marshall's Steelworks. This is probably the world's first integrated steel plant with both cementation and crucible furnaces together from at least the 1780s, something that did not occur elsewhere until the 1820s. This eventually become part of Naylor Vickers Steelworks, with Millsands Exchange Brewery occupying part of the site. In late 1864, Vickers moved to the newly built River Don Works. The bases of the cementation furnaces of Marshall's works have been preserved as archaeologically important. An excavation by ARCUS in 1999 found the wheel pit of the cutler's wheel. Much of the area was extensively damaged by 19th and 20th century foundations and cellars. The base of a cementation furnace has been preserved under a glass panel near the recent office development.

The "great waterworks" built by Peter Whalley and George Sorocold around the turn of the 18th century to pump water from the Don up to Barker's Pool was recorded as near Lady's Bridge. Its precise location is currently unknown. It seems that any evidence of the earlier waterworks has been destroyed by later development or hidden by it. It may have become the Cutler's wheel upstream of the Town Mill or near to the outlet of the tail goyt to the river. The route of the tail goyt appears to have been changed some time in the 18th century to discharge above the Wicker weir - possibly at the time the Wicker Tilt was built. It is equally possible that the Wicker Weir was used to power the waterworks pump creating a small isle just above Lady's Bridge as shown on Fairbank's Plan of 1771.

OS ref: SK 357 878

G2.1 Hillsborough Stadium of Sheffield Wednesday Football Club south entrance across the River Don footbridge.

G2.2 The Clock and finial adorning the South Stand are relics of the original Archibald Leitch designed stands.

G2.3 The North Stand is the oldest surviving cantilever roofed stand in the country.

G2.4 Hillsborough Barracks

G2.5 Artists impression of how the Sheffield New Brooklyn Bridge may have looked.

G2.6 Kelham Island Industrial Museum

(Reproduced courtesy of SIMT)

G2.7 Blast Furnace

(Reproduced courtesy of SIMT)

G2.8 Rutland Road bridge

G2.9 Ball Street bridge

G2.10   Borough Bridge and 1864 iron bridge near Bridgehouses. The latter was a replacement for the earlier iron bridge that had been damaged in the flood.

G2.11   Painting of original iron bridge. The design is typical of timber bridges of the late 18th and early 19th centuries.

"Bridge and White Railings" by an unknown artist is reproduced courtesy of Museums Sheffield.

G2.12 Doncaster Street
Cementation Furnace

G2.13 Vulcan House

G2.14   Great Sheffield
Flood Memorial stone. The
names of the known victims
of the disaster are engraved
on the stones at the foot of
the monument

G2.15   Millsands works.
From a contemporary
drawing.

(Picturesheffield.com
s09790)

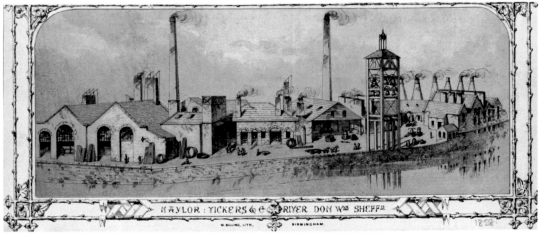

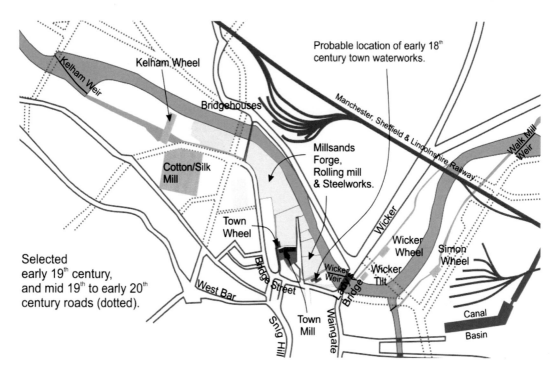

G2.16   Map of Millsands area showing location of waterwheels and works.

G2.17

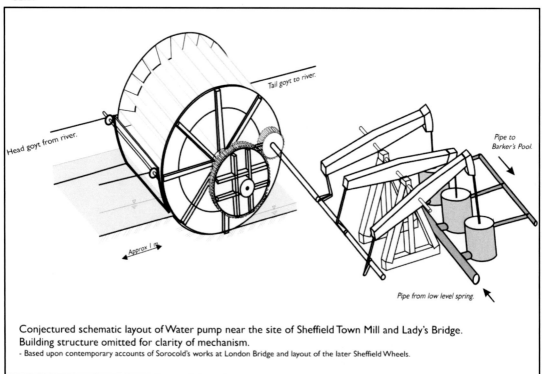

Conjectured schematic layout of Water pump near the site of Sheffield Town Mill and Lady's Bridge.
Building structure omitted for clarity of mechanism.
- Based upon contemporary accounts of Sorocold's works at London Bridge and layout of the later Sheffield Wheels.

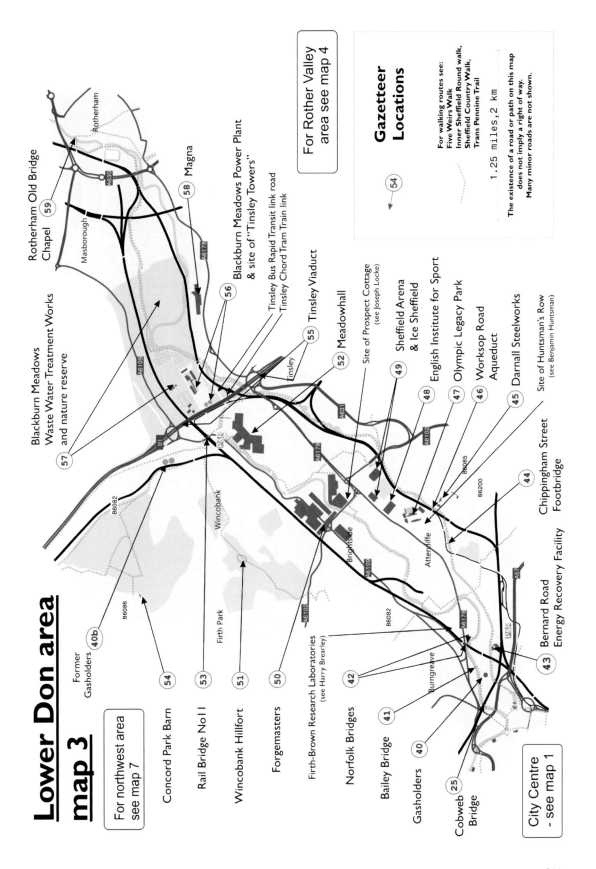

Lower Don Valley

Lower Don area
map 3

For northwest area
see map 7

Rotherham Old Bridge
Chapel (59)

Rotherham

A630

Masborough

(58) Magna

A6178

Blackburn Meadows Power Plant
& site of "Tinsley Towers"

Blackburn Meadows
Waste Water Treatment Works
and nature reserve

A6109

Tinsley Bus Rapid Transit link road
Tinsley Chord Tram Train link

(56)

(55) Tinsley Viaduct

Tinsley

M1

P&R

Wincobank

(57)

(52) Meadowhall

Site of Prospect Cottage
(see Joseph Locke)

For Rother Valley
area see map 4

**Gazetteer
Locations**

(54)

For walking routes see:
Five Weirs Walk
Inner Sheffield Round walk,
Sheffield Country Walk,
Trans Pennine Trail

1.25 miles, 2 km

The existence of a road or path on this map
does not imply a right of way.
Many minor roads are not shown.

(49) Sheffield Arena
& Ice Sheffield

A631

(48) English Institute for Sport

(47) Olympic Legacy Park

A6102

(46) Worksop Road
Aqueduct

B6085

(45) Darnall Steelworks

B6200

Site of Huntsman's Row
(see Benjamin Huntsman)

Atterclliffe

(44) Chippingham Street
Footbridge

Brightside

A6109

A6102

Former
Gasholders (40b)

B6086

Concord Park Barn (54)

Rail Bridge No I I (53)

Wincobank Hillfort (51)

Firth Park

Forgemasters (50)

Firth-Brown Research Laboratories
(see Harry Brearley)

Norfolk Bridges (42)

B6082

Burngreve

A6178

P&R

Bernard Road
Energy Recovery Facility (43)

Bailey Bridge (41)

Gasholders (40)

Cobweb (25)
Bridge

City Centre
- see map 1

211

Map 3 - Lower Don Valley

40. Effingham Street Gas holders

It is one of several sets of gas holders in the city built to store a reserve of gas to provide for the variations in demand. Like the gas holders at Neepsend these were built as part of a coal gasification plant. This plant was first built in 1835. The works were progressively modified as technology advanced and equipment required replacing.

OS ref: SK 364 881

40a. Gas company offices

The former offices of The Sheffield United Gas Light Company of 1874 are described as one of the finest 19th century building in the city, comparing favourably with those of other cities. They can be seen at the junction of Commercial Street and Shude Hill in the city centre above the Commercial Street Supertram bridge. These were extended in 1937 to accommodate the growing requirements of the company for both office and showroom space. The original offices here included showroom space to promote the use of gas to the public – cooking, water heating, mantle lamps, etc. Free cookery classes were provided to extol the benefits of cooking with gas.

The earlier gas works were on both sides of Shude Hill from here to Broad Street.

OS ref: SK 359 875

40b. At **Wincobank** a purification and storage site was built in 1932-35 as part of the South Yorkshire gas grid being fed from large out of town gasification plants such as Orgreave. The first of a pair of gas holders was ordered from Newton Chambers & Co Ltd Thorncliffe works at Chapeltown in June 1936 and completed by November the following year. At a capacity of 228,014m^3 it was the largest holder of its type in Europe at the time. The holder was 76.2m in diameter and 71.25m high rising with spiral guides in four lifts. It has recently been demolished. The capacity equates to roughly 60,000 homes average daily needs and is 33% bigger than the well known gas holder next to the Kennington Oval Cricket Ground in London.

OS ref: SK 390 919

41.   Bailey Bridge

A good example of a Bailey Bridge can be seen here. Bailey Bridges were designed to be made from simple interchangeable components to facilitate mass production by many small suppliers. The individual sections are able to be manually handled and carried on a standard 3 ton truck. It has a modular format to allow different configurations as may be required at any given occasion. This bridge is fairly typical of the size commonly used at 27.4m span.

The basic unit is a 3.0m square braced panel. This together with 5.8m cross beams and simple decking formed 3.0m long U-shaped bridge sections which could be pushed forward from one bank. By using multiple units long spans capable of carrying heavy loads could be made, even in a battlefield. The original design requirement was to create a modular bridge of 36.6m length capable of carrying a 40t load. Many configurations are possible. For instance with pontoons, bridges of 610m length have been built. Also 122m span suspension bridges have been created with the towers and deck all of bailey bridge units.

Thousands of these were used throughout Europe in the latter stages of WWII, the reconstruction works afterwards and disaster relief work world-wide since. General Montgomery considered them a key part in the success in maintaining the allied advances across Europe, while the American general Eisenhower is widely reported to have said that bailey bridges are one of the top three inventions that led to the success of the allies.

Bailey Bridging was used in Sheffield to allow the city to recover as rapidly as possible from the blitz, including to keep the city markets open to the public.

The updated versions, the "Mabey Compact and Universal", are still widely used in disaster relief throughout the world, such as in the 52m long bridge used in Cumbria following the floods of 2009. The Acrow Corporation also makes a version of the Bailey Bridge in the USA and Canada.

This bridge was refurbished to accommodate the Five Weirs Walk Trail. The designers were Sheffield City Council Design and Property Services, the contractor Mandell Engineering with Land and Marine plc.

C-ICEY&HA2007.

www.mabeybridge.co.uk

www.fiveweirs.co.uk

OS ref: SK 364 882

42.   Norfolk Bridges.

The upstream bridge of the two is a multi-span viaduct across the Don Valley. It carries the main line of the former Midland Railway over the valley of the River Don, just north of Sheffield Midland Station, and was designed by the company engineer John Crossley and built by Benton and Woodiwiss, contractors in 1868-70.

The 48-span Attercliffe viaduct is 524m long, in total. Part of this viaduct, just north of the river crossing is an elegant cast iron bridge (HEW ref: 0229) across Attercliffe Road. The bridge has a span of 18.3m square, or 24.6m in skew; it consists of six ribs, each of three segments, with a 3m rise of arch tapering from 0.76 to 0.69m deep, surmounted by N-type spandrel bracing and a 18cm timber deck. Generally by this date steel as opposed to iron was becoming more common.

The second of this pair of bridges is a grade 2 listed road bridge built in 1856. It is of 3 spans each of segmented ashlar arches between piers with ornamental cast iron railing including the Duke of Norfolk's initials.

OS ref: SK 366 882

43.   Bernard Road Energy Recovery Facility

The energy recovery facility on Bernard Road burns up to 225,000 tonnes per year of waste that would otherwise go to land fill in a carefully controlled and highly regulated way. All material is burnt at temperatures of at least 850°C. This produces superheated steam at 400°C powering a turbine linked to electricity generators and also heat exchanges connected to the district heating system. As a result it generates up to 19MW of electricity to the National Grid and up to 60MW to the Community District Energy Network. The flue gasses are treated with urea, lime and activated carbon before passing through particulate filters. The resulting flue gas is continuously monitored to ensure compliance with the regulatory standards and finally discharged through the 175m tall chimney. The flue particulates are collected for safe disposal while the ash residues are screened electro-mechanically for metal which are removed for recycling. The remaining ash is also recycled as aggregate for construction materials.

The district heating scheme provides heat to 140 public and private buildings across the city centre, the universities and public buildings being major users. This saves 21,000 tonnes of CO_2 annually.

The plant also hosts a recyclate materials recovery facility sorting 20,000 tonnes annually from the city's kerb side collections, separating paper, metals and some plastics so that they can be sold for reuse.

The plant was upgraded to improve capacity and ensure compliance with new stricter regulation in 2005. The existing plant and district heating system, commissioned in 1988, had to remain operational throughout the construction of the new plant. However, the land available was very limited posing challenges to the designer and contractor. The space restrictions forced the scheme to adopt a single line process rather than the conventional dual line thus requiring the largest individual grate and boiler in any energy from waste plant in the UK at the time. The improved facility was designed by Earth Tech and built by Clugston Construction and CNIM for Veolia Environment Ltd.

W-ICEY&HA2006
Www.veoliaenvironmentalservices.co.uk/Sheffield

OS ref: SK 366 879

44.   Chippingham Street footbridge, Attercliffe

This foot and cycle bridge, which was completed in 1991, crosses the Sheffield Canal where it is in a 12m deep cutting to link the sports stadia in the vicinity and contribute to the city's cycle network. The bridge forms a 30m span 2 pin arch in steel. Steel columns rise from the arch to carry the reinforced concrete 3.8m wide deck. The arch form makes good use of the natural support available from the sandstone bedrock through which the canal has been cut. It is sympathetic to the location with the aim of reflecting the canal heritage and city's links to steel making. It was built by Sheffield City Council to designs by their engineering consultancy.

C-ICEYA1992

OS ref: SK 382 885

45.   Darnall steelworks site

Just to the east of the Sheffield and Tinsley Canal, to the south of Darnall Road are the remains, now listed grade 2 and 2* and as a scheduled ancient monument, of

Sanderson Bros. & Co.'s Darnall Works originating in 1830s but redeveloped in 1871-4 for bulk crucible steel production with 180 melting holes. This redevelopment took place at a time when the Bessemer-Mushet process was taking over bulk steel production for general use. However, for specialist steels the "Sheffield Method" of crucible steel production remained superior. The site also contains the buried remains of a late 18th century glass cone similar to the one surviving at Catcliffe. Sanderson's took over the glass cone in 1835 and is thought to have been converted to a cementation furnace, similar to the one at Doncaster Street. However, it reverted to glass manufacture in 1859 until its demolition in 1905. Sanderson's expanded this integrated steel works in the 1870s with further cementation furnaces and crucible workshops and administration buildings. In 1873-4 a Siemens gas fired crucible shop complete with gas production plant was built to the west of the crucible shops. The cementation furnaces were demolished in the 1920s and in 1934 the plant went to entirely electric melting. Some parts of the site were demolished in the 1960s but not redeveloped, production continued into the 1980s, although the surviving crucible ranges were last used in the 1940s.

There is a surviving lodge and weigh-bridge house at the entrance on Darnall Road, within the site can be seen the office block in the style of a Venetian villa. The glass cone was to the west of this. To the east along the Wilfrid Road boundary and turning into the site are ranges of crucible shops with their characteristic chimney stacks and ancillary buildings. This includes at the southern leg some large shops capable of casting large items from many crucibles. The gas plant was to the west of this. To the west of the Sanderson's works were those of Kayser Ellison of 1913, the grand office block remains in front of two steel-framed workshops. These are two of the earliest surviving examples of steel framed construction in the city.

The two companies merged in 1960. Much of the monument was in a state of dereliction in 2002, when photographed for imagesofengland. From 2005 the site has been sympathetically redeveloped and the steel framed building re-clad and transformed into offices. Taken as a whole the monument represents a uniquely well preserved, nationally important complex tracing the evolution of the site from an early 19th century glassworks to a 20th century steel making centre.

To see a smaller, but complete crucible workshop, visit Abbeydale Industrial Hamlet.

OS Ref: SK 385 884

46. Worksop Road Canal Aqueduct.

This grade 2 listed building (HEW ref: 0001) is a masonry canal aqueduct designed by William Chapman the engineer for the Canal Company with Henry Beck as Resident engineer. Completed in 1819, it carries the Sheffield and Tinsley Canal over the Worksop to Attercliffe Turnpike of 1776.

The canal was built to a gauge to accommodate the Yorkshire Keel boats 18.29m long by 4.57m wide with a 2.06m draft capable of carrying 100 tons of cargo. These carvel built boats are thought to be direct descendants of Viking cargo boats brought to the region in the 9th century. They had a single mast a large square sail and moveable leeboards. They could be operated by a single person but were generally manned by a family.

Chapman had prepared a feasibility report on the Sheffield Canal in 1814. This was followed by an enabling Act in June 1815. He was appointed as engineer and construction of the canal began in 1816. The canal runs parallel with, and to the south of, the river Don and terminates at the head of the River Don Navigation at Tinsley 21.3m below the Sheffield Basin. Works comprised 4½ miles of canal cut with twelve locks 19.5m by 4.88m. The canal reduces to 4.88m wide and 2.1m deep to cross the aqueduct. Additionally there was a further cutting at Attercliffe, an aqueduct over a road and seven road bridges. A basin 182.9m by 30.5m was built at Sheffield with a warehouse and wharves. Steam pumping plant supplied water to the canal from disused mine workings. Opened in February 1819 the canal had cost £76,000.

William Chapman was born in Whitby and initially followed his father as a mariner. An early unsuccessful venture into coal mining led to him working as an engineer for Boulton and Watt. He soon established himself independently and worked on many canal and drainage schemes throughout Britain, Ireland and overseas. Among his projects were Hull docks and Scarborough harbour. During the Napoleonic war he returned to coal mining projects and designed several locomotives. He remained active in advising on many projects including docks in London and Leith until shortly before his death in 1832 at the age of 83.

The canal's Act stipulated a side arch for horseback travellers in the viaduct. There are side arches for pedestrians raised above the sunken roadway. It is possible that these are the horseback passages, although rather narrow, with the floor level later raised purely for pedestrian use and avoiding the flooding risk without adequate drainage. (The retaining walls supporting the walkway appear to have been built later than the piers supporting the arches.) The road had had to be lowered to pass under the canal. Alternatively, these pedestrian passageways may be a variation from the requirements of the original enabling act. There is also a smaller round-arched culvert carrying Kirkbridge Dike through the aqueduct at about walk way level on the southern side. The main arch is 6.0m wide with a highway clearance of 4.34m, slightly less than the 4.57m specified in the enabling Act. The road level may have risen in the intervening years. The side passages are 2.1m wide with semicircular arches giving a maximum headroom of 2.1m.

Prior to the construction of the railway there was a wharf on the canal just to the south of the aqueduct to service the nearby steelworks of Benjamin Huntsman.

OS ref: SK 383 886

47.   Olympic Legacy Park

Olympic Legacy Park is set to be recognised as a UK Innovation District for health and well-being research and learning.

The Olympic Legacy Park is on the site of the Don Valley Stadium that was the centre of the World Student Games in 1991. The need to have the venues ready and tested within the four years from being awarded the games to the opening ceremony gave very little time; around two years, for design and construction. The initial concept had been to develop the existing Woodbourn Road athletics track. However, it became very quickly apparent that it was not suitable. The site of Brown Baileys steelworks was selected. This posed its own challenges, not least the industrial legacy of buried foundations and some contamination. The early design process also considered how the stadium could be enlarged in future, if necessary, to a 40, 50 or even 60,000 all-seater covered stadium by building similar grandstands around the remaining sides of the track.

Clearly the intended crowd capacity is a leading factor in the design of any stadium together with the layout of the field of play. Spectators will require good unobstructed views of all the action and also score- and video-boards. This leads to large cantilevered stands providing weather protection without support at the front. The field of play also need adequate light to ensure the grass (unless artificial turf is being used) can grow well. For tall stadia such as those at Wembley and Cardiff this can prove a constant challenge to the groundsmen with the field of play regularly completely replaced. The amount of wind at the field of play also needs assessing to ensure it does not adversely affect play. The artificial lighting should produce good illumination of the entire area without glare or light pollution. This can be by independent pylons or integrated into the front of the stand roofs. Consideration for the provision of television broadcasting is also necessary. This can affect the lighting provision required and acoustic capacity of rooms at the venue. The overall design of the stadium also needs acoustic modelling to ensure the spectators can hear as well as see the action. This is particularly important for multi-use venues. A stadium cannot usually survive financially if only filled on a few days each year. Secondary uses are needed for all or part of the complex. This may be using the field of play for various sports and or as a pop concert venue. Also areas within the stands can be used for hospitality, conference, fitness club or retail uses.

The stands and concourses should allow easy flow of the crowds to their seats, toilets and refreshment suppliers and any emergency escape all with appropriate disabled access. The location needs good transport links.

Here, the international Olympic standard athletics track and field were surrounded by 25,000 seats of which 10,000 were covered. When used for concerts only 15,000 of these seats were used but 35,000 people could have been accommodated in the arena. The stadium could also host conferences and fairs using the 85m long indoor hall.

An area of shallow abandoned coal workings was drilled and grouted to stabilise the ground below the stadium. The stadium was set in an artificial bowl created by excavating the ground in the centre and creating embankments at the perimeter. This helped deal with any contamination, vastly improved wind exposure on the track and facilitated the separation of spectators and participants while affording good disabled access to the various parts of the stadium. As many major athletics events run in the evening the main home straight is to the south with the finish line at the eastern end. This meant that the grandstand, facing north could cast a heavy shadow. This suggested the use of a translucent roof material. This married well with the architect's concept of the stand being light airy and having a sense of fun about it. To provide uninterrupted views the roof is cantilevered forward from the rear of the seating area. The presence of an indoor running track within the stand complicated the arrangement of supports for the roof and seating. However, a tied A-frame neatly solved this point bridging the indoor running rack.

The roof was made of Teflon coated glass fibre tensioned into double curved geometric shapes found by computer analysis. The wind loads were checked by testing a 1:200 scale model in a wind tunnel. The roof fabric was supported by horizontal veirendeel trusses supported by stays and struts from 12m high masts, all of circular hollow steel tubing. These in turn were supported by the in-situ reinforced concrete frame and raft foundation. Installation of roof steel work and fabric roofing required detailed planning right from the design stage.

The Hillsborough disaster occurred during the early phase of construction of the stadium. The subsequent Taylor report recommended minor changes to the arrangement of turnstiles and surveillance, but no significant design alterations were needed and no additional works or cost entailed.

The stadium was designed by YRM Anthony Hunt Associates (now Jacobs) with Sheffield City Council Design and Building Services as architects. The design engineer won a special award for "striking and economic engineering in a sports stand" from the Institution if Structural Engineers.

Sadly, the lack of an anchor tenant able to generate substantial revenue leaves the Don Valley Stadium loss making and subsidised by SCC. This subsidy was withdrawn in 2013 and the site has now been demolished. The stadium always struggled to regularly attract the major international athletics competitions that might have provided a periodic income and raised its international profile increasing its chances of other income streams. The legacy of the London 2012 Olympic games is that the relative attraction of Don Valley was further diminished and so its economics imperilled, making the closure all but inevitable.

The site has recently been developed as a 1,200 place community school, 600 place University Technical College, Advance Well-being Research Centre, centre of sport science and a purpose built rugby stadium with a proposed 2,500 seat main stand and a 3,000 seat indoor arena for basketball and 50 room hotel. Organisations in the project include Sheffield Hallam University, Sheffield College, Sheffield City Council and Sheffield Teaching Hospitals NHS Foundation Trust. Athletics training and participation are now catered for in a revitalised Woodbourne Road stadium.

UTC Sheffield has two campuses, UTC Sheffield City Centre and UTC Sheffield Olympic Legacy Park. Students can join from age 13, 14, or 16 and study an academic curriculum – GCSEs and A Levels – alongside their technical specialism. The difference is that all academic study relates to employer-led projects and students gain the skills and qualifications to open up opportunities for jobs, apprenticeships and university courses. UTC Sheffield Olympic Legacy Park, specialises in Computing, Health Sciences and Sport Science. UTC Sheffield City Centre, specialises in Engineering and Creative and Digital.

Sheffield College provides education and training diverse subject from 16+ school leaver, through apprenticeships, adult learners and university level. The college is based on Granville Road but has satellite campuses at across the city.

W-BCSAA1991   (Don Valley Stadium)

Www.utc2sheffield.co.uk   OS ref: SK 383 889

Just to the west of the site across Worksop Road is the site of Huntsman's Row and the steelworks established by Benjamin Huntsman to make crucible steel in 1751. Arguably, this is the birthplace of Sheffield's specialist steel industry.

OS ref: SK 381 888

The Arena, IceSheffield, and English Institute for Sport now form part of the "Olympic Legacy Park" and are only some of the over a dozen venues across the city managed by Sheffield International Venues providing a diverse range of facilities for sport and hospitality events. These are a legacy of the World Student Games in the city.

48.   English Institute for Sport

This training centre for the nation's elite athletes covers 2 hectares under 7 bays of barrel roofing supported off 50 m high masts to give a large open area. It was completed in 2003 to designs by YRM Anthony Hunt Associates (now Jacobs) with Faulkner Browns and Sheffield CC design and Property services as architects. The main contractor was Interserve for client Phoenix Sport. The space has been carefully proportioned to accommodate the needs of the various sports and potential future users at both elite and community user levels. A grid of 20.4m by 69 and 32m neatly fitted the various playing areas. The barrel vaults to glaze trusses create northern light roofing which provides glare free natural lighting. The spans of the composite panel roofing were somewhat larger than customary. Two skins of relatively thin metal sheeting are bonded together by a thick layer of insulation material to act as a single unit. This entailed full size test construction in the Finnish factory to prove the load capacity and buildability of the system. As with the Arena ,the roof is a single structure without internal movement joints. This means that it had to be designed to accommodate stresses induced by restrained thermal movements. The floor slab is also a single fibre reinforced structure.

Jaffel Versi of Anthony Hunt Associates was the runner-up in the Young Structural Engineer of the Year Award 2004 for his work on this project.

Www.eis-sheffield.co.uk

OS ref: SK 383 892

49.   Sheffield FlyDSA Arena

In November 1987 the city won the competition to host the World Student Games. The largest international sporting contest after the Olympic games, with up to 6,000 athletes from 120 countries taking part. The Sheffield International Arena was completed in 1991 for the World Student Games by R. M. Douglas Management Ltd with ICC Sheffield and Cleveland Bridge & Engineering Co. Ltd to designs by Oscar Faber Consulting Engineers in association with Geiger Engineers and architects HOK Sport in association with Lister Drew Haines Barrow. The main feature of the building is the 120m x 90m Takenaka or "skew-chord" space truss roof covering the entire building with no internal supports. The bottom chord members of the truss are aligned to the building axes while the top chords are at 45° to these. This type of roof construction is very good at carrying the various loads applied in this type of building, where substantial loads are sometimes suspended for display. The arena provides 8629 tiered seats and up to 3120 floor level seating in the main arena together with various suites and club rooms and an exhibition space 94m x 34m. The tiered seating and main flooring are of precast reinforced concrete on an in-situ reinforced concrete frame. The high level suites are of composite steel and concrete construction built off the reinforced concrete frame. Like most contemporary building in the Lower Don Valley the ground required treatment to make safe the remains from previous uses of the site. Like the Ice Sheffield building the Arena is partly built into the slope of the land. This helps insulate the building and reduces the energy needed to chill the rinks. The building was carefully designed for airtightness to ensure that moist air cannot enter the building and cause fogs over the ice.

The adjoining **IceSheffield**, of 2003, with a twin vaulted roof structure, contains two Olympic size rinks one for community and one for elite competitive uses. The roof is of a simple series of arch trusses supporting a composite panel system. Having been built into the ground the 1500 spectators can enter at a higher level with the rinks below. Again particular attention to air movements within the operational building were needed.

Www.sheffieldarena.co.uk

OS ref: SK 387 894

Www.icesheffield.co.uk

OS ref: SK 384 893

50. Sheffield Forgemasters

The company can trace its origins back to the mid 18th century. They built the River Don works in 1864 taking advantage of the latest technologies. This continued to expand and by 1870 it had become one of the two largest steel works in the world. The company specialised in railway, marine and armament works. In the 1920s and 30s various Sheffield steel companies merged to form English steel. Nationalisation in 1967 and then amalgamation with Firth Brown as a private sector company in 1983 formed Sheffield Forgemasters. This company was subject to a management buyout in 1988 and again in 2005.

The River Don Works straddles Brightside Lane with the 1906 building creating a canyon effect once common along much of the Lower Don Valley in Sheffield.

Sheffield Forgemasters still produces the largest castings in the western world at 350 tonnes and up to 16.5 x 7.5 x 4.6m in size. The individual buildings are comparable in size to the EIS at over 2 hectares in area but taller and less prepossessing. The total building area is of the order of 14 ha. These house massive machines with complex foundations of 1,000s of tonnes to provide the stability needed. These are capable of machining items up to 22m long or 6.2m diameter to very fine tolerances. These machines are made by the likes of DavyMarkham Ltd, with structural and foundation design by the likes of Eastwood & Partners.

The "sculpture" in the centre of the roundabout on Brightside Lane is in fact the world's first prototype steel casting for joining offshore oil platform legs. This was cast in 1978 and given an IMechE Heritage Hallmark award in 2000 to mark this important innovation in both steel casting and offshore structural engineering.

The company remains at the forefront of technology, being a world leader in the manufacture of offshore castings and rolling mill rolls. It has a 10,000 tonne forging press, the largest in Europe. There is only one other forge of this size in existence in the world today.

Www.sheffieldforgemasters.com

OS ref: SK 382 901

51.   Wincobank Hillfort

Wincobank Hillfort is possibly the oldest surviving engineered structure in the city. It was built around 500 BC. The ramparts were 5.5m thick, faced with dressed stone and constructed of earth and rubble reinforced with a series of timber cribs. They survive to a height of 2.8m and the ditch below the rampart is approximately 10 m wide. However, they are buried beneath the topsoil and vegetation. The enclosed area of the hillfort is approximately 1 ha.

Although termed a hillfort, it is thought that they were primarily meeting places and not military structures. They were nevertheless places of refuge if a community was attacked and uses may have varied overtime and from place to place. There is evidence of burning of the ramparts here although the cause of the fire will remain unknown.

There is another hillfort of similar date and size at **Carl Wark** in the far south west of the city (OS ref: SK 259 815) built on the gritstone edge near Grindleford. Here the dry stone walling is clearly visible around 3m high and 30m long. Some of the stone work was dressed, that is shaped by tooling. Here the dressed stone walling is clearly visible. The other sites identified as hillforts in the vicinity are at Roe Wood, Bole Hill Totley, Castle Dyke Langsett, Worsborough Common, Ash Cabin Flats Rivelin and Caesar's Camp Scholes. Most of these are badly damaged.

Www.wincobankhill.btck.co.uk

OS ref: SK 378 910

52.   Meadowhall Shopping Centre

Meadowhall shopping centre is one of the largest and most successful in the country drawing shoppers from across the region and beyond since it opened in 1990. It is now once again expanding to increase the amount of leisure facilities in the complex. Some have blamed the success of Meadowhall for the decline of the city centre. This is an over simplistic analysis as town and city centres have suffered declining fortunes across the UK. This has in part been fuelled by the growth of car ownership allowing more people to travel further at times of their own choosing. On balance I would say Meadowhall has been a positive factor in the regeneration of the city region.

This 42 ha site was the former Hecla & Hadfield steelworks which closed in the 1980s. These left a legacy of contaminated material in the ground which were systematically identified and removed. The shopping centre is supported off 8,000 piles through the remains of the industrial landscape and river sediments below. The structure is a relatively simple steel framed building with in situ composite decking. However, the complex shape of what at the time was Britain's largest roof required careful consideration of potential snow loading and was modified to reduce the probability of excess snow building up. Parking is provided for 12,000 cars & 300 coaches in Europe's largest car park at the time. In addition, the centre is served by new rail and tram stations. The engineering designers were Bingham Cotterell.

The shopping centre has a passenger transport interchange serving tram, bus and rail services. The highways, passenger interchange and associated access bridges were design for Meadowhall Centre Ltd by Sheffield City Council. This included four major road bridges over the River Don. Meadowhall has worked with the neighbouring businesses and councils to encourage the use of public transport and mitigate the impact of the large amount of road traffic that it generates, especially at peak times.

The footbridge to the coach park was a late addition to the works and had to be designed and constructed within twenty weeks. The 4m wide footbridge is 120m long excluding the approach ramps. The three spans are of 40, 44 and 36m to ensure adequate sight lines to the shopping centre dual carriageway access road below. The brief required an "original design sympathetic to the locality" but while to be constructed as an open structure should be capable of being fully glazed in future. A through steel truss was chosen with the top chord braced from the sides with tapered members out of plane in the form of a space frame. A concrete deck helps control vibration and dynamic actions.

HC- ICEYA1991 (coach footbridge)

OS ref: SK 392 910

53. Rail Bridge No 11 Meadowhall Road

The existing multi-span masonry arch bridge carrying the railway over the A6109 caused unacceptable restrictions on traffic with the development of the Meadowhall Shopping centre nearby. The bridge was replaced with minimal disruption to either road or rail users. This involved thrusting a diversion culvert for Blackburn Brook under the railway, building abutments for the new bridge in the unused arches of the viaduct and then within 60 hours demolishing the old structure and sliding in the new bridge superstructure and reinstating the rail lines. It was built by Cementation Projects Ltd and Beazer Construction North East Ltd to designs by British Rail eastern region.

C-ICEYA1991

OS ref: SK 392 914

54. Concord Park Barn

The mediæval cruck frame, once common in the area can be considered as a crude form of an arched frame. These required the selection of trees of the correctly bent shape, something in strictly limited supply. Whereas now, with glue laminated timber we can create bends as desired at will. There are still around a dozen examples of cruck framed buildings in the villages and suburbs to the north and west of the city. However, most are now hidden behind later construction and are in private buildings.

The grade 2 listed barn at Concord Park is a good example which is occasionally open for public inspection. The barn is now the ranger station and store for the park. Its dating is unclear and as yet there have been no dendrochronological tests on the timbers. I am told there is a document mentioning a four bay cruck barn belong at the site in the records relating to a local priory in the mid 14th century. Stylistically the frames could date from the 14th to early 17th century. It is believed that the cottage, now forming the rangers offices was added in the 16th or 17th centuries by which time the property belonged to the local manor. This addition resulted in the demolition of the westernmost bay, producing the three bay structure found today. The nearby Rose Cottage and Rock House on Oaks Lane are thought to be other cottages built at the same time as this cottage.

Within the later coursed rubble stone walls there are four pairs of crucks. Over time the bases of the crucks have been much reduced by decay and are generally hidden within the masonry. However, the northern blade of the second frame is still exposed on the outside of the walling. The west end has a stud partition with wattle and daub above the tie beam. Signs of notching to take partitions are visible on other trusses. Originally, it is thought that all walls would have been of this construction, the roof being either stone flags or thatch. The date of the masonry walls of the cruck barn is uncertain but is thought to predate the addition of the cottage. The frames are of slightly different construction, the second frame notably so, and are thought to be of more than one species of timber. It seems likely that this second frame is a later replacement of an original, albeit centuries ago. There is bracing in the third bay. The first third and fourth frames have collar or block joints at the apex, none have saddles. The buildings were in a severe state of dilapidation before being utilised as the park store and offices which has ensured their survival.

OS ref: SK 373 923

55.   **Tinsley Viaduct.**

The viaduct is a 1,032.8m long and 34.0m wide dual deck steel box girder bridge of 20 spans of which only 5 are straight. It carries three motorway lanes (currently reduced to two) and a hard shoulder in each direction on the top deck and dual two lanes and walkways plus a central two lane emergency access road on the lower deck. In addition, it carries many service pipes and cables. It was built between 1965 and 1968 opening on 12 June, to the designs of Cleveland Bridge/Freeman Fox & Partners.

The innovative design allowed construction over a highly congested area of railways, roads, active stock yards and water treatment works, a river and canal. It was built progressively from the north end without interfering with the ground between the piers. It was subsequently strengthened over a number of years up to 1980 to ensure the safety of the growing amount of traffic as our knowledge of how box girders performed. Following changes in EU legislation in 1999 the bridge had to be reassessed, with many others, to accommodate heavier vehicles. This resulted in a further programme of strengthening designed by Owen Williams Highways (now Amey Consulting). This involved over 1.25 million man-hours of work over a 125 week period and was completed in 2006. Over 2,500t of steel, 53,000 bolts and 1,400m^3 of concrete were added and 155,000m^2 of paint replaced. This was completed safely and at a cost of £83.4M, some £2M less than budgeted. The viaduct carries 111,000 vehicle per day on the motorway and 22,000 on the A631 lower deck.

The "Tinsley Towers", the cooling towers of the decommissioned Blackburn Meadows electricity generating station were only 15m from the viaduct at the closest point. These reinforced concrete structures were demolished by controlled explosion in the early hours of Sunday 24 August 2008. This was the first time that explosive demolition had been used so close to a major highway structure. Amey were commissioned to inspect the viaduct before and after and monitor the structure during the demolition to ensure the safety of the structure. The viaduct was closed to traffic during the demolition but had to be open to traffic within hours. Before the demolition, the demolition company liaised with adjoining land occupiers, Amey and the Highways England to develop an appropriate method to demolish the structures. The viaduct was assessed to determine which parts were most vulnerable to damage and modelled to determine how it would behave when subjected to the blast wave. A variety of sensors were attached to key parts of the viaduct and in the adjoining ground to measure the actual response to the demolition. The actual and predicted responses were compared and the structure meticulously examined to validate the safety of the structure after the blast. This was achieved three hours ahead of schedule allowing the viaduct to open early to traffic.

HC-ICEYHA2005 W-BCIA(major Project)2005 W-BCSAA(Bridges)1969

OS ref: SK 382 920

to SK 400 908

56.   **Blackburn Meadows Bio-fuel Energy Plant.**

E.on Energy have just built the 30MW renewable energy plant that will produce enough power for around 40,000 homes by converting recycled waste wood into electricity. It will use UK sourced recycled waste wood to power the plant. It is expected that the site will create around 30 full-time jobs within the local area

The site has a strong heritage of power production and has excellent links to electricity infrastructure and transport networks. It will to breathe life back into the redundant Blackburn Meadows site and contribute to the economic regeneration of the area. A bio-mass development is a great opportunity to make a contribution to the Yorkshire and Humber region's target of reducing greenhouse gas emissions. The plant will also displace the emissions of around 80,000 tonnes of carbon dioxide every year, the equivalent of taking more than 20,000 cars off the UK's roads each year, by burning carbon neutral fuel in place of traditional fossil fuels like coal and gas. In addition to producing electricity the plant captures the waste heat to supply a district heating scheme with up to 25MW of thermal energy. Customer on this grid include Sheffield Forgemasters and Sheffield Arena. E.on has also installed 10MW of batteries at the Blackburn Meadows site in a project that will help stabilise the frequency on the national grid and balance the range of power generation available. The lithium-ion batteries will be able to hold the same amount of energy as 500,000 mobile phone batteries.

The new plant was named as one of the winners of the RIBA National Awards building of the year in 2017.

The company, at Blackburn Meadows, will support local projects throughout the lifetime of the plant, to enhance the appearance and bio-diversity of the area through landscaping, including green roofs, where appropriate, and construction of an on-site visitor centre. This will show how energy is produced as well as highlighting the industrial heritage of the site.

www.eon.co.uk

OS ref: SK 397 915

The cooling towers of the Blackburn Meadows generator - "The Tinsley Towers" - were a notable land mark adjoining the motorway for many years. Over 8,000 people turned out to watch the controlled demolition at 3 a.m. on Sunday 24 August 2008 and many more followed the television and radio coverage.

Electricity generators were initially built at Blackburn Meadows in 1921 and were successors to those at Neepsend of 1912 which had themselves replaced plant at Sheaf Street. The city's first power station was built in 1878 on the site of what is now Ponds Forge swimming centre. The first power plant here had a capacity of 28MW, one of the largest in the country at the time. By the 1930s more capacity was needed and so a second generating plant was built here in phases between 1933 and 38. The new plant had a capacity of 100MW and required significant cooling facilities, hence the construction of the "Tinsley Towers". These were built to the new hyperbolic reinforced concrete design. Each tower could cool one million litres of water by 19 ºC every hour.

Power generation ceased here in 1980. The establishment of the national power grid in the 1950s had led to the local generators being replaced by large power stations situated away from the population on major rivers or the coast through the following two decades. The Trent Valley downstream of Derby became known colloquially as Megawatt Valley.

OS ref: SK 359 875

57.   **Blackburn Meadows STW & Nature Reserve**

Opened in 1886, the sewage treatment works treats the waste from the majority of the city, with smaller plants at Woodhouse and Stocksbridge and some of the smaller outlying villages treating the remainder. Blackburn Meadows was the first plant in the country to use lime precipitation to treat the effluent. A system that then became known as the Sheffield Method. The Don Valley Interceptor Sewer delivers the waste to the plant where it is pumped to the surface for treatment before being safely discharged into the River Don. Yorkshire Water is major a partner in the Living Don project to improve the quality of the river water and the range and amount of wildlife that it can support.

The works have undergone a number of changes over the years and continues to receive substantial investment to continually improve water quality and efficiency of treatment.

Yorkshire Water has an aim to be 25% self sufficient in energy generation by 2020. As part of this a bio-energy scheme has been developed. The waste sludge is treated to generate methane gas which can then power gas turbines. The 11Gwh/year plant generates 65% of the sites energy requirements. Blackburn Meadows like all the key water and wastewater treatment plants have power back-up facilities to ensure that they can remain operational at all times. The waste heat is also used within the plant. After the Treatment the sludge is no-longer a biohazard and can be sold as fertiliser.

The design of the works is to allow for plant capacity to cater for forecast flows and loads up to the design horizon of 2025 for a population of 496,728. The current and future dry weather flow and flow to full treatment are 158,000m^3/ day and 368,000m^3/day respectively.

Parts of the site were affected by the flooding of 2007. Since then, the works have been modified to protect them against flooding and ensure that they can remain operational throughout major storm events.

Now redundant parts of the site have been transformed into the Blackburn Meadows Nature reserve in partnership with Sheffield Wildlife Trust.

HC-ICEYH2014 (bio-energy scheme)

www.yorkshirewater.com

www.wildsheffield.com

OS ref: SK 397 917

58.   Magna

A science adventure and discovery centre themed on the elements of earth, air, fire and water. There are many exhibits, displays and tours designed for children. The centre is housed in the buildings of the former Templeborough Steelworks and tells the story of steel. 'E' furnace at Templeborough has been brought back to life in a sound and light show in order to recreate the drama and power of the steel making process. In 2001 this project won the Stirling Prize for architecture due to its innovative use of space. The project architect was Wilkinson Eyre, the engineers Mott MacDonald and Buro Happold. Magna's exhibitions won the Best Exhibition category at the 2002 Design Week Awards and a tourism award in 2006.

The Templeborough steelworks were built for Steel, Peech and Tozer around 1917. Beneath the works are the remains of a Roman fort. The civil settlement associated with the fort extends into the adjoining lands. The fort was first built with earth ramparts in the sixth or seventh decade of the first century AD - when the invading army established a presence in the region. This covered an area of 6.4 acres. In the second half of the second century this was replaced with a slightly smaller stone fortification. A process repeated in the forth century by when the area was only 4.8 acres. There is evidence of iron and possibly glass manufacture through the Roman period in the vicinity.

Www.visitmagna.co.uk

OS Ref: SK 410 915

59. Rotherham Bridge Chapel

This chapel is a grade I listed building, HEW and scheduled ancient monument. Like the now lost chapel at Lady's Bridge this was built as a place of prayer for traveller. The funds raised as a result paid for the upkeep of the bridge during the mediaeval period. The chapel became an almshouse after the Chantries Act. It then survived as a gaol, private house, and shop before being re-consecrated in 1928. The chapel at Sheffield is likely to have been similar. There are only three other such chapels surviving in the country, another is at Wakefield.

The four arch bridge is recorded as dating from 1483. It was widened in 1768-9 by John Platt under John Carr's direction. It was restored in the 1930s when a new bridge was built just to the south which now takes the traffic across the River Don. You will notice that the course of the river has changed over the years and the original bridge does not extend to the present north bank.

OS ref: SK427 931

G3.1 Effingham Street Gasholder.

G3.2 Gas Company offices, Commercial Street.

G3.3 & G3.4   Bailey Bridges are made of prefabricated steel panels that are bolted together to rapidly create bridges of whatever size is required.

G3.5 Norfolk Railway bridge, cast iron over Attercliffe Road and masonry arch viaduct across the river.

G3.6 & G3.7   Norfolk road bridge carrying Leveson Road across The River Don. is of sandstone masonry arches with cast iron parapets.

G3.8 & G3.9   Bernard Road Energy Recovery Facility next to the canal incinerates much of the city's municipal waste and extract useful materials and energy for heating in the process.

G3.10   Chippingham Street footbridge is a graceful steel arch over the canal cutting.

G3.11 Although looking to be contemporary buildings the office blocks and this workshop are refurbished workshops of the Darnall Steel works and some of the oldest surviving steel framed buildings in the city.

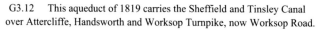

G3.12 This aqueduct of 1819 carries the Sheffield and Tinsley Canal over Attercliffe, Handsworth and Worksop Turnpike, now Worksop Road.

G3.13 & G3.14
The former Don Valley stadium used stretched fabric sheets between tubular steel trusses supported by external masts to give unobstructed views of the field of play.

(Reproduced courtesy of

G3.15   Olympic Legacy Park. 3G artificial pitch for Sheffield Eagles Rugby Club. Oasis Academy, beyond, UTC Sheffield right. The Advanced Well-being Research Centre is being built between these. A 3,000 seat indoor arena for Sheffield Sharks basketball is due to follow, off left. All sports facilities will also have community use.

G3.16 & G3.17   Sheffield Arena, built for the 1991 World Student Games has a skew chord roof truss where the upper steelwork is constructed diagonally to the lower steelwork. This allows a clear span of 120m by 90m. (Reproduced courtesy of SIV)

© SKM

G3.18   The English Institute for Sport is constructed in seven bays with pylons supporting the roof to give open spaces within. either side of the line of the masts.

© SIV

G3.19 EIS the barrel vaults span onto steel trusses supported by the external ties from the 50m tall masts. (Reproduced courtesy of SIV)

© Dave Pickergill

G3.20 & G3.21   IceSheffield is built into the ground
for economy and houses twin Olympic standard skating
rinks. (Reproduced courtesy of SIV)

© SIV

G3.22   Sheffield Forgemasters is one of the city's most successful companies providing bespoke precision large scale casting to a range of industries.

G3.23   A prototype casting for an offshore oil rig leg is now a sculpture in the centre of a nearby roundabout.

G3.24   The ramparts of over 2000 year old Wincobank iron age hillfort are discernible in the woods.

G3.25   The dry stone rampart of Carl Wark stands over 3m tall and 30m long.

G3.26 & G3.27
Meadowhall shopping centre opened in 1990 on the site of some of the city's former steelworks. The 42 ha site necessitated the country's largest roof at the time.

As one of six super regional destination shopping centres it is now proposing a further large expansion to provide more leisure facilities.

G3.28   The centre requires extensive infrastructure to accommodate the traffic it generates. This footbridge is 120m long. It links satellite car and coach parks to the centre.

G3.29   The railway bridge over Meadowhall Road was completely rebuilt with minimal interruption of traffic as part of the Meadowhall shopping centre development. This was done by constructing the new bridge adjacent to the line and sliding sideways into position.

G3.30 & G3.31   The barn in Concord Park is a rare survival of a mediaeval cruck framed construction.

G3.32   Tinsley Viaduct is an unusual twin deck box steel construction crossing the Don valley.

G3.33 & G3.34
        Opened in June 1968 it had major strengthening work in 2004 to accommodate the ever increasing amount of traffic and the increased weight of vehicles. (Reproduced courtesy of Highways England ©)

© Highways England

G3.35   Adjoining the WWTW and Tinsley Viaduct are the site of the "Tinsley Towers" cooling towers of the power station which originally dated from the 1920s and 30s. (Reproduced Courtesy of Highways England)

G3.36   The new Biomass power station burns wood waste instead of coal.

G3.37 & G3.38   Blackburn Meadows waste water treatment works processes almost all the city's sewage, discharging clean water to the river Don. It generates much of its own energy needs in the process. Even some waste from small outlying works is brought here to ensure high quality treatment and maximum environmental benefit.

G3.39   Redundant areas of the WWTW have now been transformed into a nature reserve.

G3.41   The former Templeborough steelworks became the Magna science discovery centre in 2001.

G3.42   Bridge chapel at Rotherham will have been similar to that previously at Lady's bridge.

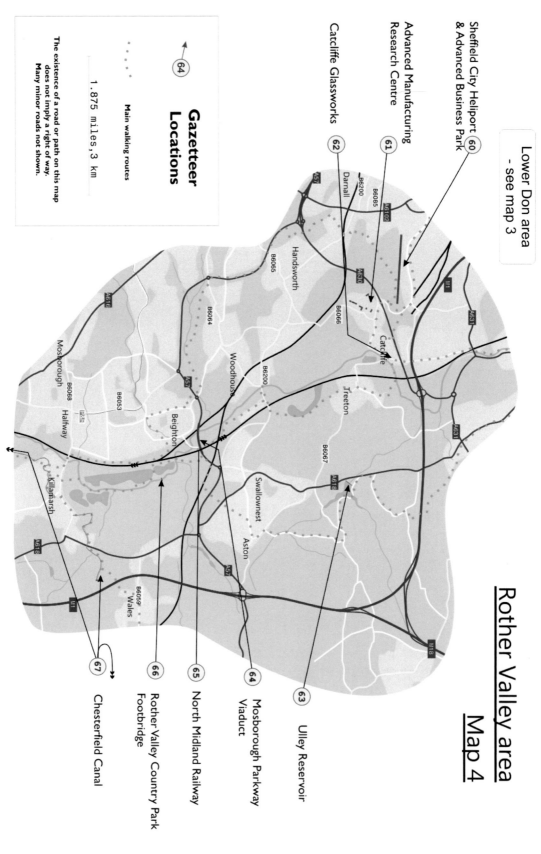

Lower Don area
- see map 3

Rother Valley area
Map 4

Sheffield City Heliport 60
& Advanced Business Park

Advanced Manufacturing
Research Centre 61

Catcliffe Glassworks 62

Gazetteer
Locations

64

1.875 miles,3 km

Main walking routes

The existence of a road or path on this map
does not imply a right of way.
Many minor roads not shown.

63 Ulley Reservoir

64 Mosborough Parkway
Viaduct

65 North Midland Railway

66 Rother Valley Country Park
Footbridge

67 Chesterfield Canal

Map 4 - East Sheffield

60. Sheffield City Heliport and Business Centre

The city Heliport was opened in 1997 as an airport. It was built on reclaimed land. The site of the former Tinsley Park steelworks had been completely cleared and the underlying coal extracted by open-cast mining. 1.5 M tonnes of coal was excavated from probably the Swinton Pottery, Clowne, Meltonfield, Two-foot and Abdy coal seams at a depth of up to around 50m. In the process, 50M m^3 of over burden was excavated and replaced. The 148 hectares of land which had been contaminated to varying degrees by the former use of the land as a steelworks was rendered safe for future use. The large earth moving operation and money recovered from the sale of the coal made it economical to safely treat the areas of contamination. The excavation was followed by careful re-instatement of the ground to make it safe for the airport and business park. The contractor was RJB Mining (later UKcoal).

As development was restricted to the area of the old steelworks the runway was limited to 1,211m long. This meant that the airport was a STOLport (Short Take Off and Landing) only capable of handling relatively small (maximum 107 seat) aircraft on relatively short flights. The noise limits further restricted the type of aircraft that could operate. In 2002, its last year of commercial operation it handled 1,000 aircraft movements. The Civil Aviation Authority licence was withdrawn in April 2008 as the operator chose not to renew it. A business park has now been built on part of this site and the former runway area is also being developed as a business park in collaboration with the Advanced Manufacturing Research Park.

The opening of the former RAF Finningley as Robin Hood, Doncaster Sheffield Airport saw the developer transfer business to the much larger facility capable of receiving all types and sizes of aircraft. It has the potential to be the region's premier airport and even serve trade from London, Doncaster being only 90 minutes or less by train to King's Cross Station.

Doncaster Sheffield Airport benefited from the opening of the first phase of the Great Yorkshire Way Link Road to the M18 motorway in February 2016. Phase two opened in June 2018 reducing congestion and shortening journey times. Plans are at an early stage to re-route part of the East Coast Main line to serve an airport station directly.

However, the Sheffield City airport remains a heliport. It was the centre of operations of both Yorkshire Air Ambulance (YAA) and the Police Helicopter surveillance unit. Today it serves a small number of private flights. The YAA moved to Nostell Priory Estate near Wakefield in 2014. The police also moved their operations there in 2016. Derbyshire, Leicestershire & Rutland Air Ambulance is based at East Midlands Airport, south of Derby while the Lincolnshire & Nottinghamshire Air Ambulance is based at RAF Waddington, south of Lincoln. All of the air ambulance services are run by independent charities. However, calls are operated through the emergency 999 service and whichever service that can best serve a case will be used. Sheffield Teaching Hospitals NHS Foundation Trust with support from their hospital charity had Henry Boot Construction build a new helipad at Northern General Hospital adjacent to the A&E department in 2016. This saved the time and complication of a land transfer across the hospital estate and allowed all weather and 24 operation. There are now plans to create a similar helipad at Sheffield Children's Hospital. YAA is one of a very few air ambulance services able to operate at night. Derbyshire and Nottinghamshire police forces operate a joint helicopter support unit from the Derbyshire force HQ at Ripley.

www.flydsa.co.uk

www.sheffieldbusinesspark.co.uk

OS ref: SK 408 888

61. Advanced Manufacturing Research Centre

The University of Sheffield with Boeing and Roll-Royce have created the Advanced Manufacturing Research Centre (AMRC) 'Factory of the Future' at the new Waverley area of Rotherham near Catcliffe. This continues Sheffield's tradition of high quality engineering. The AMRC is a collaboration between the local university and industry to further the city's long tradition of metalworking expertise and innovation. It identifies, researches and solves advanced manufacturing problems. Research can be specific to a member organisation's needs or generic to all members, as appropriate.

The site of the Advanced Manufacturing Park (AMP) and the entire Waverley site was reclaimed from its former industrial use, like Sheffield City Heliport by open-cast coaling.

The buildings are noted for their energy efficient design. The AMRC utilises natural light and heating where possible and is considered to be Carbon Neutral. The designer was Buro Happold with Bond Bryan Ltd as architects. The contractors were Bowmer and Kirkland group and Conder Structures Ltd. This is one of a cluster of buildings forming the Advanced Manufacturing Park established in 2006 by Yorkshire Forward to promote the best technology of the region. It includes the Nuclear AMRC and AMP technology centre which is aimed at the small and medium sized enterprises sector. The park is designed using the philosophy of sustainable drainage systems (SuDS). The drainage system is designed to store water during heavy rainfall and slow the flow of water off the site. The aim is to have a system so that the flow rate off the development is never any greater than it would have been if the land had not been developed.

The site includes two wind turbines, a 850 kW turbine services the AMRC building linked to a local district heating system whilst a 225 kW wind turbine linked to a 30 kWh hydrogen fuel cell system serves the AMP technology centre. The hydrogen fuel cell allows excess electricity to be stored as hydrogen through electrolysis and then at times of high demand the hydrogen is used to generate additional electricity. This reduces the amount of electricity taken from or sold to the national grid. Space heating costs are also minimised in the AMRC and AMP by not only the insulation and thermal mass of the building structure but also the use of geothermal energy from on site boreholes. This system can also store excess summer heat by reversing the heat pumps and using some of it in the winter.

F-BSCAA2009 C-IStructEA2009

Www.attheamp.com

Www.amrc.co.uk

OS ref: SK 418 881

62.   Catcliffe Glassworks.

This glass cone of c.1740 was built for William Fenney. The huge cone of brickwork is approximately 20 metres high pierced by openings. The cone is the oldest surviving structure of its type in Western Europe and one of only 4 to remain in the U. K. Previously, Fenney, had been the manager of the Bolsterstone glass works in Stocksbridge. On marrying the daughter of his then employer he left to set up on his own account and this was as close to Bolsterstone that he was permitted by his contract to work. Catcliffe was better located to export his wares than Bolsterstone, especially when the Don Navigation reached Tinsley, and his enterprise thrived as the former ceased trading a short time afterwards. There were originally two cones at this works. It operated under various ownerships until 1884, with a very brief revival in 1900-1. The cones produced bottle, flint and window glass. Flint glass is of higher optical quality, often previously using lead as an additive for high quality tablewares or chandeliers. Window glass would have been either crown glass where the glass is spun into a disk which is then cut into pieces or cylinder glass where a cylinder is blown, cut and opened out to form a sheet up to 1.7 m long. Both processes left irregularities in the glass. In the late 19th and 20th century mass production techniques of plate and then float glass, superseded the technologies of the glass cones.

Benjamin Huntsman "borrowed" the technology of these glassmakers' crucibles to create crucibles capable of withstanding the high temperatures needed for steel making, establishing a steelmaking works in 1762. His technique was subsequently "borrowed" by other steel makers in Sheffield creating a vital step in the formation of the local special steel industry.

OS ref: SK 426 885

63.   Ulley Reservoir

This 16m high 205m long earth embankment dam was built from 1872 to 74. It impounds 580M l of water from the Ulley Brook. This spring had been supplying water through filter beds to Rotherham since 1863. Even with this supply in the summer of 1874 a drought caused water rationing in the town, limiting supply to 3 hours per day. In 1894 a Typhoid outbreak in the town was thought to have been caused by pollution being washed into the reservoir. Subsequently by-wash channels were built along the sides to intercept surface water runoff and so prevent contamination of the water. After the introduction of the Reservoir safety Act 1930 a new spillway was built in 1943. The water level was originally controlled by manually operating the valve in a pipe through the dam which discharged water into the Brook downstream. A spillway provides an automatic system to discharge flood water safely. Some modifications were made in 1967 following mining subsidence.

The Yorkshire Water Authority (later Yorkshire Water plc) took over all municipal water supply and wastewater management responsibilities when it was set up in 1974. By the 1980s the reduction in industry reduced demand and the presence of the Yorkshire Grid meant that this reservoir was down graded to a standby facility and subsequently ceased use for water supply. In 1986 the council took back control from Yorkshire Water and turned the area into a country park.

The reservoir was in danger of collapse after the storms of June 2007 as flood water escaped a spillway and eroded the embankment. Emergency measures, involving teams from over the country were overseen by the recently designated panel engineer under emergency powers legislation. The panel engineer was so recently commissioned that he had not yet made the 10 yearly inspection.

It subsequently became apparent that an earlier removal of a control gate, not approved by the engineer, had prevented the spillways operating correctly. Modern developments downstream, in addition to the M1 motorway and Brinsworth electricity sub-station, had increased the potential consequences of the dam failing. In 2009, new spillway works were constructed and the embankment reinforced to ensure the safety of the structure and consequently of the people and infrastructure downstream. This work was designed by Arup, approved by the panel engineer and built by Ringway Group. The near failure of this dam has led to a review of the legislation governing reservoir safety.

HC-ICEY&HA 2011

Www.ulleyweb.co.uk

OS ref: SK 453 877

64.   **Mosborough Parkway, A57**

The Mosborough Parkway was constructed in phases from 1984 to 1994 to provide improved access to the residents and businesses of the area both to the city and M1 motorway. The final phase involved the construction of a 470m long 15m wide viaduct across the River Rother, its flood plain and nearby railway lines. The viaduct is supported off reinforced concrete piers founded on steel piles driven through the alluvial soils to the mudstone below. The viaduct is formed of plate steel girders up to 3.4m deep at the haunches of the longer 50 m spans. The shorter 34m spans are un-haunched. The reinforced concrete deck is connected to the tops of the beams so that the beam and deck act compositely, sharing the load. It is continuous along the length of the viaduct so that movement joints are only needed at the ends.

The road junction just west of the main railway line links into the old road network. This is built on an embankment of reinforced earth again founded on piles, this time of reinforced concrete. This prevents differential settlement between the different structures. In reinforced earth selected soil is carefully laid between layers of strong specially designed plastic grids and or fabrics. The sides of the embankment are retained by reinforced concrete panels tied back into the embankment with similar material so that the ground becomes self supporting. The design aimed for simple and easily maintained refinement. The designer was Sheffield City Council Design and Building Services and contractor Alfred McAlpine construction Ltd.

C-ICEYA 1995

OS ref: SK 442 844

65.   **North Midland Railway.**

This railway (HEW ref: 1583) ran from Derby (which already had connections to Rugby) via Chesterfield, Renishaw, Killamarsh, Treeton and Rotherham to Leeds. Its engineer was George Stephenson, who considered it to be the finest piece of railway engineering that he had executed.

The Sheffield and Rotherham Railway opened a 5-mile branch line in 1838 which later linked to the NMR. The NMR reached Rotherham from Chesterfield in 1840 having obtained its act in 1836.

Most of the features of particular note with regard to the listing on the Historical Engineering Works register are beyond Sheffield.

In 1865 the Midland Railway built an engine shed at Barrow Hill near Staveley. They took over the internal railway of the adjoining Staveley Iron Works the following year and amalgamated operations. Hence they enlarged the engine shed in 1869-70. The resulting round house is the last remaining operational round house engine shed in Great Britain. It is a unique, grade 2 listed, example of 19th century railway architecture. It has 24 roads and housed up to 90 locomotives at its peak in the 1920s. The numbers of engines served declining sharply in the 1960s until its eventual closure in 1991. The Barrow Hill Engine Shed Society had been formed to preserve it but it took until 1998 before it could re-open as a visitor attraction at weekends.

Www.barrowhill.org

OS ref: SK 33 to SE 3

SK 413 754

66.   Rother Valley Country Park footbridge, Rotherham.

The 300 ha Rother Valley Country Park was opened in 1983. The site had previously been open-cast mined and the landscaping for the park was a fundamental part of the restoration process of the mining operation. Nearly 1.75M tonnes of high quality coal had been removed from seams up to 50m below the surface. South Yorkshire and Derbyshire County Councils together with Sheffield, Rotherham and North-East Derbyshire Councils had already determined the need for a country park in the vicinity to provide green space and sports provision to the local population.

The River Rother was diverted into a new channel to the east of the workings during coaling. On restoration a public footpath had to be reinstated across the river. The bridge also had to accommodate horse and occasional vehicular traffic. As was common at the time, less so now, the backfill to the open-cast was loose tipped and so prone to settle over time. This complicated the bridge design as the west end of the bridge would be founded on 50m of unconsolidated fill. The eastern end however is on the natural undisturbed ground. Hence a cantilevered cabled stayed design of box tubular sections and a timber deck were chosen taking all its support from the east side of the river. The bridge does sit on a bearing at the west end as well in order to minimise deflections under imposed loads. As this west seating was expected to move, it was designed to allow the realign of the bearings with jacks from time to time.

Www.rothervalleycountrypark.co.uk

OS Ref: SK 453 834

67.   Chesterfield Canal, NE Derbyshire, Rotherham & Bassetlaw.

The canal is designated HEW ref: 1831 and includes numerous grade 2 listed structures along its length. Together with the Trent and Mersey Canal the Chesterfield Canal is the oldest canal in the East Midlands. It runs for 46 miles from Chesterfield passing through Killamarsh, Worksop and Retford to join with the River Trent at West Stockwith. However, the section through Killamarsh is now lost. The first engineer was the great pioneer of canal engineering James Brindley. After his death in 1772 he was succeeded by his brother-in-law, Hugh Henshall. John Varley assisted throughout. The route between Chesterfield and Shireoaks is largely determined by the engineering constraints. The route from Shireoaks to the River Trent was decided by the political need to include Worksop and Retford in the system. The simplest proposal would have simply followed the Rother Valley to join the Don Navigation near Rotherham. However, the backers were financial rivals to the shareholders of the Don Navigation and did not want to be reliant upon the rival company for onward navigation. Thus the limestone ridge east of Killamarsh had to be crossed to gain access to a route to the Trent.

Construction started in 1771 and the canal was opened in parts; being completed in 1777. The canal was designed to take barges 22.6m long by 2.1m wide with a draft of 0.76m and capable of carrying 20 tons of cargo. Locks were just 0.23m longer and 0.15m wider than the barge and the channel often less than 0.6m deeper than the boat draft. Even while the canal was being built there was a debate about the gauge of the canal, with some people lobbying for a wider canal as permitted in the enabling legislation. This would have allowed the Yorkshire Keel boats used on the main river to continue up the canal and prevented the need to trans-ship goods at West Stockwith. However, the works would have been considerably more expensive, especially the tunnel and locks.

The canal had 65 locks and one major tunnel. Norwood Tunnel, between Killamarsh and Worksop, is 2.6km long and it was the longest in the country when it was completed in May 1775. There is a small tunnel at Drakehouses near Retford. The River Rother at Chesterfield, together with a series of reservoirs near Harthill, for the summit pound, and several small rivers and streams along the course form the water sources for the canal.

From the mid 19th century the canal, including the Norwood Tunnel, was increasingly affected by mining subsidence between Chesterfield and Kiveton. Through traffic ceased in 1908 when a section of this tunnel collapsed and was not repaired due to the expense.

All commercial traffic on the canal ceased in the 1950s. Only the section below Worksop was retained for leisure use. However, a canal society was formed in the 1970s and pleasure craft can now navigate from Kiveton down to the Trent with the reopening in 2003 of the upper length. This involved restoring 13 listed locks including an early example of staircase lock, a listed bridge and several kilometres of towpath and canal cut. The restoration works included extensive archaeological investigations.

Several miles are also open from Tapton Lock in Chesterfield towards Staveley. There are plans to extend this navigation length and restore a link to the Worksop section. A new basin has been constructed in Chesterfield and funding achieved to link this to the canal at Tapton forming a new "Waterside" district which it is hoped will aid the regeneration of the town. The scheme to fully re-open the navigation has been identified by the British Waterways board as both achievable and of national importance. The collapsed tunnel is to be bypassed with new locks and using an existing farm accommodation tunnel to pass under the motorway. The canal will be re-routed through Killamarsh as the original line has since been developed and a basin developed at the southern end of the Rother Valley Country Park. The route from Staveley to Killamarsh is partly a simple refurbishment of the original. However, a new cut to replace subsided sections and to pass modern obstructions including the early 20th century railway line to Clowne is also required. A new basin at Staveley was completed in early 2012 forming a temporary terminus for the canal from Chesterfield.

The revised route of HS2 has removed most of the conflicts that the original proposals had created with the canal. The current route will block the approach to the new Norwood Tunnel. However, there are relatively simple ways of accommodating the canal works here and near Staveley. HS2 has committed to working with the canal trust to find solutions to allow the canal restoration to continue.

It is also proposed to make the River Rother navigable from the canal at Rother Valley Country Park down to the confluence with the River Don. The £15 M scheme is based upon European evidence that rivers can be made navigable while enhancing flood resilience and wildlife habitats. There is need to enhance both the latter and it is possible this could be a funding mechanism to achieve those aims. Economic studies suggest that by making the local canal and river network into a navigable loop pleasure traffic is greatly increased to become self financing and boosting the wider local economy by £100 Ms.

HC-ICEYH2003 (Rotherham area restoration)

Www.chesterfield-canal-trust.org.uk

www.chesterield-canal-partnership.co.uk

OS ref: SK 387 717 to SK 786 946

G4.1 & G4.2   Sheffield City Heliport and Business Park started life as the now closed Sheffield City Airport catering for short haul flights and quiet aircraft.

The runway has now been removed and the area used for advanced manufacturing business units.

G4.3 & G4.4   The Advanced Manufacturing Park is home to some of the worlds most important manufacturing companies. Like the Airport it is the site of a former open-cast coal mine.

G4.5 Catcliffe Glass cone is the last visible evidence of the once thriving local glass industry and was the inspiration for key developments in Sheffield special steel industry.

G4.6 & G4.7 Ulley reservoir is now just used as a country park and sports venue. It originally supplied much of Rotherham's drinking water. Following the storm of 2007, in which it came close to failure, new weirs were built.

G4.8 & G4.9 The A57 Mosborough Parkway link road to the motorway was upgraded in 1994 with a new viaduct above the Rother flood plain.

Reinforced earth behind the interlocking precast concrete panels makes the abutment partly self supporting.

G4.10   The North Midland Railway from Derby to Leeds, via Rotherham was the first long distance railway in the area. It is crossed here by the Manchester Sheffield and Lincolnshire Railway and also numerous high voltage electricity cables linking to Brinsworth's major substation.

G4.11   Barrow Hill, near Staveley, is home to the country's last operational engine round house. (Reproduced courtesy of Barrow Hill Roundhouse.)

G4.12 Rother Valley Country Park footbridge shortly after the creation of the park.

There are plans to make the River Rother navigable downstream from the park while maintaining and improving flood resilience and wildlife value. (Reproduced courtesy of Rotherham MBC)

G4.13   The original Norwood Tunnel has been blocked for around a century, but a new route is planned at a higher level using an existing passage under the motorway in the area.

G4.14   Chesterfield Canal Trust is working to reopen the section of canal between Chesterfield and Kiveton Park and has created a new basin at Staveley and are heading towards the Renishaw section, but have some complex obstacles to navigate around including new road and rail lines.

G4.15   Sections of the canal such as at Renishaw have been restored by volunteer labour.

© Paul Brunt Chesterfield Canal Trust

G4.16   The Chesterfield Canal now provides tranquil navigation from Kiveton Park to the River Trent at Stockwith.

© Paul Brunt Chesterfield Canal Trust

Sheaf Valley

Sheaf Valley Area
map 5

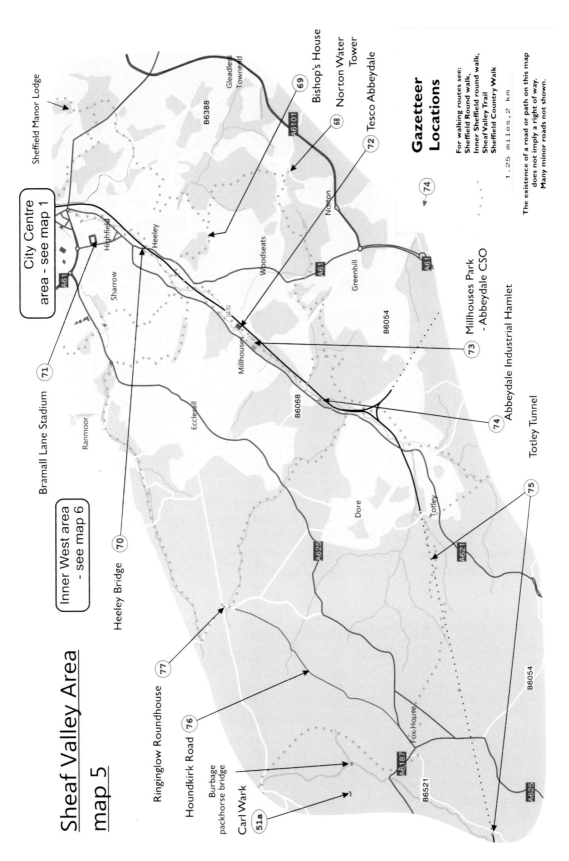

City Centre area - see map 1

Inner West area - see map 6

Sheffield Manor Lodge

Bramall Lane Stadium ⑦1

Heeley Bridge ⑦0

Ringinglow Roundhouse ⑦7

Houndkirk Road ⑦6

Burbage packhorse bridge

Carl Wark 51a

Bishop's House

Norton Water Tower

Tesco Abbeydale

69
68
72

Gleadless Townend

B6388

A6101

Heeley

Highfield

Sharrow

Ranmoor

Ecclesall

Woodseats

Norton

A61

Greenhill

Millhouses

B6054

B6068

Dore

Totley

A625

A621

Fox House

A6187

B6521

B6054

A625

Gazetteer Locations

For walking routes see:
Sheffield Round walk,
Inner Sheffield round walk,
Sheaf Valley Trail
Sheffield Country Walk

74

1.25 miles, 2 km

The existence of a road or path on this map does not imply a right of way. Many minor roads not shown.

Millhouses Park - Abbeydale CSO 73

Abbeydale Industrial Hamlet 74

Totley Tunnel 75

261

Map 5 - Sheaf Valley area

68. Norton Water Tower

This reinforced concrete tower was built in 1960-1 to provide a constant feed of treated water to the south of the city. Previously the area had been supplied purely from the service reservoir at Ringinglow by gravity. However, the expanding population of the south of the city and increase in water use meant that at peak times flow was inadequate. The Norton tower was therefore fed by a pumped supply directly from Redmires / Rivelin Water Treatment Works. It was operated so that normally the Ringinglow supply was used until pressure dropped to a critical point whereupon supply would be drawn, under gravity from the tower. When the tank in the tower was nearly empty water was pumped up to it at night using cheap rate electricity ready for future use.

The 66m³ water tank is 5.5m deep and 18.3m in diameter. It is raised on 26 columns to create a structure 33.2m high and 19.5m in diameter. This prominent landmark also housed the water company short wave radio transmitter. This allowed the company to keep in touch with its workforce across a 50 mile radius area before the advent of mobile phones. The structure was also designed with a viewing platform on the roof, accessible by lift and was periodically opened for public viewing days.

OS ref: SK 367 824

69. Bishops' House

An interesting example of traditional timber framed construction is the Bishops' House in Meersbrook Park, now a museum run by volunteers through a charitable trust and so open to the public at weekends. This is thought to date from around 1500 with various later alterations and additions and is probably not the first building to have been on the site. An exact date by dendrochronology has been obtained for samples of the surviving timbers of the cross wing and main hall ranges. The timber for these was felled in 1537 and 1579 respectively.

A cruck framed barn similar to that in Concord Park was recorded adjoining Bishops' House until the late 19th century.

Www.bishopshouse.org.uk

OS ref: SK 354 840

70. Bramall Lane Football ground

Sheffield United Football Club's Bramall Lane Ground is arguably the oldest major football ground in the world. Little is known of the earliest construction.

Bramall Lane sports connections begin in 1855 when a group of local cricket teams acting together as the Sheffield United Cricket Club leased the site for a cricket ground. The ground was the first home of the Yorkshire County Cricket Club (YCCC) when it was formed, in the city, in 1863. The year before the ground hosted its first football club match. The ground was the city's principal sports stadium and hosted numerous major football competitions through the 1870s & 80s with attendances in excess of 20,000 people.

The world's first floodlit football match took place here on 14 October 1878. As an electricity grid was not yet established, this used mobile generators to power arc lights. A steam engine was set up behind each goal linked to two Siemens dynamos to supply the arc lights on 30 foot high arc lights at each corner of the pitch. The attendance on this occasion, to see two teams from the Sheffield Football Association play, is thought to be 30,000 people. John Tasker who went on to set up the city's first electricity company was responsible for this feat. These generators continued in use at various locations ending up in Malta, where they are still to be seen in one of the museums.

In 1893, YCCC moved their headquarters to Leeds, but the ground continued to be used for county matches, hosting a 1902 Test. The last county match played here was in August 1973, whereupon Sheffield's Cricket moved to Abbeydale Park. The removal of the cricket square to the south of the football pitch allowed the construction of the South Stand and so a fully enclosed pitch. It was not until 1889 that a Sheffield United Football Club was formed as a home team.

New stands were built on Shoreham Street and John Street in 1896 and 1897. The latter was designed by Archibald Leitch, and built by the Clyde Structural Iron Company, and was one of their first commissions. The Bramall Lane Stand was remodelled in 1911 and the Kop in 1936. This was paid for by Richard Lawrence- a Director who also built the lido pool at Hathersage. Permanent floodlighting was installed in 1953. Running and cycle tracks have been features at times and the Cricket Pavilion was rebuilt in 1900 and finally demolished in 1982. However, the earliest surviving stand is of 1966. A few of the turnstiles and base of the boundary wall on Bramall Lane may date back to the 19th century developments and the original foundations and parts of retaining walls of the Kop remain below the current stand.

The current Bramall Lane Stand was built in 1966 to designs by Husband & Co. (now Mott McDonald). The stand has upper and lower tiers and a total capacity of 5,680. It also houses the Scoreboard. The roof was replaced with a cantilever construction to improve sight lines in 2006. The designer for this was Mott McDonald and contractor Mowlem. Linked to the upper tier, at the South end is a new corner in-fill housing 2,000 seats. This was also completed in 2006. The installation of the new cantilever roof entailed the closure of Bramall Lane to all traffic for a period to allow two large cranes to lift the girder truss into place. This girder spans the full length of the stand, a distance of over 100m.

The South Stand, also by Husband & Co., is the closest to the pitch and, like the Bramall Lane Stand, was refurbished in 2005-6 giving a capacity of 7,500 in a single tier. The box office, media facilities and corporate function rooms are also housed here. In 2018, there are plans to increase the capacity of the south stand by adding a second tier with 5,400 seats bringing the total stand capacity to 13,995. There will be new executive accommodation, press facilities and improved disabled access. The height of the stadium will rise by 20m to 45m, 15m above the adjoining Copthorne Hotel. The new stand will also include 10,000 m² of event space. The location of original cricket crease is below this stand and the pavilion was located in what is now the car park. The bowling green was to the east of the pavilion up to the corner of Shoreham Street.

The Shoreham Street Stand also known as the Kop is built into the natural slope of the ground at the eastern end of the Ground. It was re-roofed in 1982 with a simple goal post construction - with a series of four slender columns supporting the front edge of the roof. The 10,221 seats were installed in 1991. The design engineer was Eastwood & Partners. There are plans to extend and re-roof this stand when funds permit adding an extra 3,215 seats. The 1975 stand was one of the first in the country to be completed following the Safety of Sports Grounds Act 1975 requiring for the first time strict regulation of larger sports stadia. This Act was the result of the Wheatley Report into the 1971 Ibrox disaster in Glasgow.

The John Street Stand was completed in 1996 to designs by Eastwood & Partners. The capacity is approximately 7,000 and includes executive suites and boxes. Linked to this stand is the Kop Corner completed in 2001 with an additional 900 seats. This replaced the original stand which was designed by Archibald Leitch and constructed by the Clydeside Structural Iron Company. This was one of his first projects having established himself as a consultant in 1896 with the design of Ibrox stadium.

The total capacity is currently 32,609. The largest attendance was over 68,000 and happened in 1936.

The pitch is laid with special turf comprising specially selected grasses combined with polymer fibres laid on a sandy bed. Daylight spectrum lights are shone onto the turf when it is in shadow to ensure even growth of the grass which is mown up to three times a day. With underground heating to protect it from frost, the pitch can be used several times a week throughout the year. (The Mansfield Sand used has also been widely used as foundry moulding sand. It is now exported worldwide, including to Arabia, for use in sports venues.)

There is also a 158 bedroom hotel in the South west corner of the ground and the Blades Enterprise Centre, providing facilities for local small business attached to the John Street Stand. The proposed new development will also provide a new club store and 97 "studio" houses at the corners of John Street and Cherry Street. Whtittam Cox Architects with Glid Livignum structural engineers are the designers of the new scheme.

Www.sufc.co.uk

OS ref: SK 353 861

71.   Heeley Bridge

The bridge was strengthened to be able to carry the heavier lorries now on the roads. The cast iron bridge of c. 1869 is historically important and spans the River Sheaf. This was built by the Midland Railway company when they constructed the adjoining railway line. It presumably replaced a stone arch bridge from the turnpike. The ancient Sheffield to Chesterfield road had been turnpiked in 1756. There was likely to have been a crossing here or hereabouts long before that date. The bridge was relieved of the load of the traffic by the construction of a temporary girder bridge a few centimetres above it while the strengthening works were designed and financed. The A61 highway is extremely busy both with traffic and local pedestrians and had to remain open through the strengthening works, apart from a few short night time closures, as there were no suitable diversions. This required careful phasing of the works. The work was done by SOL Construction Ltd to designs by Sheffield City Council Design and Property Services Engineers.

C-ICEY&HA2002

OS ref: SK 351 852

Also of potential interest is Stumperlowe Crescent Road bridge over Storth Lane. This is a wrought iron plate girder bridge with cast iron parapets built in approximately 1892 to carry the crescent over the old lane for the new housing development taking place in the area. This has been sensitively restored as part of the Sheffield Streets Ahead project by Amey and Sheffield City Council winning a certificate of excellence in the 2015 ICE Yorkshire and Humber Awards.

OS ref: SK 314 860

72.   Tesco Abbeydale

The store has an elegant wave form curved roof sitting on "tree form" columns. A standing seam roof membrane system is supported off Universal beams cold rolled to the sinuous profile via cold formed purlins. These beams are supported off sets of four tubular struts fixed to the top of the main hollow columns which cantilever vertically from their bases. The overall effect produced an efficient roof system and an open and flexible floor area. The structure and services are deliberately visible, with the full height glazed front elevation creating a light and airy space.

The design engineer was Robinson Consulting Engineers with architect Michael Aukett Architects Ltd and contractors Kier North East & Tubemasters Ltd.

C-BCSAA1998

The British Constructional Steelwork Association (BCSA) awards are judged on a range of criteria including: Economy of material and fabrication requirements; Skill and workmanship in fabrication; Durability and adaptability; Energy conservation; Integration of structure with architectural and service needs; Innovation in design and techniques.

Www.tesco.com

www.bcsa.org.uk

OS ref: SK 338 836

73.   Millhouses Park - Abbeydale Road CSO

As part of a wider programme of works to prevent flooding of the city's combined sewer outfalls (CSOs) into the local rivers, a very large storage tank has been built in the park between the children's play area and the cricket pitch. Historically, both foul and storm water flowed through the same pipes. The pipes were sized to accommodate a storm surge and so overflowed rarely. Since they were built many more houses have been built and so more foul waste water flows through them. This reduces the spare capacity for storm water and results in more frequent overflows into the city's rivers. We are, rightly more alert to the harm of discharging untreated sewage into the rivers and so wish to prevent such overflows as much as possible.

There is a series of storage tanks at strategic points across the city, including Endcliffe Park and Hillsborough Park - where a shaft 21m diameter and 20m deep was built. These range in size from a few metres long to the size of a football pitch. (see page xx for more information on the waste water network)

The location of the emergency outfall from the CSO is just upstream of the Archer Road bridge over the River Sheaf in the easternmost corner of the park. In the very worst storms even these large storage tanks would become full. This should happen only a few times a century. However, in these circumstances it is necessary to allow some dilute screened effluent to discharge into the river which will then be flowing rapidly.

These works are preventing flooding from the sewer network within the streets of the city but do not protect against flooding of the river from the natural water flow with a rainstorm. The inner city rivers are to have their banks raised in places to prevent localised flooding. However, such measures are expensive, disruptive, visually intrusive and tend to simply move the area at risk of flooding else where. Therefore an integrated approach is being developed to control the river flows. This starts with improved management of the land at the heads of the catchment to slow the flow of water into the rivers. Secondly, at suitable points in the river new temporary flood storage is to be provided where land can hold water safely for a few hours or days from time to time to reduce the maximum flood flows in the rivers. At the time of writing quite where these will be is still being determined. However, Millhouses Park is a prime candidate for this. It is likely that open areas such as the Cricket Pitch will be carefully sculpted bowl to create areas holding up to 20,000m^3 in an entirely controlled and safe way. This will also enable the park drainage to be improved and spectator areas enhanced.

The CSO outfall point was also the location of the exit from the tail goyt from the Ecclesall Corn mill. The weir to which can be seen near the children's play area approximately 500 m upstream. Recently a fish pass was constructed as a bypass channel for use at those times of year when fish are migrating. The corn mill building still remain near Abbeydale Road adjacent to the cricket pitch. These are the only corn mill buildings surviving in the city. A corn mill was on this site from the 13th century. The existing buildings probably largely date from the 1679 rebuild, albeit altered in a major programme of works to the mill in 1825 and also subsequently. The 1825 works introduced a 12 hp steam engine which probably worked alongside the water wheel system for around 30 years after which the water wheel went out of use. Corn continued to be ground here until 1942. The buildings are now used as a park store but plans are in place to convert them to diverse community uses with solar power, geothermal and/or bio-mass energy sources. The goyt and dam were long since filled in and the route is now obstructed by the CSO works preventing a return to hydro-power use.

HC-ICEY&HA2006

Www.friendsofmillhousespark.org

OS ref: SK 336 832

74.   <u>Abbeydale Industrial Hamlet.</u>

A group of Grade 1 and 2* listed building. (HEW ref: 0951 and Heritage Hallmark award since 1988.) It is an excellent museum displaying the complete manufacture of scythes from the crucible steel onwards. It has working water wheels and tilt hammer, grinding hulls and the only surviving complete crucible steel furnace shop.

Of the 35 known water power sites on the River Sheaf and its tributaries there were 12 corn mills, 11 forges, 25 grinding shops, 4 rolling mills, 1 slitting mill, 1 wire mill, 1 saw mill, 8 lead smelters, 1 lead mill, 1 slag mill and 2 paper mills at various times. The earliest dates to the 1200s the last was built in 1782.

The earliest known date associated with this site is 1676 as a cutler's grinding wheel. However, there is speculation that it may be of much earlier origin associated with the nearby Beauchief Abbey, founded in 1175. The dam was enlarged and wheel renewed in 1777 and rebuilt in 1817. The tilt forge is dated 1785, making it the oldest surviving in its original location. Within 10 years three houses had been built on the site, with further warehousing and workshops in 1811. The manager's house is of 1830. The steel furnaces are thought to date from c. 1829. Again this would make them the oldest surviving in place. The site suffered severe damage in a "rattening" incident in 1843. (Rattening was action taken by workers to force employers and fellow workers to accept union membership. It ranged from annoying pranks to the explosive demolition of buildings.) In 1855 steam power was introduced to supplement the water wheels.

The tilt hammers are driven by an 5.64m diameter 1.68m wide oak water wheel developing 22.5kW. A similar size wheel drives the grinding shop while there are two smaller wheels to power the boring shop and blower for the forges.

The site was bought as a museum in 1935 when production ended. However, production resumed for a short while in 1941 for steel melting following damage to a steel works in the blitz.

The museum recently won Heritage Lottery funding to allow much improved presentation of the exhibits and site history as a whole.

See also Doncaster Street Cementation Furnace, Shepherd Wheel, Wortley Top Forge, Darnall Steelworks and Kelham Island Industrial Museum.

Www.simt.co.uk

OS ref: SK 325 820

75.   **Totley Tunnel.**

Totley Tunnel (HEW ref: 0671), which at 5.70km long is the longest railway tunnel not under sea or estuary (excluding the London Underground) in Great Britain. It was constructed from 1888 to 1893 on the Midland Railway's Dore and Chinley line, having been given its act in 1884. This was the last trans-Pennine line to be constructed and provides a more direct route to Manchester avoiding the steep climb to Woodhead or the long diversion to Ambergate.

The portals have an imposing horse-shoe shaped masonry arch carrying the inscription '1893 Totley Tunnel' and the M. R. monogram. However, only the western portal at Grindleford is readily accessible, that at Totley being in a steep cutting. The line opened to goods traffic on 6 November 1893 and passenger traffic on 16 May 1894. The railway company was very satisfied with the work and awarded the contractor a substantial unsolicited bonus of £14,500.

The Tunnel was driven from the two ends a series of four shafts within 1200 yards of the Totley Portal. The main bores met in October 1892 with a deviation of under 12cm. The fifth and deepest shaft of 152m depth, was only sunk from Totley Moss after completion of the tunnel and it became clear that the extra ventilation was necessary. Provision for this had been made in the original act but to assuage the landowner of the moor it had not been built initially.

The tunnels are 8.2m wide with a clear height from the rails of 6.86m. The tunnel is extensively lined with brickwork. Over 30 million bricks being used.

The works were troubled with vast quantities of water up to 10,200m^3 per day from the Totley heading and 34,000m^3 from the Padley heading. Extensive use of compressed air pumps and machine drill were made.

Generally, the villagers and navvies got along although there was some friction especially when the navvies were drunk! Many of the workforce resided in a camp near shaft 3, above Totley Bents which had been built by the contractor for them. However, some lodged with villagers and houses on Bricky Row (now Baslow Road shops at the rise) and Lemont Road were constructed for the workers. In some cases the houses were badly over crowded and so when smallpox reached the area in the winter of 1892 many were affected. Over 60 cases were recorded and the convalescent hospital in Totley re-opened. Sanitary conditions in the camp were poor with pit latrines being used. A typhoid outbreak occurred in the summer of 1893. Of the deaths that occurred during the construction almost all were attributable to the disease epidemics which also affected the families and locals. One notable casualty of the typhoid was Percy Rickard the resident engineers supervising the works. Rickard was born in Derby in 1859 to the town's Silk Manufacturer and in due course was apprenticed to the locomotive workshops of the Midland Railway in the town. His early duties included surveying and preparing contract drawing for various railway projects. He was proposed for Associate membership of the Institution of Civil Engineers in 1884 and went on to be elected a member in 1891. His paper on the construction of the Tunnel was presented to a meeting of the institution in 1894.

The engineer for the work was the firm of Parry & Storey of Nottingham and Derby. Edward Parry had been elected to membership of the ICE in 1879. He went on to work on many railway schemes including the London extension of the Manchester Sheffield and Lincolnshire Railway - the line from Sheffield to Marylebone in London. The contractor was Thomas Oliver and sons of Horsham. Thomas Oliver was born in Newton le Willows the son of a railway contractor from NE England. However, he grew up in Hasland near Chesterfield where the family had then settled. Oliver undertook his training with Charles Bartholomew of Doncaster and later J. T. Leather of Sheffield working on a variety of mainly railway and drainage projects. By 1870, when he was elected an associate member of ICE, he was able to establish his own contracting business. He was able to use the experience gained on the Totley Tunnel in subsequent work when he built part of the Great Central Railway line up to 1897. He died aged 86 in 1920.

OS ref: SK 251 788 to SK 306 802

76.   Houndkirk Road turnpike

Houndkirk Road is a rare survival of an unimproved turnpike road. This was the route of the Sheffield to Buxton turnpike from 1758 to 1812. After which time the Ecclesall and Dore Moor road opened. Most turnpikes still lie beneath the modern highway surface, such as Ecclesall Road.

Although badly damaged signs of the road construction and drainage can be seen.

OS ref: SK 283 825

77.   Ringinglow Road Round House Toll Booth

The round house at the corner of Ringinglow Road and Houndkirk Road was built by the Sheffield and Sparrow Pit Turnpike Trust at the junction of the Sheffield to Buxton turnpike (Houndkirk Road). The design of the house allowed the toll keeper to see along the approach in all three directions.

OS ref: SK 291 837

G5.1 Norton Water tower

G5.2 Bishops' House was built for a wealthy 16th century family and is the best preserved example in the area.

© Ken Dash Friends of Bishops' House

G5.3 & G5.4   Bramall Lane stadium south stand, above, and John Street Stand, below.
(Reproduced courtesy of Sheffield United Football Club.)

© Sheffield City Council

G5.5 & G5.6 Heeley Bridge carries the A61 Chesterfield Road over the River Sheaf. As a principal HGV route into the city it was a priority for strengthening.

G5.7 Storth Lane bridge carrying a suburban road has also been strengthened recently.

Both these bridges are built of cast iron.

G5.8 & G5.9   Tesco Abbeydale superstore's graceful steel roof. (Reproduced courtesy of Tesco.)

G5.10 & G5.11   Millhouses Park Abbeydale Combined Sewer Outfall storage tank lies below the car park and adjoining area. The pumping station and emergency outfall are in the bottom corner of the park..

G5.12 & G5.13   Abbeydale Industrial Hamlet museum. (Reproduced courtesy of SIMT)

G5.14   A 30 hp water wheel powers the tilt hammers.

G5.15   Contemporary sketch of the working at Totley Bents for the Totley Tunnel.

G5.16   Vent shafts and wooded spoil heaps at Totley Bents. The previous sketch is the same area viewed from the opposite direction.

 The black drum shaped object in the foreground is No. 3 Shaft. Number 2 shaft is beyond the green barn and the tree covered hillock beyond is a large spoil heap by number 1 shaft and Penny Lane.

G5.17   Totley Tunnel - Grindleford portal.

G5.18   The original cobble paving can still be seen on Houndkirk Road Turnpike.

G5.19   Ringinglow "Round house" an octagonal toll gate keeper's lodge.

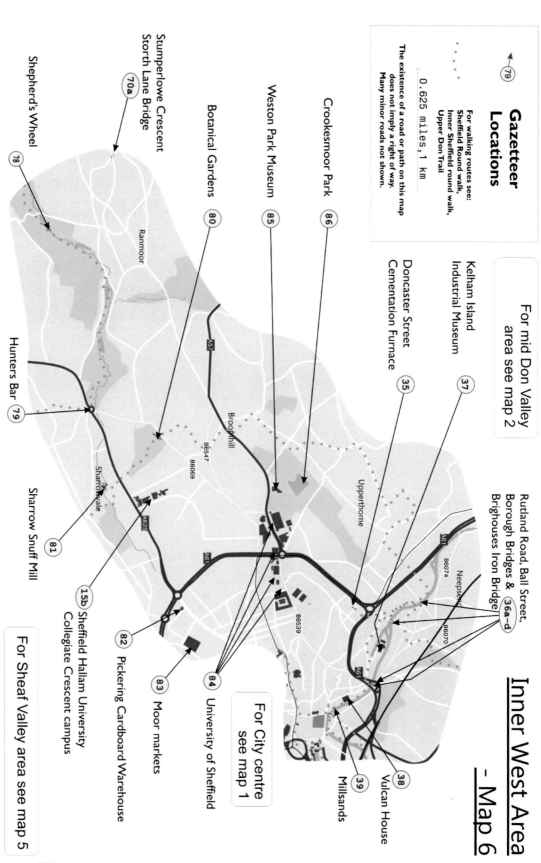

Inner West Area
- Map 6

Gazetteer Locations

For walking routes see:
Sheffield Round walk,
Inner Sheffield round walk,
Upper Don Trail

0.625 miles, 1 km

The existence of a road or path on this map
does not imply a right of way.
Many minor roads not shown.

For mid Don Valley
area see map 2

Rutland Road, Ball Street,
Borough Bridges &
Brighouses Iron Bridge ⑯36a–d

Kelham Island
Industrial Museum ㊲

Doncaster Street
Cementation Furnace ㉟

Weston Park Museum ㊷

Crookesmoor Park ㊸

Botanical Gardens ㊿

Shepherd's Wheel ㉘

Storth Lane Bridge
Stumperlowe Crescent ㉙70a

Hunters Bar ㊴79

Sharrow Snuff Mill ㉛81

Sheffield Hallam University
Collegiate Crescent campus ㉕15b

Pickering Cardboard Warehouse ㉒82

Moor markets ㉓83

University of Sheffield ㉔84

Millsands ㊴39

Vulcan House ㊳38

For City centre
see map 1

For Sheaf Valley area see map 5

278

Map 6 - Inner West area

78. Shepherd Wheel

This water powered grinding wheel, parts of which date back to 1584, has been restored. It is now owned by Sheffield City Council and managed by Sheffield Industrial Museums Trust and supported by the Friends of the Porter Valley. It ceased working in 1930. The grinding shop is typical of the many wheels once found along the Sheffield rivers.

The Porter Brook had 20 water power sites, the earliest known date is 1531 and the last built in 1779. These provided 4 corn mills, 1 forge, 16 grinding shops, 1 wire mill, 1 saw mill, and 1 snuff mill at various times.

www.sheffieldportervalley.org.uk

www.simt.co.uk

OS ref: SK 317 854

79.   Hunter's Bar

In the centre of the roundabout are the re-sited original turnpike gate posts and a replica of the toll bar. The original bar was destroyed by the crowd when the turnpike ceased in 1884. It was the last toll to be removed in Sheffield. By that time it was causing considerable annoyance as the city had grown beyond the toll point and so many more people were subject to the tolls.

OS ref: SK 332 858

80.   Sheffield Botanical Gardens

The Botanical gardens were opened in 1836 and laid out by Robert Marnock, who was also responsible for Weston Park, after a design competition. The buildings however, were designed by the runner up, Benjamin Broomhead Taylor. The domes are redolent of Paxton's Chatsworth conservatory (now demolished) and occasionally mis-attributed to him. The main lengths of glass house between the domes have a ridge and furrow profile. This was a system devised by Paxton to maximise the light entering the glasshouse. The glasshouse range faces south and so the sun in the morning and evening shines at a low angle along the length of the glasshouse. By using inclined glazing in that direction, more light is transmitted through the glass rather than reflected off the surface. It also was an effective use of the size of glass panes then available with minimal framing material which, being opaque, necessarily reduces light transmission.

The grade 2* listed pavilions of c. 1834 had fallen into disrepair by the middle of the 20th century and were unsafe. As part of a Lottery funded project to restore the gardens they were to be brought back into a viable use with full public access. The basic conservation philosophy of limited replacement was applied with the need to have a modern functioning environment. Where possible, existing structures were carefully repaired and new hand blown glass installed in the domes. However, the interlinking glasshouses have new roofs in modern materials to re-create the form of the original ridge and furrow form. Originally of timber and with manually operated vents they are now of stainless steel and have automatic ventilation control systems.

C-ICEY&H2005

Www.sbg.org.uk

OS ref: SK 335 863

81.   Sharrow Snuff Mill

This was originally a cutler's wheel and may date back to 1588 but was enlarged in the mid 18th century. The unusual feature of the tail goyt being culverted under the river before joining further down stream is first recorded in 1757. This allows a greater operating head of water and so power output within the land available. Six years later the Snuff mill was built and shortly afterwards steel grinding ceased. This is still a working snuff mill, in the hands of the Wilson family since 1774, capable of using water power, although electric power is now generally used.

Frog Walk is a good place to view the Mill buildings, pond and goyt.

Www.sharrowmills.com

OS ref: SK 338 858

82. Pickering cardboard warehouse

The Pickering cardboard warehouse at the junction of Moore Street and Young Street near the city centre was a notable example of early steel framed building dating from 1908. The steel frame allowed a flexible work space and grand frontage with large windows. When this site was redeveloped in the late 1990s only the independent elaborate terracotta frontage was retained and the entire building behind replaced.

OS Ref: SK 348 886

83.   Moor Markets

The new market building was a finalist in the Wood Awards 2014. (The Wood Awards were not active at the time of the Winter Garden construction.) Glulam timber has been used to roof a space with an open market feel with all stalls on one level below a 10m high roof. The main entrance to the building is formed in the shape of a geodesic arch as a landmark while the main market area used tree columns to achieve 10m spans for the roof beams while minimising interference in the floor space. Integrated with the market hall are several two and three storey retail units.

Www.sheffieldmarkets.com

OS ref: SK 351 866

84.   The University of Sheffield

The University of Sheffield traces its origins back to the Sheffield School of Medicine founded in 1828. In 1879 the local steel magnate and philanthropist Mark Firth set up Firth college as part of the Cambridge education extension movement to bring higher education to the new industrial cities. The Sheffield Technical School was set up in 1884 to help further the education of the managers of industry. Two years later this moved into new premises at St George's Square. These three institutions merged in 1887 to form a university college that gained its own charter in 1905 as the University of Sheffield. The university has expanded from around 2,000 students 50 years ago to 28,000 today with 6,000 staff. The university is ranked in the UK top ten percent and world top 100. The University is also ranked at number 25 in the Sunday Times 100 Best Not-For-Profit Organisations to Work For 2017. The university has been awarded the Queens Anniversary Prize four times including in 2001 for environmental work relating to waste incineration and most recently in 2007. The department of Civil and Structural engineering was formed in 1917 under Joseph Husband as head of Department. Mr Husband had been the first lecturer in the subject at the technical school from 1892. The department today has approximately 500 undergraduate students, 170 Postgraduates and 70 researchers. Of the research, 85% is classed as internationally excellent or world leading giving the department a 4th place in national rankings. 100% of graduates achieve graduate level employment or higher education studies.

St George's Church was built in 1825 for the sum of £15,181 by Benjamin and James Newell of Dewsbury, part of a family of Stonemasons and contractors throughout the 18th and 19th centuries. They went on to be successful railway contractors. This was part of a scheme by the Church Burgesses. They developed a large tract of land to the west of the town between the Porter Brook and The River Don extending from the old town head area outwards to roughly the present ring road. This formed the new parishes of St Philip's, St George's and St Mary's. These are sometimes called "Million Pound Churches" as they were built from the national fund for new churches of that amount operated by the Church Commission under the 1818 Church Building Act. St George's Church became redundant and was converted to a lecture theatre, meeting rooms and student accommodation by the University in 1994.

The Sir Frederick Mappin Building was built in three phases from 1902 to 13 to house the new Department of Applied Science. Behind lies the 1885 Technical School, the oldest purpose built building in use by the University. Further buildings were added to the faculty creating a central courtyard from the earlier streets. The space between the Mappin Street building and Technical School is now being enclosed to form a four storey glass roofed atrium, new laboratories, offices and social space and the complete refurbishment of both buildings. This is with the object of promoting communication and collaboration to create a dynamic social and research collaboration environment.

Opposite the present engineering department beyond the church is the new post-graduate engineering building, *The Diamond Building*, on the site of the former Jessop Hospital annexe. This contemporary piece of architecture has caused much angst in the heritage sector as it entailed the demolition of a listed building and the design to some people does not enhance the setting of the neighbouring listed buildings. However, it does provide world class facilities for the researchers and most critics have been won over by the design. It houses lecture theatres, formal and informal learning areas totalling 5,000 study spaces. There are also specialist laboratories, a pilot chemical plant, an aerospace simulator and an operational jet engine. The building incorporates post-tensioned concrete floors and load transfer beams. This is a form of construction long used in bridges but not widely used in buildings in the UK. High strength steel cables pass through the reinforced concrete sections. The carefully induced stress in the cables applies a compressive stress to the concrete which counteracts tensile stresses that develop from the loads applied. This allows thinner sections to be used while actively stiffening the structure to control possible movements. This had the effect of increasing space available for services. Delivering the architects complex design earned this building a high commendation in the 2016 ICE Yorkshire and Humber Awards and a short-listing for the 2016 BCI awards (building costing more than £50 M category). It was also a finalist in the 2016 Carbuncle of the year award! It also won the IstructE Yorkshire Large Structure Award in 2017. The judges said: "This building showcases innovative engineering at its best through its quality of design and sustainable practice – it is a beacon of striking contemporary architecture and engineering."

The university is also building a new energy centre to provide uninterrupted power supply to research experiments and will have the capacity to supply power and heat to a number of key university buildings. It will also save 15 tonnes of carbon per year and lower the cost of heat and electricity for the University. Some university buildings are able to be heated from the Sheffield District Heating scheme. This will supplement this while proving the necessary electrical power generation.

The university Information Commons building is a new facility that provides students and staff with state of the art library and digital information services and study environments. This is part of an extensive programme to improve the facilities across the university.

W-SCT2008

Www.sheffield.ac.uk   OS ref: SK 345 873

85.   Weston Park Museum

The museum is located in Weston Park which was the first municipal park in Sheffield being opened in 1875. The park had been the grounds of Weston House which had been built by Thomas Harrison (1758-1818) a successful saw manufacturer. The town council had bought the property for a sum of £15,750 from the Harrison Trust under the powers of the Public Health Act 1848. This may have been to accommodate a fever isolation hospital which was subsequently built on adjoining land.

Eliza Harrison, one of Thomas's daughters, set up the forerunner of the Sheffield Royal Society for the Blind in 1860 in remembrance of her late sister's interest in the welfare of the blind.

Weston House was converted into the town museum to house the collection of the Sheffield Literary and Philosophical Society and applied arts collections. The Mappin Art Gallery was built next to the house in 1887. In 1934 the house was demolished and a purpose built museum opening in 1937, including an extension to the art gallery.

The original gallery layout was innovative with effective natural display lighting and an overhead travelling gantry to help move exhibits. The gallery core was destroyed in the blitz but the main facade escaped without serious damage. After the war, in 1965, the gallery was rebuilt. It is grade 2 listed.

By 2005 it lacked modern facilities. The basement has been enlarged within the building and new large opening created in sensitive load bearing walls. The floors were removed or replaced with stronger ones and the facades tied and stabilised. A new roof was also created to one of the galleries. Almost all of this difficult work is now hidden. The work was carried out by Mowlem (now Carrillion) and Turner and Townsend to designs by Arup with Purcell Miller Tritton architects.

Since re-opening in 2006, Weston Park museum has surpassed all visitor targets and now welcomes almost 300,000 visitors each year. As well as the permanent galleries which tell the story of Sheffield from pre-history to the present day, a temporary exhibition space welcomes shows from partners such as the British Museum and the V&A Museum of Childhood.

HC-ICEY&H2008

Www.museums-sheffield.org.uk   OS ref: SK 339 863

86.   Crookesmoor Park

Below Weston Park at Crookesmoor are the remains of the 18th century water supply reservoirs built by the Sheffield Reservoirs Company. Only one, the Great Dam, originally called Ashlar Dam, now holds water. Previously there were five reservoirs above it. New Dam which was enlarged in 1809, Butcher's Dam and Misfortune Dam. Godfrey Dam was enlarged in 1853 and lay above New Dam, and Ralph's Dam above Misfortune Dam. Both these were west of Northumberland Road. I don't know the reason for the name Misfortune, but it may be that it proved difficult to construct - it was not in use long. The nearby Hadfield Reservoir encountered difficulties when old coal workings were found in the excavation, significantly increasing the cost. In addition, there were smaller reservoirs in the valley below the Great Dam; Low Dam, Works Dam, Wall Dam, Tom Dam and Clough Dam. These were filled-in in 1839.

These are shown on John Leather's Map of Sheffield of 1832 together with the new cistern at Portobello which replaced the Barker's Pool and the small reservoirs at the Whitehouse near Primrose Hill, Upperthorpe. The highest of the White house reservoirs which were all very small, fed a culvert passing below the Great Dam to the Portobello cistern. The upper Crookesmoor reservoirs also fed into this culvert. All the lower reservoirs must have supplied the lower parts of the town. The Portobello cistern was approximate 66m by 44m in area and located under what is now Upper Hanover Street in front of the University Information Commons building. This cistern was replaced by Hadfield reservoir in a later scheme.

The Hadfield or Pisgah dam created a supply reservoir and was built nearby at Reservoir Road by J. T Leather in 1853-4. This stored water from the Redmires reservoirs for use in the town. This is shown on the first edition Ordnance Survey map. In 1953 this was replaced by a reinforced concrete covered service reservoir occupying approximately a half of the area of the earlier reservoir.

OS ref: SK 339 863

G6.1 & G6.2   Shepherd Wheel was one of many small water-powered grinding workshops along Sheffield's rivers. It is the earliest complete example of this key industry to the area, with evidence dating it back to the 1500. It is now a museum.

(Reproduced courtesy of SIMT)

G6.3   Hunter's Bar. Standing within the landscaping of the roundabout are the stone gateposts and a replica toll gate. They mark the spot where the last toll bar stood in Sheffield in the 19th century.

G6.4   Sharrow Snuff mill is perhaps the last traditional wheel site still capable of operating commercially by water power.

G6.5, G6.6 & G6.7
  Botanical gardens pavilions. The domed lights were restored using traditional techniques. The ridge and furrow glazing uses modern materials and technology to recreate to original form in a manner that allows effective use of the glasshouses.

G6.8   Weston Park museum.

G6.9   Crookesmoor Park Great lake is the oldest surviving water supply reservoir for the town, but is now an ornamental feature of the park.

G6.10 The frontage of Pickering cardboard warehouse was retained when the site was redeveloped in the 1990 but the original 1908 steel frame was removed to make way for the new office block construction.

G6.11   Sheffield Markets moved from the heart of the old township to Moorfoot in 2014.

G6.12   The new market area is light and spacious under the timber roof structure.

G6.13 The University of Sheffield was founded in 1905.

G6.14 It has buildings of many ages including the redundant St George's Church of 1818, that is now a lecture theatre and accommodation.

G6.15 The Engineering Department on Mappin Street, one of the oldest purpose built buildings in use on the campus, is undergoing a major refurbishment now that the Diamond Building provides extra space. It will continue to serve its role in the research and education of engineers.

In recent years the university has built many new buildings to cater for the expanding student numbers. Much of this is of a notably contemporary design such as the Information Commons (G6.16), above, and Diamond building (G6.17), below.

Many former factories near the city centre are being converted to uses related to the universities. The former Henderson's Relish factory on Leavygreave Road is now own by the university and is to be a café/bar (G6.18), left.

The former Eye-Witness (previously Saynor) Cutlery Works on Milton Street are to be converted to student accommodation (G6.19), right.

In both cases the businesses thrive and have moved to new premises.

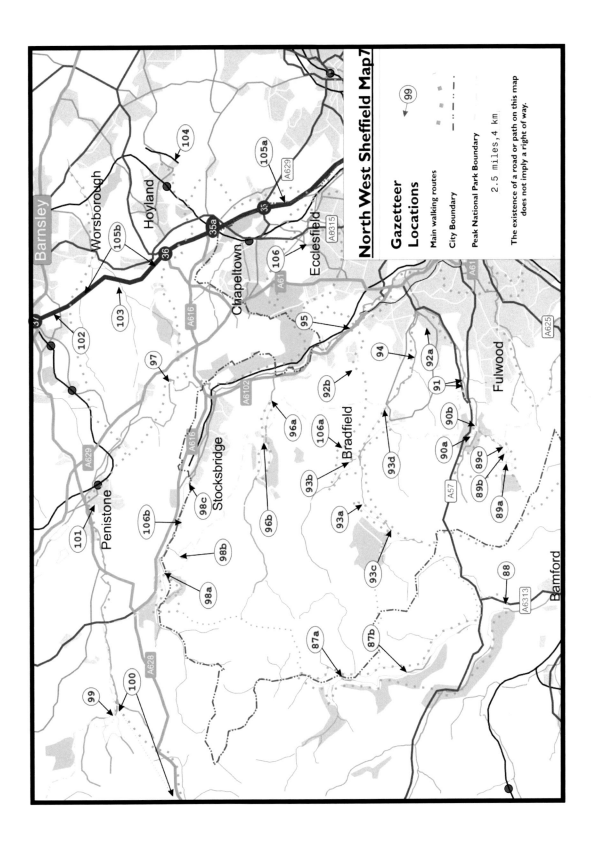

Map 7 - North west area

87. Derwent Valley Reservoirs.

In 1909 Sheffield joined Derby, Nottingham and Leicester corporations in the Derwent Valley Water Board and takes 25% of the water delivered by the scheme. The DVWB was responsible for the construction of the Howden, Derwent and Ladybower reservoirs on the head waters of the Derbyshire Derwent, below the high moorland of Hope Forest.

The first two were made under the Derwent Valley Water Act of 1899.

Derwent & Howden Reservoirs

87a. **Howden Dam**, (grade 2 listed structure & HEW ref: 0185) the most northerly of the group was constructed from 1901 to 1912. It is a masonry dam of stone set in concrete with a gritstone facing. The stone was quarried at Bole Hill near Grindleford and brought to site on a purpose built railway system. An aerial rope-way system was employed at the dam sites. Cables were stretched across the valley above the line of the dam. From these hoists carried the materials to the place required avoiding a lot of manual labour. Howden dam has a length of 329.1m, a height of 35.7m above the valley floor and maximum thicknesses of 53.4m reducing to 3.0m at the crest. Had it been built of rock fill construction, as most of the local dams, the base width would have been approximately 183 m.

Its overflow level is 265.2m AOD. The dam has a castellated tower at each end of the spillway. The 2.1km long reservoir has a capacity of 9.0M m^3 covering an area of approximately 29 ha.

OS ref: SK 170 924

87b. The **Derwent Dam** (grade 2 listed structure & HEW ref: 0539) is of similar design, dimensions and construction to the Howden dam. It was constructed from 1902 to 1916. It has a length of 338m, height of 34.7m. The thicknesses are 52.1m reducing to 3.0m and overflow level 236.5m AOD.

The reservoir has a capacity of 9.6M m^3 and stretches 2.5km to the foot of the Howden Dam, covering an area of approximately 72 ha. The Derwent Dam was used by the RAF in preparation for the famous Dambuster raid of 1943 due to the similarity with the targets.

OS ref: SK 173 898

The engineer for both these reservoirs was Edward Sandeman, who was Engineer to the Board. Sandeman was the first president of the Institution of Water Engineers and influential in the 1918-21 board of Trade enquiry into reservoir safety leading to the Reservoirs (Safety Provisions) Act 1930. The construction was carried out by direct labour. A settlement was constructed to house the workforce and cater for their needs. At Birchinlee, a model village was built it gained the nick name "Tin Town". It provided extensive infrastructure for the workforce and their families. The population reaching a maximum of 900 people. Village accommodation consisted of workmen's huts, foremen's huts and married workmen's huts. However, a canteen, post office, recreation hall, public bath house, school, hospital and police station were also built together with several shops. The shops were independently run and not tied company shops. All that remains are foundations which can still be seen in the woodland. Some of the hut were reused in local farms and villages, at least one still survives in Hope.

A 7.2km long 2.0m diameter tunnel was built in 1909 under Bamford and Hallam Moors to take Sheffield's water from the Derwent aqueduct at Priddock Wood to the water treatment works at Rivelin. The remaining flows are taken by gravity aqueduct from the Derwent reservoir to a treatment plant at Bamford and thence piped to a storage reservoir at Ambergate to serve Nottingham Derby and Leicester.

Between 1921-1930 weirs were built in the Ashop Valley, so that water from the river could be diverted to the reservoir. A 914m long tunnel was made under the ridge between the Derwent Reservoir and the Ashop Valley to the West to take the water.

The Board obtained another Act of Parliament in 1920 giving them the powers to make the Ladybower Reservoir. It is sited 4.8km down the valley from the Derwent Dam.

The Peak District National Park have a visitor centre at Fairholme next to the Derwent Dam offering information on the many walking and other activities available in the vicinity. The 55 mile long Derwent Valley Heritage Way follows the river valley from here down to the confluence with the River Trent and explores the World Heritage Site.

88.   Ladybower Reservoir, Derbyshire

The Ladybower Dam (HEW ref: 0540) is an earth embankment with a clay core and faced on the upstream face with gritstone to protect it from the erosion of lapping water. Construction of this dam started in 1935 and was completed in 1943, after two years filling it was operational in 1945. The cut-off trench, below, was excavated to an average depth of 54.9m with a maximum of 77.7m and filled with concrete. This extends 500 ft each side of the dam into the valley sides to block any water seepage. The embankment when built was 381m long, its maximum height 41.1m, and its greatest thickness 202.6m, reducing to 5.2m at the crest. The overflow level is 203.6m AOD. The embankment crest was raised slightly in the late 1990s and the embankment strengthened to comply with the current safety standards. This work was to ensure that there was enough spare capacity above the weir level to accommodate the extra water coming into the reservoir in very rare storm events. Our understanding of rainfall patterns across the UK had grown considerably over the intervening decades.

An unusual feature of the reservoir is the stepped bell-mouth spillways, colloquially known as the "plug-holes". These take the overflow water into two separate pipes passing below the dam to the river down stream. Bellmouth spillways remained innovative at the time of construction. The proposed design was subject to rigorous model testing at Manchester University to prove it had the desired flow capacity – and some to spare. The first bell-mouth spillway was designed by J.

Mansergh for the 1898 Blackton Reservoir in the upper Tees Valley. However, very few others were built until the early 1930s. Generally, such spillways have a smooth profile reflecting the natural flow pattern of water. Here a stepped profile was adopted to make construction easier. The spillways were designed to accommodate 360 m^3/s between them, but should be able to pass nearly twice that safely – more than satisfying safety requirements.

The capacity of the reservoir is 28.6M m^3. One arm of the reservoir stretches 3.2 km up the Ashop Valley while the other reaches nearly to the Derwent Dam, 4.6 km upstream of the dam. The reservoir covers an area of approximately 2 km^2.

Construction of this dam started in 1935 and was completed in 1943, after two years filling it was operational in 1945. G. H. Hill & Sons were the engineers and the contractor was Richard Baillie of Haddington, East Lothian.

Two villages (Ashopton and Derwent) were submerged, and reinforced concrete viaducts were constructed to carry the A57 and A6013 roads across arms of the reservoir.

OS ref: SK 199 854

The catchment area of all three reservoirs was increased by 29.5km² to a total of 156km² when the waters of the River Noe in Edale were diverted through another tunnel into the Ladybower reservoir in 1951. The Ladybower reservoir acts as a regulating reservoir to ensure adequate flows in the river below the scheme.

www.severntrentwater.co.uk

89.   **Redmires Reservoirs**

Perched high above the valley floor are the Redmires reservoirs on the edge of Hallam Moor.

89a.   The **middle** reservoir was completed in 1836 and at 14m high by 689m long was the first dams built by the Sheffield Waterworks Company. The reservoir covers an area of approximately 19 ha with a top water level of 336.8m AOD.

89b.   The **lower** reservoir was completed in 1849 and has a 14m high and 579m long embankment, creating a lake of approximately 12 ha area. The top water level is 325.5m AOD.

89c.   The **upper** reservoir is formed by an embankment 15m high and 686m long. This creates a reservoir of roughly 24 ha area. The upper dam was completed in 1854. The top water level is 350.5m AOD. You will notice that the dam wall curves as it follows the high water line of the Middle reservoir. The three reservoirs cover a very compact site and operate together. An aqueduct skirts Brown edge to the north to tap a tributary of the Rivelin Brook and augment the supply catchment of the reservoirs feeding into the upper reservoir. In about 1960 a bell-mouth spillway was built into the aqueduct close to the outfall to the reservoir to act as a supplementary overflow for the reservoir. Collectively the reservoirs drain an area of 1,041 ha producing a supply of water of 2.77M m^3.

All can be regulated by adjusting the drainage valves if necessary. A common practice at the time. Accommodation was built nearby to ensure staff were available at all times. Recent works have altered the spillways to improve the safety of the reservoirs. All these are earth embankment dams and were designed by John Towlerton Leather.

Water was fed by conduit from here to the Hadfield Supply Reservoir at Upperthorne where it was stored before being piped to the town. A small water treatment plant with filter beds was built before 1923 in Redmires Plantation. In 1987/8 the Australian SIROFLOC process was pioneered in the UK to remove discolouration from the water prior to purification treatment. The process uses recyclable magnetic powders (magnetite) to remove colour and turbidity from surface and groundwaters. Clarification involves the magnetisation of the particulate matter, which aggregates and settles rapidly, so the clarifier is much smaller than in the conventional plant. There is no filter and the clarifying agent can be re-used. The Redmires plant was mothballed when the Rivelin plant was subsequently enlarged. It proved cheaper to operate a single larger plant and pump the treated water back up to Redmires than operate two small works. Raw, untreated water from the Redmires reservoirs flows freely down Wyming Brook to Rivelin reservoirs.

The open water conduit to the Hadfield supply reservoir was subsequently covered over to prevent contamination and later replaced with a pipeline in 1909. The covered treated water storage tank is still operational and feeds water to the upper parts of the city.

Yorkshire Water have created two walking routes from the car parks at these reservoirs allowing visitors to explore the area, in addition to the general walking opportunities the location provides.

Www.yorkshirewater.co.uk

OS ref: SK 260 854
OS ref: SK 264 854
OS ref: SK 267 855

90. Rivelin Valley Reservoirs

The two (Upper and Lower) Rivelin reservoirs are towards the head of the valley. They were built in 1848 to the designs of J T Leather and are 12 and 15m high and 220 and 305m long with reservoir areas of approximately 5 and 12 ha respectively. There is also a small (4.5m deep 1.6 ha) reservoir immediately downstream of the WTW which is operated by Yorkshire Water. This was built in 1869 and operates as a de-silting pond and river gauging point to measure and record the flow of water in the river accurately.

The weir and spillway to the lower reservoir were altered in around 1960 to improve their capacity. The spillway was lined with reinforced concrete and the stilling basin amended at the bottom of the slope. Instead of the water flowing over rough stone cobbles down the slope it runs freely down the smooth concrete with only a small step part way down to dissipate the kinetic energy before the base. The water flow forms a waterfall at the foot of the spillway plunging onto carefully placed large boulders to prevent erosion of the river banks and bed.

The Rivelin Water Treatment works, originally opened in 1914, has a capacity of 75 Ml/day and treats water piped here from several reservoirs including the Derbyshire Derwent Valley scheme to customers in the west of Sheffield. A tunnel was built under Hallam Moor to carry the water by gravity to the works from the Derwent Valley. The waters from the Agden, Dale Dyke and Strines reservoirs also flow by aqueduct through the hills to this water treatment plant.

Yorkshire Water have recently carried out works to improve the finished water quality due to increased raw water colouration. This involved the design construction and commissioning of six manganese contactors together with associated pipe work, control equipment and a 600m³ holding tank. The integrated project team used Building Information Modelling (BIM) - an electronic means of describing all elements of a project in space, time and also items attributes. This allowed them to thread a new 1 m diameter pipe through the existing structure and reuse much of the existing system. Pre-fabrication was used where possible to simplify on site works and ensure minimal disruption on site. A change to the originally determined pump specification allowed the system to operate within the existing electricity supply capacity thus obviating the need for an expensive new HV connection.

W- ICEY&H 2013.

OS ref: SK 271 869
OS ref: SK 276 868

91.   Rivelin Valley Trail

Down stream of the reservoirs the Rivelin Valley Nature Trail explores many of the sites of the 21 former water wheels on this river. The earliest was in existence by 1581 and the last dam built in 1853. Several sites had a series or multiple uses. In all, there are known to have been 2 corn mills, 2 forges, 18 grinding wheels, 1 rolling mill, 3 wire mills, 1 saw mill, 1 smelter, 2 paper mills and 1 rope mill. There is a car park near Rails Road.

Also of note is a **Packhorse bridge** on the route from Dore to Bradfield approximately 70m downstream of Rails Road. This is an 18th century bridge which would have replaced an earlier timber or stone clapper bridge. When Rails Road was built from the old trail route, a new bridge was built the short distance upstream, hence preserving the old bridge. Similar bridges are still to be found at Wharncliffe Side (re-sited from the Ewden valley when flooded for the reservoirs), upstream of Howden Reservoir (again re-sited), on Burbage Brook, below Carl Wark, over the Loxley near Rowell Lane, Bradfield and over the Don at Oxsprings.

OS ref: SK 292 873

One of the better preserved wheels is the **Wolf Wheel**, about 1km downstream of this bridge. This was built around 1722 and the dam still holds water creating a wildlife haven. The site went through a succession of owners and developments. By 1830 there was a wheel 4.57m diameter and 1.93m wide powering 19 troughs, probably making this the largest grinding shop in the valley. The wheel came into the ownership of the Sheffield Waterworks Company and continued in use until 1930. Signs of the building can just be made out. The water control devices have been replaced.

There is a car park off Rivelin Valley Road near Wolf Wheel this is approximately ¾ mile down the trail from Rails Road.

OS ref: SK 302 875

92. Forge Valley Community School & Bradfield School

92a. The **Forge Valley** school was developed for Sheffield City Council under the Building Schools for the Future programme by Vinci Construction with Mott MacDonald Ltd + BDP Architects as designers. The main buildings include significant open plan areas and a 3 storey atrium allowing natural lighting and ventilation. The two storey sports block is built into the landscape to reduce visual impact. There is a separate on site energy centre to house energy generating plant and other mechanical and electrical equipment. Throughout the design and execution there was considerable attention to detail lifting the project above the ordinary.

The Building Schools for the Future programme is a central government funded initiative to improve the quality of the environment in which pupils learn. They are designed to be able to readily incorporate the latest teaching technologies.

HC-ICE(Y&H)A2011 W-IStuctE(Y)A 2012

OS ref: SK 320 891

92b. The **Bradfield School** was developed for Sheffield City Council under the Building Schools for the Future programme by the same team of designers. There are four teaching blocks and a community sports hall fitted on to a steeply sloping site. There is also a separate on site energy centre to house the bio-mass powered energy generating plant and other mechanical and electrical equipment. Much attention was given to providing a building that has a low impact on the environment, with green roofs and on site storm water storage. Throughout the design and execution there was considerable attention to detail again lifting the project above the ordinary.

HC-ICE(Y&H)A2014.

OS ref: SK 303 921

There is some evidence that the new schools have been associated with improved educational outcomes. However, It is not clear if this is a direct cause and effect.

93. Loxley Valley Reservoirs

The upper Loxley Valley is home to four reservoirs built by the Sheffield Waterworks Company in the late 1860s, 70s and 90s.

93a. The first to be built was **Dale Dyke** and is on Strines Dike above Bradfield. It was completed in 1864 by Craven, Cockayne and Fountain to designs by John Towlerton Leather. Under the supervision of John Gunson. The embankment was 29m high and 382m long with a puddle clay core taken down to bed rock. The top water level was to be 212.1m AOD and it had a 19.5m wide weir. It was designed to provide river flows of $0.28m^3/s$ 24 hours a day six days a week all year round and a water supply for 12 hours per day during summer.

It collapsed in a great storm on the night of 11th/12th March 1864 causing catastrophic flooding. The incident has since been known as the Great Sheffield Flood. The reservoir was just complete and being filled for the first time. Up to 0.2m of rain fell over the two days leading up to the disaster causing the water level to rise very quickly by 15.2m. This put considerable strain on the dam. The number of people who died is not known precisely, 241 names are known and shown on the flood memorial near Vulcan House. However, scores more may have died in the following months as an indirect result. However, due to the action of the engineer, public health officer and the head of the local dispensary there were no outbreaks of disease amongst the population with the streets quickly disinfected and cleaned and people given assistance to cleanse their own properties. The Water company paid out £373,000 in compensation to individuals and businesses.

This was the worst engineering disaster in Britain and eventually, led to better oversight of all large dams in the country - see Ulley Reservoir. The puddle clay core had had to be considerably deepened to reach an impermeable stratum during construction. Initially intended to be 10 feet deep it was extended to 60 ft over sections. However, the step in the trench as it became shallower towards the side of the valley was too great. Differential settlement at this point created a crack. The fill material either side of the relatively narrow puddle clay was not as well selected or placed to provide adequate support to the core. When the storm arrived, the reservoir filled for the first time and the water level rose rapidly. This was too quickly to safely monitor the effect upon the dam. When the water reached a sufficiently high level it seeped through the crack and disturbed some of the fill near to it de-stabilising the central section of the dam wall. This collapsed allowing the water to rush out and erode a complete breach. As was common at the time only a small spillway was provided with the intention that the water level could be controlled by manual operation of the drain valves. However, these could not drain the reservoir quickly enough when required.

The current reservoir was built between 1867 and 1875 under the design and supervision of Thomas Hawksley the new engineer to the water company. The design was substantially the same at 25 m high by 380 m long embankment with a similar composition. However, the location was moved a short distance upstream of the original. This meant that the trench for the core did not need to be as deep as had proved previously. Also an improved spillway was constructed. The 3km long reservoir covers an area of 25 ha and impounds 2.2M m³ of water. The storage capacity was somewhat reduced at about 2/3 of the capacity of the original.

Yorkshire Water have created walking routes. There is limited road side parking at SK2456 9204 and SK2270 9088 from where footpaths circles the reservoir. Please note the roads are narrow in the area so do take care if visiting.

OS ref: SK 244 917

93b. **Agden** is on Hobden Moss Dike, again above Bradfield, where the two dikes form the River Loxley. It is 29m high and 458m long and was completed in 1869 to the designs of Leather and hardly modified by Hawksley. This dam impounds 2.9M m³ of water under a lake of 31 ha and 3km long. Yorkshire Water have recently undertaken safety improvements - modifications to the wave wall and spillways.

Over time engineers understanding of rainfall intensity and frequency has improved considerably as much more data is now available. Major research projects took place in the 1960s and 70s using the availability of computers to process large quantities of data and derive empirical rule with complex sets of parameters. These have subsequently been refined and modified. This means that engineers are better able to better predict the probability of varying severity of floods than Leather and Hawksley possibly could. The modifications ensure that the dam will remain safe in the maximum probable flood event. The understanding of climatic factors continues to grow with continuing research. The complexities of global, and local climate change adds extra uncertainty into the science of predicting future rainfall patterns that engineers have to take into account when assessing the safety of reservoirs and flooding in general.

Yorkshire Water have created walk routes here. Car parking (SK2622 9200) is at Low Bradfield which can also be reached by public transport.

C-ICEY&H2010

OS ref: SK 260 922

93c. Strines is above the Dale Dyke Reservoir and was completed in 1871 to Hawksley's design with a 382m long, 35 m high embankment impounding 2.3M m³ of water in a lake 2.8km long covering 21 ha. Again Hawksley's design was substantially the same at that previously proposed by Leather, but with larger spillways. It also recently received safety improvement works.

C-ICEY&H2009.

OS ref: SK 284 906

93d. Damflask was completed in 1893 to the designs of Leather as modified by Hawksley. Damflask dam is 26m high 351m long and impounds 5.3M m³ of water. The reservoir is over 2km long with an area of approximately 49 ha.

When built there was a small leak of water through the south bank of the reservoir. This was not sufficient to prevent the reservoir to come into use but did require action to ensure the long term stability of the reservoir. An additional cut off trench was dug to seal the flow. This was 670m long up to 2.7m wide and 30m deep and filled with concrete and puddle clay.

Damflask does not directly contribute water to the city's drinking water supply. Its purpose is to store water to ensure there remains an adequate flow in the river at all times allowing more water to be held in the supply reservoirs upstream. This maintains river levels in times of drought to protect the river ecology and provide water for any hydro-power schemes (formerly this was paramount when there was so many active water wheels powering the city's industry in the 19th century) or down stream water extraction for drinking water supply or industrial purposes. The length allows Damflask to be used by several rowing and sailing clubs.

A short distance downstream of Damflask is the Loxley Water treatment work. This treats the water from the upper reservoirs before it is pumped to service reservoirs to then feed the city supply under gravity.

OS ref: SK 232 905

The land around these reservoirs is available to the public for walking Yorkshire Water have created an easy going accessible trail around the reservoir. There is no official car park but on street parking is possible at some points and it is also accessible by public transport.

Www.yorkshirewater.co.uk

94.   Loxley Valley water wheels

The Loxley Valley was home to 27 water wheels. The remains of some of these can still be seen from the river side walk. The oldest mill site in the valley is at Low Bradfield at the confluence of the Agden and Dale Dyke streams. A corn mill was in existence here in 1219 and continued until destroyed in WW2 having been completely rebuilt after the Great Sheffield Flood of 1864 like many others in the valley. The 27 sites provided, over time, 6 corn mills, 11 forges, 22 grinding wheels, 5 rolling mills, 5 wire mills, 1 smelter, 1 glass mill, 4 paper mills and 3 snuff mills. The most recent addition to the list of sites was 1777, with many being built that century.

Low Matlock Rolling mill is an excellent example. This steel rolling mill building is dated 1882 having been rebuilt on existing foundations after the flood of 1864. The earliest known date for a wheel at this site is 1732, with both forging and grinding being carried out here at times before the rolling mill took the entire site. The large rectangular gritstone and brick building until very recently housed an operational rolling mill for specialist production. The late 19th century rolling mill became powered by electricity through 19th century gearing and the massive flywheel.

There is a large, 5.64m diameter by 3.56m wide, overshot water wheel, now immobile, with 8 cast-iron spokes to each side and 42 buckets, last used circa 1956. Above it is a sectional cast-iron pentrough supported by a cast-iron stanchion. In the adjacent wall is a blocked shouldered-lintel opening that formerly allowed access to the wheel from inside the works. Both the dam and tailrace survive. A second shallow weir in the river just upstream of the tail race outfall allowed the river bed to be lowered thus maximising the water level difference available at the wheel and so its operating power. The wheel is the largest example of its type to survive in Sheffield.

OS ref: SK 310 894

95.   A6102 Road at Middlewood

The repairs to the A6102 that collapsed in the storms of June 2007 required innovative solutions. Heavy rains had caused the River Don to Flood undermining the support for the A6102 perched on a narrow ledge on the valley side. Not only is this a major highway link in the city it also carried major water and gas mains. These all had to be temporarily diverted and secured before any repairs could begin. The damaged slope continued to deteriorate until the final repair was completed increasing the potential hazards to the construction team. The need to keep some through public access and not obstruct the river and reinstate the road as soon as possible ensured an integration of the design of the final works with the methods of construction. This allowed the work to be completed by 12 December 2008, ahead of programme. A contiguous bored pile wall anchors the base of the slope and prevents further undermining from the river. A reinforced earth slope up to 10m high was then constructed, with a shallower slope above. Care was taken to allow the finished face to re-vegetate with native grasses. Outline design was by Sheffield City Council Design and Property Services, Contractor Carrillion, detailed design WYG. The project team worked closely with the Environment Agency and the affected Utilities to ease progress throughout.

W-ICEY&H2010

OS ref: SK 316 922

96.   **Ewden Valley Reservoirs**

Sheffield water works company obtained legal powers to abstract water from the Ewden Brook in 1867. The company obtained powers to prevent the waste of supplied water in 1870 which delayed the need to construct the new reservoirs. Both these powers were transferred with the company take-over to the council in 1897.

The Ewden Valley scheme commenced in 1913 with a budget of £1.25M. Broomhead and More Hall reservoirs on the Ewden Brook were completed in 1929 and 1936 respectively as part of the River Don compensation pumping scheme. The supervising engineer was Colin Clegg for Sheffield City Council Water Works with T & C Hawksley the consulting engineers who carried out the design.

96a.   Broomhead earth fill embankment dam is 30m high and 305m long and impounds 5.4M m^3 of water in a reservoir 1.6km long over 36 ha. As with the original Dale Dyke dam the cut off trench had to be deepened to achieve a stable water tight stratum. In this case the trench is up to 48.2m deep and contains 31,300 m^3 of concrete. During its construction 11.3Ml/day of water had to be pumped out. The puddle clay core is up to 7.3m wide and sits within an embankment tapering from 181m wide at its base to 6m wide at the top. The discharge tunnel was dug through the hillside of the northern bank around the end of the embankment it is horseshoe in profile and 3m wide and 3.6m high.

Yorkshire Water have created a circular walk around the reservoir, but there is no car park.

OS ref: SK 269 960

96b.   More Hall, downstream, is the smaller at 24m high and 280m long to impound 2.4M m^3 in its 28 ha area and 1.3km length. Again a deep cut off trench was required at up to 31.4m deep with 16,200 m^3 of concrete. The puddle clay core is up to 5.2m wide and sits within an embankment tapering from 141m wide at its base to 6m wide at the top.

There is a narrow private road along the northern side of More Hall, to which there is concessionary access and parking is possible at some points, with care and consideration affording access to Yorkshire Water walking routes.

OS ref: SK 287 957

Both dams have grit stone facing to the weirs and wave walls quarried from the south side of the valley. A branch railway line up from Wharncliffe Wood was built to bring in other materials.

The combined yield is 20,700 m³/day supply and 11,800 m³/day compensation flow.

Ewden Water Treatment Works was begun in 1913 but work was interrupted by the first world war. It was completed in 1935. The WTW was completely replaced with a new plant nearby in 1994. The 45 Ml/day processed by the plant is pumped to Brightholmelee storage reservoir from where the 17M l capacity can flow under gravity to the 120,000 customers in north Sheffield.

Ewden village was constructed as a model village to house the work force. There were two types of house, one for married workers or foremen with a living room two or three bedrooms a bathroom and WC. The second type for the general working men was for 13 lodgers and had a shared dining room, bathroom and WC plus 13 sleeping cubicles and a house keeper's sitting room and two bedrooms. In addition to the houses there was a church, school, recreation room and hospital plus a canteen, co-op store and allotment gardens. The village had a 440V DC electric supply from the construction site power station fuelled by coke. None of the original huts remain although some have been replaced with more modern buildings.

Www.yorkshirewater.co.uk

97.   **Wortley Top Forge, Barnsley.**

This is an excellent museum run by volunteers with working water wheels and drop forge. A grade 1 listed building, it is the oldest surviving iron forge in the country. (HEW ref: 1157) . Although records of iron working in Wortley go back to 1579 the location is uncertain - the earliest record for the site is of 1657. Kirkstead Priory had a licence to dig iron in the general area since 1160.

There are extensive additions from the 18th & 19th centuries. From 1850 onwards the works became an important centre for railway axles under Thomas Andrews. These were exported throughout the world. His son Thomas who took over became a respected metallurgist. Earlier John Cockshutt had also pioneered work on steel production. Production ceased at Top Forge in 1912 although the workshop remained in use for a further 17 years. The number one hammer wheel is 12' diameter and 20' wide and constructed of cast iron with eight spoke to the iron rim with wooden paddles operating as a breast shot wheel. Its operational speed is a swift 35 rpm operating five cams to give 180 blows per minute. The force of each blow of the hammer being amplified by a timber spring beam. Number two hammer operated in a similar way from a 4.11m diameter and 1.14m wide wheel of iron and timber construction.

The smaller blower wheel is thought to have been put to use to drive an electric generator for a local factory during WW2.

The site became a museum in 1957 and is now in the care of the South Yorkshire Industrial History Society. It is a surviving early example of an integrated engineering facility incorporating research, design, manufacture and testing on one site. The site was awarded an IMechE Heritage Hallmark award in 1993.

Www.topforge.co.uk

OS ref: SK 294 998

98.   **Upper Don reservoirs.**

98a.   The **Langsett** reservoir (HEW ref: 2035) was built between 1897 and 1904 and exemplifies the state of the art of earth dam building, being "thoughtfully detailed, amply dimensioned and soundly constructed". William Watts, Works engineer for Sheffield Corporation designed it with construction being by direct labour. As with the Derwent Valley reservoirs temporary "tin towns" were built to house the work force and their families which included the provision of a school and chapel and other welfare facilities often omitted by contracting companies at the time.

The embankment dam is of conventional composition, including a central puddle clay core above a concrete-filled cut-off trench. This averages 27.7m in depth and had to be extended by a 140m long wing trench at the northern end. It contains in total 32,900m^3 of concrete. The 352m long embankment stands 35.7m high and contains 636,875m^3 of material, including 53,135m^3 of puddle clay in the core.

The tunnel passes beneath the northern end of the dam and is notably large, 6.1m^2 in section area. This contains the delivery pipelines. The valve house that stands above it has the 'waterworks baronial' appearance of that era. To help with illumination, the shaft beneath is not only of larger diameter, 2.4m but is lined with white glazed bricks. The valves themselves, at three water depths, are operated by hydraulic cylinders with small feed ports to give slow movement of the valve gates. This helps prevent potentially damaging pressure surges in the pipework. The overflow weir is 61m long and dressed in Ashlar. The spillway channel contains a series of curved steps which concentrate the flow in the centre of the channel.

The reservoir is approximately 1.4km long with a flooded area of up to 56 ha of the 21km^2 catchment. The normal top water level is 247m AOD.

Before the construction of the reservoir, Stocksbridge drew its water from a variety of small local sources – directly from the river and springs and wells as needed. There was a small supply reservoir at Machin Spout operated by the Sheffield Corporation Waterworks by 1893.

Langsett water treatment works were rebuilt in 1986 to accommodate the latest technology. Further improvements to the plant were undertaken in 2007.

Yorkshire Water have created several walking and cycling routes near the reservoir from their car park at Langsett Barn (SE2103 0046).

HC-ICEY1986, HC-ICEYH2007 (Water Treatment Works)

OS ref: SE 214 003

98b.   **Underbank** was completed in 1907 as part of a joint project with Rotherham and Doncaster corporations using the same construction methods. It was built by Samuel Fox & Co. The embankment at Underbank is 466m long and 16m high to create the reservoir 1.3km long flooding approximately 40 ha of the 946 ha catchment. Samuel Fox owned major business interests in the Stocksbridge area. They had previously opposed plans to build reservoirs in the Little Don Valley above Stocksbridge. By the end of the 19th century their own expansion saw their interests change to favouring construction. Underbank primary role is to regulate the flow of water in the river below Langsett and Midhope reservoirs to reduce the risks of flooding and ensure adequate flow to safeguard the environment and for any other uses when rainfall is low.

OS ref: SK 224 997

98c.   Midhope is 262m long and 27m high to create the reservoir 1.8km long flooding approximately 21 ha of the 552 ha catchment. It was built in the mid 1890s by Barnsley Corporation Waterworks following the construction of Ingbirchworth Reservoir on Moss Brook, a Don tributary north west of Penistone. There was a small water purification works near the reservoir filtering the water. This closed in the 1980s when all treatment was taking place at the improved Langsett works. There is now a visitor car park there. Water was pumped from the Don Valley to Barnsley at Wortley.

As the demand for water grew in the 19th century it became quite common for West Riding boroughs to seek water supplies beyond the borough boundaries and frequently in the head waters of other rivers. Sheffield borough and city amalgamated with neighbouring boroughs through the 19th and 20th centuries to retain a unified control of an area's development even before the council had formal planning powers or ownership of the water supply. Barnsley added Scout Dike reservoir downstream of and Royd Moor reservoir near to Ingbirchworth in the late 1940s and early 1950s respectively.

Www.yorkshirewater.co.uk

OS ref: SK 253 993

99.   Winscar Dam, Barnsley.

Winscar Dam (HEW ref: 2036) was built between 1972 and 1975. The use of rock fill for the embankment allowed steep faces to be used and so enabled the 53m height of dam to be fitted onto the site between an existing earth dam and Dunford Bridge village, below. It was the first in Britain to have an upstream face membrane of asphaltic concrete. This membrane is 120mm thick and was formed in two layers. It was renewed in 2001. The Dewsbury and Heckmondwyke Water works Company had built a set of reservoirs here in the mid – late 19th century feeding the water by aqueduct out of the River Don catchment to the communities to the north. Upper and Lower Windleden, Harden and Snailsden were built as supply and Dunford Bridge as a compensation reservoir. The last dammed the River Don upstream of the confluence with Harden Clough. The new Winscar dam is downstream of that point flooding both valleys significantly increasing the reservoir capacity.

The dam is 520m long and contains 900,000m³ of rock fill, which is graded from 1.2m down to 2mm in size. Water is drawn at four points into the pipe work in a longitudinal gallery near the upstream toe. The pipe work continues through a reinforced concrete culvert under the rock bank. The kinetic energy of water falling down the overflow chute in the eastern mitre is dissipated in a hydraulic jump pool at the foot, an innovation at an English dam.

The dam was designed by consulting engineers Mander, Raikes and Marshall, whose panel engineer in charge was John D. Humphreys. There is no valve tower in the reservoir, nor valve house on or near the dam. It was built on the headwaters of the River Don for the Mid Calder Water Board, based in Dewsbury, by Gleeson Civil Engineering Ltd. Such inter-valley transport of water is quite common in Yorkshire and increasingly so elsewhere. The reservoir is approximately 1.4km long covering an area of approximately 69 ha.

The asphaltic waterproofing membrane was renewed in 2003 by Morrison Construction Ltd with CARPI Tech SA to the designs of MHW.

The Ingbirchworth and Broadstone Reservoirs, together with a feeder weir on the Moss Brook, near Penistone were built for the Barnsley Corporation Water Works in the latter part of the 19th century. Scout Dike Reservoir was added post world war one and Royd Moor reservoir on the Moss Brook below the weir location in the early 1950s. There is a small water treatment works downstream of the Ingbirchworth Dam.

HC-ICEYHA2003 (membrane renewal)

Www.yorkshirewater.co.uk

OS ref: SE 154 025

100. Woodhead Tunnels, Barnsley - Glossop.

The Sheffield, Ashton-under-Lyne and Manchester Railway was incorporated by Act of Parliament in May 1837 and six months later the construction of the tunnel (HEW ref: 0235) began. The engineer was Charles Vignoles. However, a dispute with the board caused him to resign and he was replaced by Joseph Locke. Locke doubled the estimate first made by Vignoles for the driving of the tunnel, but proceeded with the original design. However, as work progressed the bore was reduced in section and so only accommodated a single track rather than the double line envisaged. The tunnel has a maximum elevation of 293m above Ordnance Datum and lies up to 183m below ground level. There is a fall of 24.4m to the west portal. The average cover is 137m.

The tunnel was driven from both ends and also from five intermediate shafts of 2.4m diameter, creating a total of twelve faces. The single track tunnel was opened in December 1845, at which time it was the world's longest, at fractionally over 4.8km. Excavation had totalled 208,482m^3 and it had cost approximately £200,000, more than twice the original estimate. Severe problems had been encountered as a result of water ingress. The eastern end was driven by Thomas Nicholson and the western by Richard Hattersley. The tunnel is 4.57m wide and 5.49m high with an 0.46m thick brickwork lining.

The railway company remained short of money and were reluctant to pay for even the most basic of facilities even on the bleak isolated moors. The tunnel became notorious for the conduct of the up to 1500 navvies employed on the project and the many deaths that occurred, largely as a result of the drunkenness, but also to the harsh working conditions and some work practices. It was said that before the line reached the tunnel in early 1845 the encampments at the shaft tops on the moor were as difficult to provision as Balaclava.

The camps were mostly of crude hut of mud and stone with heather thatch roofs erected by the work men themselves with little or no sanitary provisions. Wages were high but so were the prices in the Tommy shop controlled by the contractors. The high prices were partly a result of the shear difficulty of getting provisions there but there was also an element of profiteering. Wages were paid in arrears - up to 3 months late - and the Tommy shop bills deducted from the wages.

The conditions here were infamous at the time and led to a parliamentary enquiry into railway workers conditions. Although no action was taken by parliament to enforce better conditions at the time it was the first step towards improving the conditions of the workers on temporary sites.

The 3% death rate and 14% wounded was comparable to that suffered by the army during the peninsula campaign of the Napoleonic wars. The second tunnel also suffered a serious outbreak of cholera with around 250 people dying of the disease in the summer of 1847. However, generally work and welfare conditions were much better and far fewer accidents occurred.

A second single track tunnel was built between 1847 and 1852, by G. C. Pauling, contractor to the same design. In anticipation of duplication, 25 side-access connections had been provided when the first tunnel had been built, thus facilitating construction using the original shafts and the completed tunnel as access. This provided the second line to the railway and so removed a bottleneck from the system and allowed unhindered two way running of the line. Work was quicker and a lot safer on this second bore.

Both these tunnels suffered from poor ventilation and were closed to traffic in 1909. The ventilation shafts were subsequently enlarged and the line re-opened in 1915. These single line tunnels, were superseded by a double-track tunnel 10m in diameter built between 1949 and 1953 for overhead electrification of the line. Balfour Beatty were the contractors and they employed a similar number of men as on the first scheme. Sir William Halcrow and Partners were the design engineers. However, the contractor created a temporary village on the moor to house their workers and cater for their needs with extensive facilities. By this time the original tunnels were in urgent need of repair but were not large enough to accommodate the over head lines. The new tunnel also posed difficulty to the contractors and engineers. Despite being so close to the earlier tunnels the complex geology made progress harder than expected. Much of the drive is in highly variable shales, some of which are highly susceptible to swelling when exposed to air and contain large amounts of water. The larger diameter exposed a larger area to the air before it was lined and so some rock falls occurred. This led to alterations in the working method employed so that small areas were worked upon and lined as soon as possible. To maintain progress a series of tunnel faces were worked at the same time using side access tunnels from a small access bore parallel to the tunnel in a procedure similar that that used on the second bore a century before. The tunnel is lined with concrete with a drainage system behind.

The line was closed to passenger traffic in 1970 and all other traffic in 1981. The tunnels are now used to carry national grid power cables. The Victorian "up" tunnel was refurbished to take the new 400kV trans-pennine cable link over a period of 5 years powering up in 1969. The "down" tunnels being used for oil storage tanks. All the tunnels have deteriorated over time. The 1953 tunnel has just been reconditioned to take new power cables and the original tunnels may well be abandoned.

Much of the approaching rail route is now part of the Trans Pennine Trail walking, riding and cycling route. This trail links Southport and Liverpool in the West to Hull and Hornsea in the East with branches to Wakefield & Leeds and Sheffield & Chesterfield. There have been several proposals to reopen the tunnel to rail traffic to improve the trans-pennine capacity. It seems unlikely this will happen in the foreseeable future as the tunnel is now used for major power cabling.

Www.transpenninetrail.org.uk   OS ref: SK 114 999 to SE 157 023

101. Penistone Market Hall

This now can lay claim to be the largest publicly accessible timber framed building in the country. A new open market hall was built in 2010 to house the farmers' market using traditional green oak framing techniques on over 100m³ of oak timber. The open sided hall is 35m long 24m wide and 13m high. Penistone Open Market won the South Yorkshire and Humber Local Authority Building Control - Building Excellence in 2011. After a 10 week preparation off site the works were completed in a little over 2 weeks on site.

www.penistonetowncouncil.gov.uk/local_facilities.html

OS ref: SE243 034

102. Needle Eye Footbridge, Barnsley.

This is one of the most eye-catching structures on the motorways in Yorkshire. It is a reinforced concrete arch bridge (HEW ref: 1319) of 86.9m span between springings. Including the back spans the length is 132.2m between abutments. It spans across the M1 motorway a short distance south of junction 37 where the motorway is in an approximately 10m deep cutting as it climbs the hill. The bridge provides a public footpath link and farm access. It was designed by the West Riding County Council highway unit as part of the original motorway construction.

OS ref: SE 326 051

103. Rockley Furnace, Barnsley

Built between 1698 & 1704 it is thought to be the oldest surviving blast furnace in the country. It produced cast iron from the locally quarried ores and charcoal from the adjoining woodland until the 1740s. It is thought to have been reopened in the Napoleonic wars to cast guns, this time using coke as a fuel. It was part of a larger iron working complex. The ruin of the Newcomen engine house is nearby. This was built c. 1813 to improve the drainage of the iron ore mine. A bloomery forge is now buried under the motorway. The site is now in the care of the South Yorkshire Industrial History Society.

Www.topforge.co.uk

OS ref: SE 338 022

104. Elsecar Engine House, Barnsley.

The engine house (HEW ref: 0220), dated 1787 contains a Newcomen beam engine completed in 1795. The engine received modifications in 1801 and 1836. It remained operational until 1923 and was capable of occasional use until the colliery closed in the 1950s. The world-famous beam engine, shaft, and engine house have recently undergone a two-year project to restore them to full working order. It is now in full working order and demonstration steaming events are held periodically. The 7.3m beam operated a 227l capacity cylinder giving a pump capacity of 2.73m³ per minute. John Bargh of Chesterfield was the designer.

The engine is part of what is now Elsecar Heritage Centre, a former iron works and colliery complex. A year after the beam engine was installed the ironworks were producing 950 t of iron per year. Shortly afterwards a second smelter was built to double production, which continued until 1885. Many of the workshop buildings are from the time when a railway link was made to the works.

The centre of the village was created as a model village for the Fitzwilliam estate colliery workers in the late 18th century. Some of the early cottages were designed by John Carr of York. The Earls showed a keen interest in the village and often took visiting nobility and royalty around the village including the forge and colliery.

The Elsecar branch of the Dearne and Dove Canal was completed in 1798 to serve the colliery and forge. The principal engineer was Robert Mylne. The canal company was taken over by the Don Navigation company in 1846. Four years later they were taken over by the South Yorkshire, Doncaster & Goole Railway Company which itself was taken over by the Manchester, Sheffield and Lincolnshire Railway in 1874. This resulted in reduced investment and yet increased tolls. In 1850 the railway company laid a new railway line to Elsecar moving the canal basin in the process. The line took the freight via Swinton to Mexborough and so to Doncaster. In 1895 the Sheffield and South Yorkshire Navigation Company bought out the local canal network from the railway company. However, the canal branch suffered from the effects of mining subsidence and closed in 1928. In the early 20th century the canal reservoir at Elsecar was developed as a "Seaside Resort in the Yorkshire Coalfield" for the local workers.

A section of the Elsecar branch railway line now operates occasionally as a steam conservation line. It plans to extend the current line through to Cortonwood.

The centre of the village was created as a model village for the Fitzwilliam estate colliery workers in the late 18th century. Earl Fitzwilliam of Wentworth Woodhouse was clearly very proud of his enterprise and frequently gave tours of the village and colliery to noble and even royal visitors to the great house. Some of the early cottages were designed by John Carr of York. Elsecar village was one of the first areas in the country to be designated a Heritage Action Zone with the aim of improving the understanding of of the area and creating new uses for many buildings in the conservation area. It also plans to create new sympathetic housing and community engagement and retraining the local work force.

Www.elsecar-heritage-centre.co.uk

OS ref: SK 385 999

105.   Smithy Wood footbridge

This is the last remaining of the three "Wichert Truss" footbridges built across the motorway in South Yorkshire. The eponymous truss was designed in 1930, by E.M. Wichert of Pittsburgh, USA to address the problem of settlement of intermediate piers in bridges. Here a continuous truss is created along the entire length of the bridge with hinged quadrilateral sections over the intermediate piers. This provided both continuity and flexibility at the intermediate pier positions. The motorway had to be designed to accommodate large movements that might occur as a result of deep coal mining in the region, with potential settlements of several metres. These elegant and simple reinforced concrete structures provided effective crossing for footpaths over the motorway.

OS ref: SK 370 949

The other two bridges, at Birdwell and Stainborough have been replaced by steel truss bridges. The bridges were replaced in advance of a potential widening of the motorway and to enhance the crash resistance of the structures. The slender intermediate piers of the original bridges were relatively vulnerable had they been struck by a heavy vehicle. Those at Smithy Wood are far enough back from the motorway not to need alteration.

The bridges were demolished in one night, and the new deck erected in one night thus minimising any disruption to the traffic on the motorway. For Birdwell this was 10 September 2005 and 19 November 2005 respectively. In the intervening time the foundations, piers and abutments were replaced. Another consideration in the removal of these structures was the possibility of widening the motorway to four lanes, which would require the current hard shoulder to become a running lane with or without a new hard shoulder beyond. This was not possible at Birdwell and Stainborough as the current hard shoulder had been taken up locally with protection barriers for the old bridge piers.

OS ref: SE 346 005
OS ref: SE 333 040

106.   St Mary's Church, Ecclesfield.

This is probably the oldest surviving building in the city still in use. The earliest written record surviving for this church indicate it was in existence by 1141. There has probably been a church on this site since perhaps the late 7th or early 8th century, although it was not recorded in the Domesday Survey of 1086 (Particularly, in Yorkshire the survey failed to record many features that must have existed at the time of the conquest. This may have been because of the wasting of much of the county following the failed uprising.) An Anglo-Scandinavian cross was discovered in the church yard and is now resting in the south aisle. The very place name suggests a Celtic Christian tradition here. It is thought that this was the principal church of Hallamshire in this early mediaeval period. The piers in the nave are believed to be part of the early Norman church. However, much of the remainder of the fabric dates from 1478-1500 when the church was expanded to become "the Minster of the Moors".

Www.stmarysecclesfield.com/History

OS ref: SK 353 942

106a. The beautiful and imposing **St Nicholas Church, High Bradfield** was for a long time a chapel of ease of Ecclesfield church. It too has what is thought to be a Saxon Cross fragment in the nave. This had been found elsewhere in the village some decades ago. The church contains reused masonry of c. 1200 forming the bases of the nave piers. The majority of the fabric seems to be 14th century. The church stands close to the remains of the motte and bailey castle.

OS ref: SK 267 926

106b. The charming small church of **St James, Midhopestone** was also a chapel of ease of Ecclesfield parish. Although the church as it stands now primarily dates from 1705, the north and south walls contain mediaeval masonry.

OS ref: SK 234 995

G7.1, G7.2 & G7.3
Howden dam has a central overflow cascade between two towers in the masonry wall.

G7.4 Section through Howden dam showing cut-off depth.

Cross section through Howden dam.

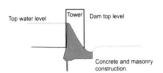

G7.5 Derwent dam is very similar to the Howden dam upstream. The valley is almost continuously full of water for approximately 8 km length below the mass of high surrounding moorland.

Longitudinal section through Howden dam.

G7.6, G7.7 & G7.8 The reinforced concrete box arched Ashopton and Derwent viaducts carry the A57 and A6013 roads across the Ladybower reservoir.

G7.9 Ladybower dam, like most of the local dams, but unlike Derwent and Howden, is made of carefully placed rock fill and gains its strength purely from its weight.

Cross section through Ladybower dam.

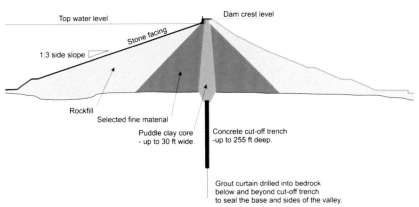

Top water level

Dam crest level

Stone facing

1:3 side slope

Rockfill

Selected fine material

Puddle clay core - up to 30 ft wide.

Concrete cut-off trench - up to 255 ft deep.

Grout curtain drilled into bedrock below and beyond cut-off trench to seal the base and sides of the valley.

G7.10 & G7.11   It has unusual "bell mouth" spillways discharging into a pipe under the dam, rather than a linear weir, leading to the river downstream.

313

G7.12, G7.13 & G7.14 The Upper, Middle and Lower Redmires Reservoirs were the first large upland reservoirs serving Sheffield. (top, centre, bottom)

G7.15 A collector channel feeds additional water to the upper reservoir. A bell-mouth spillway was added in the 1960s to supplement the weirs on the reservoirs.

G7.16   Upper Rivelin reservoir dam seen above the lower reservoir.

G7.17   Lower Rivelin reservoir.

G7.18   Lower Rivelin dam spillway.

G7.19   Packhorse bridge Rivelin.

G7.18   Packhorse bridge Rivelin.

G7.19   Wolf Wheel mill pond.

G7.20 & G7.21   Forge Valley School.
(top and right)

(Reproduced courtesy of Sheffield City
Council)

G7.22   Bradfield School.
(below)

G7.23 & G7.24   Strines reservoir.

Cross section through Dale Dyke dam

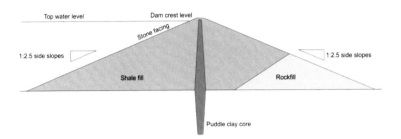

Longitudinal section through dam

G7.25 The section drawing through the original Dale Dyke dam shows the depth of the puddle clay core and large steps in the bottom of the cutoff trench. Significant factors in the failure of the dam.

© Dave Pickersgill

G7.26 The rebuilt dam created a smaller reservoir and was constructed on more favourable ground a short distance upstream of the original.

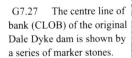

G7.27 The centre line of bank (CLOB) of the original Dale Dyke dam is shown by a series of marker stones.

319

G7.28   Agden, Dale Dyke and Strine reservoirs in the head waters of the River Loxley create part of the "Sheffield Lake District" popular with walkers.

G7.29   Agden was built successfully to its design.

G7.30   Agden reservoir spillway improvements.

cc-by-sa/2.0 - Damflask Reservoir - March... by Alan Murray-Rust - geograph.org.uk/p/2873004

G7.31 & G7.32
    Damflask reservoir in the lower valley provides a continual supply of water to the river system downstream to protect the river environment.

cc-by-sa/2.0 - Damflask Reservoir by Graham Hogg - geograph.org.uk/p/2195020

G7.33   Low Matlock Rolling mill still has the mechanism to be powered by the river although it is no longer used and neglected.

Until very recently the company provided specialist steel rolling services from this historic site. An expansion of the business has seen Pro-Roll move to new premises.

G7.34   A new retaining wall supports the A61 by the River Don at Middlewood.

(Reproduced courtesy of Sheffield City Council)

G7.35 & G7.36   More Hall Reservoir, like Damflask provides compensation water to the river system allowing Broomhead reservoir, upstream, to be fully utilised for water supply.

G7.37 Ewden village was purpose built to house the workforce and had diverse amenities for the population. (Reproduced courtesy of Stocksbridge & District History Society - EAWV020)

G7.38, 39, 40 Broomhead reservoir.

© Helmut Kohler, South Yorkshire Industrial History

G7.41 & G7.42   Wortley Top Forge.

© Helmut Kohler, South Yorkshire Industrial History

G7.43   Underbank reservoir. (right)

G7.44   Underbank spillway. (right)

G7.45   Langsett reservoir. (centre right)

G7.46   Midhope reservoir. (bottom)

G7.47   Midhope spillway. (centre left)

2.0 - Underbank Reservoir by Andrew Hill - geograph.org.uk/p/3579040

cc-by-sa/2.0 - The Dam Wall and spillway... by Dave Pickersgill - geograph.org.uk/p/3356550

C-C by sa 2.0 © Dave Pickersgill Geograph.org.uk/p/2900004

C-C by sa 2.0 © Dave Pickersgill Geograph.org.uk/p/3664956

© Dave Pickersgill

G7.48   Winscar Reservoir.

G7.49   Winscar dam waterproofing.

G7.50   Winscar dam section.

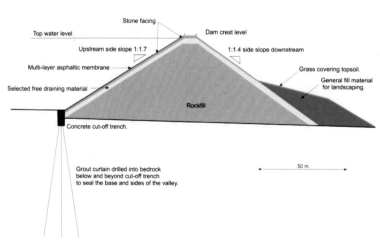

Stone facing

Top water level

Dam crest level

Upstream side slope 1:1.7

1:1.4 side slope downstream

Multi-layer asphaltic membrane

Grass covering topsoil.

General fill material for landscaping.

Selected free draining material

Rockfill

Concrete cut-off trench.

Grout curtain drilled into bedrock
below and beyond cut-off trench
to seal the base and sides of the valley.

50 m.

G7.51 & G7.52
      Woodhead Tunnel,
Dunford Bridge (eastern)
portal, above, and
Woodhead (western) portal,
below.

G7.53   Penistone timber market hall.

G7.54   Rockley engine house.

G7.55   Needle's Eye footbridge over the M1 motorway.

G7.56 Rockley blast furnace.

© South Yorkshire Industrial History Society.

G7.57 Elsecar Newcomen Engine.

© Highways England

© Highways England

G7.58 & 59   Birdwell former Wichert type footbridge and new steel truss replacement on more robust piers. Ground settlement from coal mining will have largely ceased and so a conventional design could be used.

G7.60   Smithy Wood footbridge. Notice the diamond shaped space formed by the sections of bridge over the slender piers. This is the last surviving example of this type of bridge in the UK.

© Rose Tanner

G7.61   Ecclesfield Parish Church "Minster of the Moors".

G7.62 & 63   Saxon Cross and Norman Columns in the nave.

G7.64   St Nicholas' Church Bradfield.

G7.65   St James' Church Midhopestone.

Acknowledgements

I am indebted to my mother Connie, brother Douglas and Arnie Cotton for their generous support, encouragement, helpful comments and advice. Thanks must also go to Angela Harpham for her excellent photography, and her husband, Martin, for his assistance.

I am grateful for the assistance of Sheffield City Council Libraries and Archives Service, the Institution of Civil Engineers Information Services, Trevor Hodgson (ICE Yorkshire representative, Panel of Historical Engineering Works - now retired from that post), Institution of Structural Engineers Information Services, North Yorkshire and West Yorkshire Archives, Sheffield City Council Parks and Countryside, Sheffield City Council Design and Project Management Services, Sheffield City Council Highways, AECOM, Amey, Ancon Ltd, ANF Consulting, Arqiva, Arup, Balfour Beatty, Barn Energy, The Big Tower.com, BSP Consulting, British Constructional Steelwork Association, Buro Happold, BT, Chesterfield Canal Trust, The Company of Cutlers' of Hallamshire, DavyMarkham Ltd, Eastwood and Partners, E.On, The Friends of Bishops' House, Mott MacDonald, National Grid, National Gas Archive, Network Rail, Outokumpo, The Railway & Canal Historical Society, Ryedale Folk Museum, Sheffield Forgemasters, Sheffield Industrial Museums Trust, Sheffield International Venues, Sheffield Museums and Galleries, Sheffield Transport Study Group, SKM Consulting, South Yorkshire Industrial History Society, The University of Sheffield, WSP consulting and Yorkshire Water, also Jon Carr, Sheila Harris, Andy Hughes, David Leather, Sue and Richard Lee, Nalin Seneviratne, Andy Tyas, Ian West, Alan Wood.

If I have not credited anyone who should have been this is entirely accidental.

I readily acknowledge my debt to all those local historians and engineering researchers who have gone before me.

Finally I must thank David Tattersall, former ICE Regional Director whose idea this was.

I also acknowledge that some of the points of interest are in neighbouring boroughs. I hope the people of these boroughs will allow me to borrow them for the purposes of telling this story.

Picture Credits.

Angela Harpham, Ancon, Arqiva, Barn Energy, Carpenter Oak, Chesterfield Canal Trust, DavyMarkham, Ken Dash - Friends of Bishops' House, Duncan Froggatt, Catherine Harpham, Sheila Harris, Highways England, Institution of Civil Engineers, Institution of Structural Engineers, Leather Family, Mott MacDonald, Museum Sheffield, National Portrait Gallery, Network Rail, Outokumpu, Dave Pickersgill, Anna Ravetz, Rotherham MBC, Ryedale Folk Museum, Sheffield Cathedral and Chapter, Sheffield City Council, Sheffield Forgemasters, Sheffield International Venues, Sheffield Libraries and Archives, Sheffield Museums and Galleries, South Yorkshire Industrial History Society, Stocksbridge District History Society, Rose Tanner, The Big Tower.com, West Yorkshire Archive Service, WSP consulting, Yorkshire Water.

Ken Bagnall, Peter Barr, Jonathan Clitheroe, Don Cload, Steve Fareham, Paul Glover, Derek Harper, Andrew Hill, Graham Hogg, Christine Johnstone, Trevor Littlewood, Peter McDermott, Christine Matthews, Chris Morgan, Andrew Murray-Rust, David Pickering, Stephen Richards, Terry Robinson, John Slater, Wayland Smith, Neil Theasby, Andrew Tyron, Richard Webb, James Wood, Peter Wood.

Sources and Further Reading

Batty, S. R., 1994, *Railways of Sheffield*, I. Allen (Sheffield) 07110-2236-4

Badcock, A., 2009, *Inside Tinsley Towers*, ARCUS (Sheffield)

Ball, C. et al (eds)., 2006, *Water Power on the Sheffield Rivers, second (revised) edn.*, Sheffield Trades Historical Society (Sheffield) 0-9556644-0-3

Ball, C. 1992 *Millwrights in Sheffield and South Yorkshire 1550 - 1900* (unpublished MA Thesis, University of Sheffield)

Barnes M., 2013, *Joseph Locke: pioneer civil engineer project manager.* Proc ICE - Engineering History and Heritage 166(2): pp 65-72, Institution of Civil Engineers (London) ISSN 1757-9430

Barraclough, K.C., 1976, *Sheffield Steel*, Moorland Publishing Co. (Buxton) 0903485-31-1

Bayliss, V., 2012, *Building schools for Sheffield 1870-1914,* Victorian Society / ALD Print (Sheffield) 1901587951

BCSA, 2006, *Centenary of steel Construction 1906-2006,* British Constructional Steelwork Association 085073-050-3

Binfield, C & Hey, D.(eds), 1997, *Mesters to Masters - A History of the Company of Cutlers in Hallamshire*, Oxford University Press (Oxford) 0-19-828997-9

Binfield, C et al.(eds), 1993, *The History of the city of Sheffield 1843-1993* Vol. 2: Society, Sheffield Academic Press (Sheffield) 1-85075-431-4

British Geological Survey, 1993, *Sheffield, England and Wales Sheet 100 Solid and Drift* Geological survey map 1:50,000

Clarke, J., 2014, *Early Structural Steel in London Buildings - A discreet revolution*, English Heritage (Swindon) 1-84802-103-7

Coleman, T., 1965, *The Railway Navvies,* Hutchinson & Co (Publishers) ltd (London)

Cresy, E, 1861 (2010 Facsimile) *An Encyclopaedia of Civil Engineering, Historical, Theoretical and Practical, Volume 1*, Thomas Telford Ltd (London) 978-0-7277-3635-2

Cross-Rudkin, P & Chrimes M. (eds.), 2008, *Biographical Dictionary of Civil Engineers Volume 2 - 1830 to 1890*, Institution of Civil Engineers (London) 978-0-7277-3504-1

Dalgleish K., 1992, *Transport Studies & Infrastructure Development in Sheffield.*

Davies, H., 2006, *From Trackways to Motorways - 5000 years of Highway History*, Tempus (Stroud) 07524-3650-3

Defoe, D., 1724 (1986 reprint), *A Tour Through the Whole Island of Great Britain*, Penguin Classics (London) 0-14-043066-0

Devey, J, 1862, *The Life of Joseph Locke Civil Engineer*, M.P. F.B.S.

Dulieu, D., 2013, *Stay Bright, A History of Stainless Steels in Britain*, Outokumpu Stainless Ltd., (Sheffield)

Dunstan, J. 1970 *The Origins of the Sheffield and Chesterfield Railway,* Dore Village Society (Sheffield).

Edwards, B. H., 1989, *Totley and the Tunnel*, Shape Design (Sheffield) 0952506416

Ferguson, H. & Chrimes, M., 2011, *The Civil Engineers,* The story of the Institution of Civil Engineers and the people who made it, ICE Publishing (London), 0-7277-4143-1

Freeman, J. F., 1979, *The growth and Changes in the H.V. And L.V. Ditribution Systems in the Sheffield Area*, (unpublished chairman's address to the Institution of Electrical Engineers Sheffield Centre)

Gifford, A., 1999, *Derbyshire Watermills - Corn Mills*, The Midland Wind and Water Mills Group (Shropshire) 0-9517794-3-5

Gifford, A., 2003, *Derbyshire Windmills Past and Present,* Heage Windmill Society & The Midland Wind and Water Mills Group (Heage) 0-954486-0-7

Griffiths, P.,1999, *The Five Weirs Walk - Sheffield East End History Trail 3*, Hallamshire Press (Sheffield) 1-874418-27-X

Harman, R. & Minnis, J., 2004, *Sheffield - Pevsner Architectural Guide*, Yale UP (London) 0-300-10585-1

Harrison, D., 2004, *The Bridges of Medieval England*. Transport and Society 400-1800, Oxford UP (Oxford) 0-19-922685-6

Harrison, S., 1864 (1974 reprint) *A complete History of the Great Flood at Sheffield*, Evans & Langley Associates (Dewsbury)

Hey, D., 1997, *Forging the Valley*, Sheffield Academic Press (Sheffield) 1-85075-647-3

Hey, D., 1998, *A History of Sheffield*, Carnegie Publishing (Lancaster) 1-85936-045-9

Hey, D., 2001, *Packmen, Carriers and Packhorse Roads - Trade and communication in N. Derbys. And S. Yorks.* Landmark Publishing (Ashbourne) 1-84306-016-7

Hey, D., 2011, *A History of Yorkshire: 'County of the Broad Acres'*, Carnegie Publishing (Lancaster) 1-85936-210-5

Hill, A., 2002 *The South Yorkshire Coalfield*, Tempus (Stroud)

Hopkinson, G. G., 19??, *Road Developments in South Yorkshire and North Derbyshire, 1750-1850*, Trans. Hunter Archaeolgical Society Vol. 10 pp14-30.

Huber, W., 1876, *A comprehensive treatise on the water supply of cities and towns.*

Johnson, S, 1998, *From Bailey to Bailey, A Short History of Military Buildings in Sheffield*, 09519351-3-5

Joiner, J. H., 2011, *The story of the Bailey Bridge*, Proc ICE Engineering History and Heritage Vol 164 Issue EH2 pp65-72.

Jones, P. 1996, *John Smith and England's First Iron Bridge*, Journal of Railway and Canal History Society Vol 32 pp178-185.

Labrum, E.A., 1994, *Civil Engineering Heritage - Central England*, Institution of Civil Engineers (London) 07277-1970-X

Leader, R. E., 1905, *Sheffield in the Eighteenth Century (2nd edn)*, Sir W. C. Leng & Co Ltd (Sheffield)

Leader, R. E., 1903, *Surveyors and Architects of the past in Sheffield*, Independent Press

Leather, D. 2005, *Contractor Leather, John Towlerton Leather (1804-1885), Hydraulic Engineer and Contractor of Railways and Sea Defences*, Leather Family History Society (Ilkley) 09520545-3-1

Lightman, B. et al., 2004, *The Dictionary of Ninetenth Century British Scientists*, Theommes Continuum (Bristol) 1-85506-999-7

Lodge, H., 1999, *Henry Bessemer: Sheffield's Radical Steelmaker*, in Aspects of Sheffield Vol. 2 pp 164-181, Wharncliff Publishing Ltd (Barnsley) 1-871647-58-4

Matthew, H. C. G. & Harrison, B. (eds) 2004-9, *Oxford Dictionary of National Biography (Online version)*, Oxford University Press (Oxford) 0-19861412-8

McWilliams, R.C. & Chrimes, M. (eds) 2014, *Biographical Dictionary of Civil Engineers Vol. 3 1890-1920*, Institution of Civil Engineers (London) 978-07277-5834-7

Medlicott, I. R., 1999, *John Curr, 1756-1823, Mining Engineer & Viewer*, in Aspects of Sheffield Vol. 2 pp 63-78, Wharncliff Publishing Ltd (Barnsley) 1-871647-58-4

Newland, C., 2004, *A Historical Archaeology of mobile phones in the UK*, University of Bristol MA dissertation. www.academia.edu/468072/An_Archaeology_of_Mobile_Phones accessed 22/04/13

Ogden, S.,1997, *The Sheffield and Tinsley Canal, Sheffield East End History Trail 3*, Hallamshire Press (Sheffield) 1-87418-26-1

Rennison, R. W., 1996, *Civil Engineering Heritage - Northern England (2nd)*, Institution of Civil Engineers (London) 07277-2518-1

Reynolds T. S., 1983, *Stronger than a hundred men, A History of the Vertical Water Wheel*, John Hopkins University Press, (Baltimore) 0-8018-7248-0

Richardson, C., 1992, *The Waterways Revolution: From the Peaks to the Trent, 1768-1778*. Self Publishing association Ltd, (Hanley Swan) 1-85421-161-7

Rickard P., 1894, *Tunnels on the Dore and Chinley Railway*, Proc ICE vol. CXVI pp 115-145, Institution of Civil Engineers (London)

Robinson, B., 1993, *Walls across the valley - The building of the Howden and Derwent Dams*, Scarthin Books (Cromford) 0-907758-57-6

Ryder P.F.,1979, *Timber Framed Buildings in South Yorkshire*, South Yorkshire County Council County Archaeology Monograph No 1, South Yorkshire County Council (Sheffield) 086046-015-0

Scott & Campbell, 1954, *Woodhead New Tunnel*, Proc ICE vol. 13 No 5 pp 506-541 & 541-556 (Discussion), Institution of Civil Engineers (London)

Skempton, A W et al (eds.), 2005, *Biographical Dictionary of Civil Engineers Volume 1 - 1500 to 1830*, Institution of Civil Engineers (London) 07277-2939X

Soil Survey of England and Wales, 1983, *Soils of England and Wales Sheet 3 Midlands and Western England*, Soil Map 1:250,000

Smith, H. 1998, *Sheffield's Turnpike Roads*, in Aspects of Sheffield Vol.1 pp70-83, Wharncliff Publishing Ltd (Barnsley)

Smith, H. 1999, *Visual reminders of Sheffield's Turnpike Roads*, in Aspects of Sheffield Vol.2 pp52-62, Wharncliff Publishing Ltd (Barnsley) 1-871647-58-4

Sutherland. R.J.M., 2008, *Materials and Structural techniques*, The Structural Engineer, Vol 86, No. 14, pp118-122, The Institution of Structural Engineers, London, ISSN 1466-5123

Terrey, W. 1908, *History and Description of Sheffield Waterworks*.

Usherwood, G. F. 1934(?) *The Early Waterworks of Sheffield*.

Vickers, J.L., 1992, *A Popular History of Sheffield*, Applebaum Books (Sheffield) 0-906787-04-1

Wells, M., 2010, *Engineers, A history of engineering and structural design*, Routledge (Abingdon) 0-415-32526-9

Wray, N. et al, 2001, *One Great Workshop - The Buildings of the Sheffield Metal Trades*, English Heritage (London) 1-873582-66-3

Yorkshire Electricity Board, 1986, *100 Years of Electricity in Sheffield*, Yorkshire Electricity Board Institution of Electrical Engineers, Sheffield.

Thomas Jeffries' map of Yorkshire 1771 Peter Burdett's map of Derbyshire 1791 Ralph Gosling's map of Sheffield 1736

Wm Fairbank's maps of Sheffield 1771, 1795, 1808 E Baines' map of Sheffield 1822

John Leather's map of Sheffield 1823

John Taylor's map of Sheffield 1832

Ordnance Survey mapping various dates.

ICE Yorkshire and Humber Award submissions and adjudication.

www.adeptnet.org.uk

www.bwea.com/ukwed

www.ciob.org.uk

www.concrete.org.uk

www.english-heritage.org.uk

www.forgottenrelics.co.uk

www.breedongroup.com/

www.bgs.ac.uk

www.ciht.org.uk

www.ciwem.org.uk

www.engineering-timelines.com

www.erih.net

www.graceguide.co.uk

www.ice.org.uk

www.icheme.org

www.iom3.org

www.maps.thinkbroadband.com

www.nationalarchives.gov.uk/a2a

www.nce.co.uk

www.ofcom.org.uk

www.ordnancesurvey.co.uk

www.picturesheffield.com

www.samknows.com

www.stocksbridgehs.co.uk

www.theiet.org

www.turnpikes.org.uk

www.visionofbritain.org.uk

www.windmillworld.com

www.yorkshirewater.co.uk

www.imeche.org

www.istructe.org.uk

http://motorwayarchive.ihtservices.co.uk/

www.nationalgrid.com/uk

www.networkrail.com

www.oldmapsonline.org

www.pastscape.org.uk

www.riversheaf.org

www.sheffield.gov.uk

www.sytimescape.org.uk

/www.thinkdefence.co.uk/2012/01/uk-military-bridging-equipment-the-bailey-bridge/

www.veoliaenvironmentalservices.co.uk/sheffield

www.windengineering.org.uk

www.worsbrough-mill.com/

Web-site as listed in the gazetteer section.

Please note I cannot accept any liability for the content of these web-site or indeed their continued existence.

Index